Deterioration and Maintenance of Pavements

Deterioration and Maintenance of Pavements

Derek Pearson
Chartered Engineer
Institute for Transport Studies
University of Leeds

Published by ICE Publishing, 40 Marsh Wall, London E14 9TP.

Full details of ICE Publishing sales representatives and distributors can be found at http://www.icevirtuallibrary.com/info/printbooksales

First published 2012

Also available from ICE Publishing

Principles of Pavement Engineering.
N. Thom. ISBN 978-0-7277-3480-8
ICE Manual of Highway Design and Management.
I. Walsh (ed.). ISBN 978-0-7277-4111-0
Pedestrian Facilities: Engineering and Geometric Design.
J. Schoon. ISBN 978-0-7277-4069-4

www.icevirtuallibrary.com

A catalogue record for this book is available from the British Library

ISBN 978-0-7277-4114-1

Associate Commissioning Editor: Victoria Thompson
Production Editor: Imran Mirza
Market Development Executive: Catherine de Gatacre

Typeset by Keytec Typesetting Ltd, Bridport, Dorset, DT6 3BE
Printed and bound by CPI Group (UK) Ltd, Croydon, CR0 4YY

Contents

Foreword

The contribution of good transportation networks to a nation's economic growth and wellbeing is widely recognised. These networks can be rail, air, sea and canal based but the major contributors, carrying by far the greatest volume of freight and people, are the highways. It is therefore of great importance to ensure a good maintenance regime to extend the serviceability of the network to the optimum. The main requirement to establishing these maintenance regimes is a full understanding of how the materials used interact, and of the mechanisms of the deterioration that will ensue.

This book sets out to identify the types of deterioration of highway and footway and other pavements and the appropriate maintenance that is needed. It does this admirably well by being based around a series of lecture notes for an MSc course on pavement engineering that the author, Derek Pearson, has delivered over a number of years at the University of Leeds.

He has utilised this experience to expand and enhance his lecture notes to provide one of the most comprehensive and instructive manuals on the deterioration and maintenance of pavements that it has been my privilege to study. The format of the book is entirely logical with extensive indexing and relevant illustrations, figures and tables for supportive data throughout. The whole book has been written in a narrative style, which is very readable and informative, and provides both easy access and assimilability to the information contained therein. It covers the full range of the work needed very well indeed, and includes one of the best descriptions of drainage that I have seen, and it is not confined to major highway pavements but to a broad range of pavement types. It is also applicable to a wider international audience.

This book should be required reading for all students and undergraduates studying pavement engineering. It would also serve well as a reference work for practitioners in pavement design and maintenance. I have no reservation in commending this book to all who require knowledge and understanding in these important areas of work.

W.J. McCoubrey
CEng, FICE, FCIHT, FIAE, MIQ
Past president, Chartered Institution of Highways and Transportation
Former chief executive, Roads Service, Northern Ireland

Acknowledgements

I started my working life in 1959 as an Articled Pupil to the local Borough Engineer studying part-time before becoming Chartered in 1968 and subsequently working for several large Local Authorities, County Councils and Consulting Engineers, before establishing my own practice in 1993.

In 1994, I met Joe Cabrera, Professor of Civil Engineering Materials at the University of Leeds, who at that time was organising an MSc(Eng) course entitled, Repair and Maintenance of Civil Engineering Structures, and was invited to become involved and develop a module entitled Repair and Maintenance of Pavements.

Joe Cabrera was one of the most inspirational people I have had the good fortune to meet in a long and interesting career. Under his guidance, I developed a series of notes, which, over the years, have grown in both breadth and depth, influenced by interaction with students – many of whom have been from overseas. Joe effectively became my mentor ably assisted by Dr Salah Zoorob and to both I record my sincere gratitude.

At about the same time, I was fortunate to work with Dr Per Ullidtz of the Danish Technical University and his colleagues, especially Richard Stubstad, and Dr Anders Sorensen of Dynatest International A/s in Denmark – three pioneers in the development and practical implementation of the Falling Weight Deflectometer.

As my involvement at the University of Leeds progressed, so did the notes, which have developed into this book and I hope will be of interest as a source of learning and reference to, both, students and practicing Engineers.

On the way, I express my sincere gratitude to a number of colleagues, listed in alphabetical order, for their help and support over the years.

- David Cudworth
- Jeff Farrington
- Dr Allan Dowson
- David Green (Past President of the Institution of Civil Engineers)
- Iain Mc Gregor
- Len Parker
- Dr Geoff Rowe
- Keith Nowak
- Mike Shaw

Finally, I would be remiss not to express my most sincere gratitude to my wife, Anne, and my sons, Adam and Marc, for putting up with somebody whose focus may well not have been compatible with family priorities.

Derek Pearson
Chartered Engineer

Deterioration and Maintenance of Pavements
ISBN: 978-0-7277-4114-1

Chapter 1
Pavements and their Management

> Although pavements appear to be very simple
> structures they are in reality very complicated, possibly
> the most complicated of all civil engineering
> structures.
>
> Ullidtz, 1987

1.1. Types of pavement

The word 'pavement' should not be confused with the colloquial
UK usage of pavement as a name for a footway. The term
'pavements' covers a considerable range of application, including
the examples listed below

- footway/cycleway/pedestrian precinct
- highway – unpaved track to motorway
- parking areas – HGV/cars
- airfield – runway/taxiway/apron
- heavy duty – port/industrial – internal and external.

Pavements are generally classified by construction type, the
principal types of which are

(*a*) unpaved
   (i) soil – unsealed/sealed
   (ii) gravel
(*b*) asphalt
   (i) flexible (bituminous composite)
   (ii) flexible composite (lean mix concrete and other
        hydraulically bound bases)
(*c*) concrete
   (i) rigid discrete concrete slabs (unreinforced/reinforced
        dowelled or undowelled)
   (ii) rigid continuous concrete slab
   (iii) rigid composite (rigid base bituminous composite surface)
(*d*) elemental
   (i) concrete blocks/pavers
   (ii) brick pavers
   (iii) natural stone setts (evolved or designed).

1.2. Definition and a principle

A pavement, in engineering terms, is a horizontal structure
supported by in situ natural material. Its purpose is to distribute
the applied traffic and other loading to such levels that they can
safely and reliably be carried in a sustainable manner by the
supporting soil. The bearing capacity of the supporting soil is
critically dependant on particle size distribution, shape and its
moisture content.

Road builders were aware, from ancient times, that water is the
greatest enemy of a stable long-lasting pavement. The Romans
who started building the 50 000 mile Imperial Roman Road
network in 312 BC knew of the damaging effects of water and
tried to keep their roads above the level of the surrounding
terrain. In many of these roads they often provided a drainage
blanket on top of the subgrade.

Little progress was made for the next 2000 years. In 1820,
McAdam made his often quoted statement:

> The roads can never be rendered thus perfectly secure until the
> following principles have been fully understood, admitted and
> acted upon: namely that it is the native soil which really supports
> the weight of traffic; that while it is preserved in a dry state, it
> will carry any weight without sinking ... That if water passes
> through the road and fills the native soil, the road, whatever may
> be its thickness, loses support, and goes to pieces.

The merits of effective subsoil drainage were again commented
on by Frost (1910), who observed:

> There are three things that are necessary to get a good roadbed
> and they are – drainage, drainage and drainage.

These observations relating to drainage have not always been
complied with and it is interesting to note that the recent issue of
TRL (Transport Research Laboratory) Road Note 42 (Nicholls *et
al.*, 2008) has highlighted this.

1

1.3.   The incidence of pavements

Pavements are to be found worldwide; they provide access to basic services as well underpinning the economic wellbeing of a country. An indication of scale and distribution is set out in Table 1.1.

No comprehensive data relating to the international distribution of port and /or industrial pavements are available.

1.4.   Range of loading

Traffic, which can vary from a single pedestrian to a large airliner or a straddle carrier at a port, can deliver a considerable range of load, both static and dynamic, to a pavement. The range of load and applied stress is shown in Table 1.2.

1.5.   Objectives of a pavement

Prior to developing any system of management it is necessary to define objectives, or an objective, for a pavement. While traffic levels will vary at different points within a network, it is nevertheless important to place any pavement section within some hierarchal grouping. This can be based either on total traffic flow or on cumulative damaging effect. With a paved road network the latter may be found to be the most convenient indicator: with this method of evaluation, there is a more clearly defined relationship between HGV flow and overall condition.

The following objectives provide a starting point. A pavement must

- permit unhindered passage by a defined level of traffic
- provide an acceptable level of ride comfort (roughness)
- have a minimum level of skid resistance to ensure safety
- not permit more than a defined amount (depth) (area) of standing water to ensure safety
- not exhibit more that defined levels of surface distress as the greater the distress the more rapid the overall deterioration
- carry traffic and ensure the load transmitted to the formation does not exceed its bearing capacity

Table 1.1 Incidence of pavements
Data taken from https://www.cia.gov/library/publications/the-world-factbook/index.html. Information in the public domain

Country	Population: $\times 10^6$	Airports and runways: no				Roadways: km $\times$ 1000		
		Total	Paved	Unpaved		Total	Paved	Unpaved
World	6525	49 024				32 345	19 403	12 942
					%	100	60	40
China	1313	486	403	83		1810	1448	362
EU	457	3115	1863	1252		4634	4161	473
UK	61	471	334	137		394	394	
USA/Canada	328	16 195	5628	10 567		7440	4575	2865
					%	100	61	39
Aus/NZ	24.4	583	356	227		903	396	507
					%	100	44	56
S Africa	44	731	146	585		362	74	288
					%	100	20	80

Table 1.2 Range of loading on pavements

Source	Load: kg	Contact stress (MPa)	Comment
Stiletto heel	55	15	6 mm $\times$ 6 mm heel
Car	1500	0.035	
Truck	44 000	0.700	Tyre 100 psi
Airliner	560 000	1.5	A380–800
Fast jet	25 000	2.5	Fighter jet
Port straddle carrier	36 000	0.800	

MPa = MegaPascal

- ensure materials of construction are not overloaded or excessively fatigued
- be sustainable in economic terms.

It is then convenient to allocate the sections of the highway network into a series of traffic classes, and the banding represented in Table 1.4 may be found to be a useful starting point in a developed country. In a developing country, the third column may be more relevant.

It will be necessary to develop investigatory levels for each attribute in Table 1.3 and to differentiate between the several usage bands in Table 1.4.

The network must be segmented into reasonably homogeneous sections, which can be done using traffic flow and/or construction. In some cases, it may be appropriate to use convenient maintenance lengths between junctions. Depending on condition and deterioration, sectioning may become dynamic rather than static.

Once this has been done the basis of a management system exists, as there is now something to compare the individual pavement sections against.

1.6.   Questions relating to pavement management

A pavement may be considered to be a major economic asset and must be managed as such. As part of developing an overall strategy of pavement maintenance and management, the following questions must be examined in detail and options considered.

- What is the bearing capacity of the pavement structure?
- How good is the ride quality?
- What is the desired standard of maintenance?
- What would happen to the future condition if maintenance and rehabilitation were/were not carried out?

Table 1.4 Possible pavement loading design bands

Description	Cumulative msa	Vehicles/day
Access (unpaved)	<0.5	0–50
Low usage	>0.5 <2.5	50–250
Medium usage	>2.5 <10	250–500
High usage	>11 <30	500–1000
Very high usage	>30	

msa = million standard axles

- What is the economic value of the asset?
- What is the replacement value of the network?
- At what rate is the value of the asset declining?
- How much should be invested in maintaining the road network in order for society to get the highest rate of return on investment?

1.7.   Highway statistics in the UK

1.7.1   Road lengths

It is estimated that local roads sustain 15% and national roads 85% of the overall damaging effects of HGV traffic (see Table 1.5).

1.7.2   Road traffic – growth

Figure 1.1 shows that the principal growth in traffic has been on the motorways – 250% in 30 years, compared with that on local roads, which have seen 167% growth on urban major roads and 200% on rural major routes in the same period. An article published in NCE magazine stated that 'Isolated sections of the motorway network have seen significantly higher growth, for example M1 Jct 25–Jct 28 was originally designed for 13 000 vehicles/day and has been carrying 65 000 vehicles/day prior to the addition of a fourth lane to cater for up to 85 000 vehicles/day' (Greeman, 2010).

1.7.3   Traffic volumes

On the heavily trafficked sections of motorways traffic flows can be as high as an average flow of 100 000 vehicles per day, and

Table 1.3 Pavement investigatory performance limits

Number	Attribute	Maximum	Minimum
1	Traffic (light) level free flow	< X vehicles/hr	
2	Traffic (HGV) defined in standard axles	< X msa	
3	Longitudinal roughness (separate wheeltracks)	IRI < X m/km	
4	Transverse rutting (under X m straight edge)	< X mm	
5	Skid resistance in wheelpath (50 kph)		> X SRV
6	Surface texture		> X mm
7	Surface distress (may need to list individually)	< X % area	
8	Surface deflection (falling weight deflectometer)	< X microns	
9	Standing water (depth and area)	< X deep < Y area	

IRI = International roughness index; SRV = skid resistance value

Table 1.5 UK road lengths

2009 statistics published in the Department for Transport's website, www.dft.gov.uk/pgr/statistics/datatablespublications/tsgb/

	Rural: km	Urban: km	Total: km	%
National roads				
Trunk	8179	417	8596	
Motorway	3310	250	3560	
Subtotal national	11 489	667	12 156	3.08
Local roads				
Major	27 460	10 714	38 174	
Minor	212 880	131 220	344 100	
Subtotal local	240 340	141 934	382 274	96.92
Total roads in UK	251 829	142 601	394 430	

Figure 1.1 Traffic growth in the UK

From www.dft.gov.uk © Crown copyright

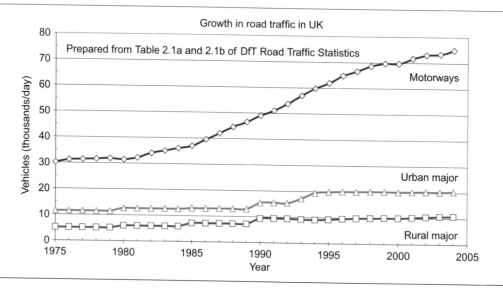

maximum flows of up to 173 000 vehicles per day have been recorded. Heavy goods vehicle flows are generally in the range 10–35% of total vehicle flows.

1.8. Funding and delivery of highway maintenance in the UK

There are two overall sources of funds that facilitate highway maintenance in the UK. In addition, there is a limited number of toll roads, and a small number of PFI arrangements. (See Figure 1.2.)

First, the national roads (motorways and trunk roads) are funded directly by the government from overall taxes collected. The maintenance of the national road network is managed, on behalf of the Department for Transport (DfT), by the Highways Agency (HA); both of these are government bodies employing civil servants. Essentially, the DfT is the asset owner and the HA the

asset manager. The national spending in any one year is not very easy to access; nevertheless an attempt is made and the information sources used are identified.

On the national roads in England, where delivery of the highway maintenance service comprises a series of 13 areas, there is currently a managing agent/contractor (MAC) arrangement. The MAC is generally a joint venture between a traditional contractor and a consulting engineer whose collective responsibility it is to manage and deliver the maintenance of the national asset within the defined area to HA standards and protocols.

The HA has detailed standards, specifications and administrative procedures, which are set out and can be accessed at http://www.standardsforhighways.co.uk/dmrb/index.htm.

Figure 1.2 Highways Agency MAC areas
www.highways.gov.uk/aboutus/143.aspx, accessed 08/07/2011 © Crown copyright

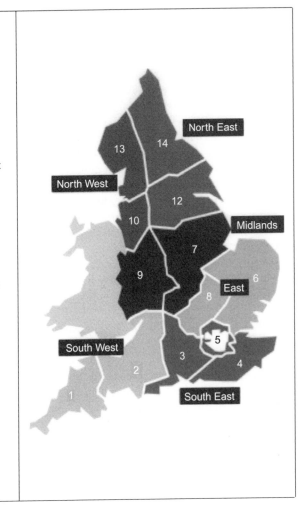

1 Cornwall and Devon

2 Somerset, Avon, Wiltshire and Gloucestershire

3 Hampshire, Berkshire, Surrey, Oxfordshire, Dorset and Wiltshire

4 Kent, Surrey, East Sussex and West Sussex

5 M25, link roads to GLA boundary, Berkshire, Buckinghamshire, Hertfordshire, Essex, Kent and Surrey (M25 area)

6 Essex, Cambridgeshire, Suffolk and Norfolk

7 Leicestershire, Northamptonshire, Derbyshire, Nottinghamshire, Lincolnshire, part of Warwickshire, Rutland and part of Oxfordshire (includes former Area 11)

8 Cambridgeshire, Bedfordshire, Hertfordshire and part of Suffolk

9 West Midlands, Hereford, Worcestershire, Shropshire, Warwickshire and Staffordshire

10 Cheshire, Merseyside, Greater Manchester and part of Lancashire

11 Not used

12 Yorkshire and Humberside ports motorways

13 Cumbria and parts of Lancashire

14 Northumberland, Tyne and Wear, Durham and North Yorkshire

This website is split into three sections

- *Design Manual for Roads and Bridges* (15 volumes)
- *Manual of Contract Documents for Highway Works* (7 sections)
- Interim Advice Notes.

The relevant expenditure figures for the national network are shown in the Table 1.6.

Second, within their own defined area the Local Highway Authorities (LHAs) are autonomous, although they normally work to the HA contract procedures and specification – which are accepted as national benchmarks. The local performance standards are set out in *Delivering Best Value in Highway Maintenance (Code of Practice for Highway Management)* which, with various supporting documents on highway asset

Table 1.6 National roads

	£ bn (£ × 10⁹)
Overall spend on operations 2004–2005	2.1
Value of asset	73.0
Return period in years (value/operations)	36 years

Expenditure on operations for financial year 2004–2005. Data taken from the Highways Agency Annual Report and Accounts, at www.highways.gov.uk/aboutus/documents/annl_rept_2004_05.pdf (accessed 08/07/2011).

management and highway asset valuation, can be found at www.ukroadsliaisongroup.org.

What a local highway authority spends on its own asset is for it alone to decide, but there are two things that it must be aware of – first, public opinion and the need to consult the users and, second, the legal situation whereby if anybody has any form of accident, vehicular or tripping, there is the possibility of the aggrieved/injured person claiming compensation from the highway authority, based on negligence. It is not appropriate to examine this in any detail here, as it would need a separate chapter to explain. The overall legal position is set out in Sections 41 and 58 of the Highways Act 1980. Again accurate figures are very difficult to assemble but the total cost of dealing with third-party claims nationally is believed to exceed £500 million annually! Money which could be much better spent.

Central government provides a substantial proportion of the funds expended by the local authority – over a range of programmes, namely education, personal social services, police, fire, highway maintenance, environmental protective and cultural services, and capital financing. This takes the form of a 'standard spending assessment' (SSA) more recently called 'formula spending shares' (FSS). Essentially, this is a 'top-down budgeting' exercise: the government defines a sum of money and attempts to appear to allocate it rationally.

The overall SSA/FSS allocation set out in Table 1.7 relates to financial year 2004–2005.

The major problem here is that each local authority gets an allocation defined discretely for a number of programme areas, and how it spends that total sum is for it to decide. For example, it might decide to spend all its money on education and let all other programmes come to a stop. Alternatively, and most unlikely, it could decide to keep a very good standard of maintenance of its highways and let education stand still. While the possibility is there for it to decide, it is most unlikely that this will happen.

Table 1.7 National funding for local services, 2004–2005
Data taken from www.hm-treasury.gov.uk/spending_review_sr02/press/spend_sr02_pr

Service	£ M	%
Education	26 828	44.6
Personal social services	11 856	19.7
Police	4395	7.3
Fire and rescue	1703	2.8
Highway maintenance	**2105**	**3.5**
Environmental, protective and cultural services	10 024	16.6
Capital financing	3323	5.5
Total SSA/FSS	60 234	100.0

Regardless of what an individual highway authority budgets to spend on individual programmes, it must report annually to the centre (government) on a series of key performance indicators (KPIs) – for the performance of different programmes and aspects of the asset. This is argued by government to ensure that some degree of reality prevails and is effectively an overall discipline.

An illustration of the difference between SSA/FSS and the budget allocated to highway maintenance over several years by Rotherham MBC is shown in Figure 1.3.

In Figure 1.3, it can be seen that the budget allocated by Rotherham MBC is only 71% of the funds allocated by the government. Rotherham must be congratulated as the only highway authority to have been sufficiently open to declare the SSA/FSS compared with the allocated highway maintenance budget.

In performance terms, the significant data missing from Figure 1.3 is first, the overall trend of highway condition and second, the overall trend in damage and injury payments to third parties (the travelling public).

While there are many ways in which overall pavement condition can be reported, and there is much debate as to which is the most relevant, Figure 1.4, taken from the Nevada Department of Transportation (DOT) annual pavement condition report, clearly illustrates the improvement in overall condition, taking account of three distress types. When producing information of this type careful consideration should be given to how it is presented. In the case of Figure 1.3, the trend of expenditure is clearly a negative one. In Figure 1.4, the y-axis could be inverted such that the trend in condition would be demonstrated to be positive. In addition to what is presented, how it is presented can be of equal or greater importance.

There is, however, a move toward requiring individual highway authorities to be more rational – namely to move towards formal asset value management, which is a principle being used progressively by the UK government for all spending programmes and is already used internationally by an increasing number of national highway authorities. In the case of highways, this work in the UK is drawing on experiences in New Zealand and Australia.

The principle is relatively simple: the highway is considered to be an asset, with a capital value – generally described as the gross replacement cost (GRC), and this value must be maintained – or any depreciation quantified. Overall the principle is that the maintenance budget must be equal to or greater than the value of the total economic worth of the deterioration, to maintain the value of the asset. This principle is a distinct move towards rational management, as it requires assessment of the asset value and the determination of a rational budget. In the present difficult

Figure 1.3 Proportion of funding spent on highway maintenance in Rotherham

From *Streetpride Annual Report 2005 – Rotherham* at http://moderngov.rotherham.gov.uk/mgConvert2PDF.aspx?ID=7073. Information in the public domain

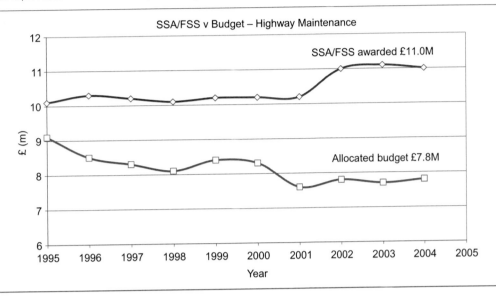

Figure 1.4 Monitoring of overall pavement condition

Nevada Department of Transportation (DOT), USA. Information in the public domain

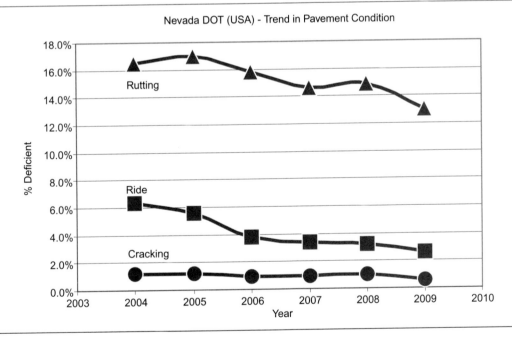

economic climate, time will tell whether it leads to more realistic budgets.

1.9. Estimated value of highway asset

In an attempt to make a first-order estimate of worth of the overall UK highway network, work undertaken in Sheffield in 1987 indicated that the 2000 km urban network, including bridges, had a replacement value of about £650 million (1986 prices). In terms of highway length it can be seen that Sheffield equates to approximately 0.52% of the overall English local highway network, in which case the overall highway asset for Sheffield, allowing for an inflation multiplier from 1986 to 2004 of 2.00 (www.statistics.gov.uk), suggests that the overall UK network (excluding motorways and trunk roads – dealt with earlier in this chapter) could be worth about £194 billion (2004 prices) – nearly three times the asset value of the national roads. Local road highway maintenance allocation for 2004–2005 was about £2 billion. Using a similar format to the national roads summary previously set out, the overall statistics for local roads can be illustrated in the following way:

	£: bn (£ × 10^9)
Value of asset	250
Overall spending on operations 2004–2005	2.1
Return period in years (value/operations)	119 years

The estimate of a return period of 92 years may be over-optimistic. The government argued, at the time, that there had been a significant under-spend, and estimated spend achieved by local highway authorities was nearer to £1.6 billion, in which case the return period can be seen to be as high as 156 years.

This overall return period may be taken as a first-order indicator of the likely highway condition. Bearing in mind that a surface course may be expected to last between 15 and 20 years and a pavement may be expected to require strengthening at 20-year intervals, a return period of about 40–60 years seems to be a reasonable expectation. The return periods calculated in the previous paragraph go some way towards explaining the very poor condition of the local road network in the UK.

As the result of a national move towards calculating GRC, much effort has been put into deriving guidance, and the CIPFA code (CIPFA, 2010) sets out typical unit rates with regional variations, treatment lives, and depreciation models (see www.cipfa.org.uk/pt/infrastructure/support.cfm). This site links to a series of presentations from Hamfig (Highways Asset Management Finance Information Group), which are available at: www.leics.gov.uk/highways/transport_plans_policies.amp/hamp_events/.

Work in a unitary authority in southern England, some years ago, revised using the currently advised CIPFA unit rates, is shown in the Table 1.8. This indicates how an initial first-order assessment of the value of the highway asset (i.e. its GRC) in an individual authority may be calculated. It also illustrates the significance and importance of a comprehensive and detailed inventory.

1.9.1 Assessment of highway asset worth (GRC)

See Table 1.8.

Table 1.8 Assessment of highway asset worth (GRC) in a unitary authority in southern England

Item	Length: km	Width: m	Area: sq. m	Number	Rate	£ m
Carriageways						
A	74	8	592 000		125	74.00
B	31.3	7.5	234 750		106	24.80
C	217.2	7	1 520 400		95	144.40
Unclassified	749	6.5	4 868 500		76	370.00
Redways	250	4	1 000 000		45	45.00
Street lighting						
Class A				15 000	1000	15.00
Class B				32 500	800	26.00
Bridges						
Principal				33	160 000	5.28
Non-principal				402	85 000	34.17
Unclassified				114	60 000	6.84
Drainage (5% roads)						32.10
Barriers						1.00
Traffic signs						2.00
Traffic signals				30	35 000	1.05
Pedestrian areas			150 000	30		4.50
Footways	1200	2.5	3 000 000	70		210.00
Parking areas			200 000	50		10.00
Planting/trees						10.00
Total £m						1016.14

1.10.   Highway management

The highway network is a major economic asset of any country or community, a fact which was recognised in Victorian times by Smiles in *Lives of the Engineers*:

> Roads have in all times been among the most influential agencies of society: and makers of roads, by enabling men readily to communicate with each other, have properly been regarded as amongst the most effective of pioneers of civilisation. Roads are not only the pathways of industry, but of social and national communication.
>
> Smiles, 1862

It can be argued that the highway is used by more of the population on a daily basis than any other services provided by the government and local authorities. It can also be demonstrated that it is used for the entire lifespan of the population, unlike other elements of infrastructure – for example, education, which is formally used for only a part of a person's life, and social services, which many people do not use at all.

From the point of view of the highway's owners, the major management parameter is the value of that asset and the manner in which it is being managed. In these circumstances the need for a sophisticated management process can be readily appreciated.

1.10.1   The principle of asset management

One of the major problems at the moment is rationally developing a case for adequate funding for highway maintenance, which is considered alongside other services. In times of financial stringency all services tend to be cut arbitrarily. Alongside this is the growing dissatisfaction expressed by the travelling public about the state of the network (the asset). While there have been, and there continue to be, surveys such as the National Road Maintenance Condition Survey (NRMCS) which chart the on-going condition of the various sections of the network, the results are relative – one year to the next – with no rationally defined starting point.

The evolving concept of asset management is one that involves considering each element of infrastructure as an asset and estimating its worth in financial terms. Each element is assigned a service life – for example, a surface course will have a typical service life of 12–15 years, and a bridge perhaps 150 years. Based on this concept a depreciation profile can be constructed. A regular inspection can estimate the overall condition of the particular asset element and this can be compared with what might be expected. Any difference in these two estimates may be considered to be the 'consumption'. Simply put, the relevant overall budget would then be the sum of all the estimated consumption. If the allocated budget is less than this summation of consumption, the value of the asset will reduce. This can be expressed in monetary terms rather than in terms of relative condition. The relative condition would most probably be related to the user's perception of the ride condition, however; this is dealt with in Chapter 10.

1.10.2   Maintenance systems (see Figure 1.5)

Prioritisation takes many forms. To consider two contrasting positions: prioritisation by decibel (he who makes the loudest noise and causes the most embarrassment is given first place) can still be observed, and is perhaps still the case, in the allocation of public finances internationally, but in the UK this is progressively giving way to the application of economic factors, ensuring that the best financial use is made of scarce resources.

In the UK, the first attempt at defining standards of maintenance was set out in the Marshall Report (Marshall, 1970), which was not widely implemented. Despite the fundamental philosophy being correct, the cost of achieving the recommended standards was argued to be well beyond the financial resources available in the 1970s.

The Local Authorities Association (LAA) published *Highway Maintenance: A Code of Good Practice* (LAA, 1989), which continued to promote the overall philosophy of the Marshall Report. The recommendations in these documents were somewhat more widely implemented than had been those of the Marshall Report, but again scant financial resources were a problem.

A third and major revision of the series was *Delivering Best Value in Highway Maintenance: Code of Practice for Highway Maintenance* (DETR, 2001).

Figure 1.5 Maintenance system

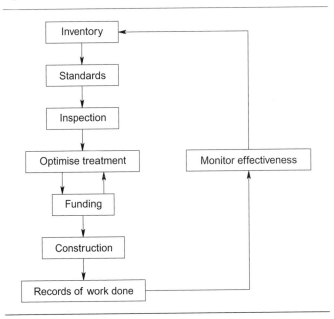

This publication adopted the concept of best value – which is essentially a system of continuous improvement, involving detailed internal examination of systems, external benchmarking of similar systems, and the definition and monitoring of service delivery improvement programmes. Because the concept of best value is rooted in the academic pursuit of quality, one fundamental addition to past practices was the introduction and appreciation of the requirements of the user. In this respect the 2001 Code had in its foreword the following challenging statement: 'The Code of Practice is founded on the key principle of best value – that services should be based on the needs of the community rather than the convenience of the service providers.'

A further document in this series, *Well Maintained Highways – A Code of Good Practice for Highway Maintenance Management*, was issued in 2005 (RLG, 2005). This and other relevant advice documents listed below are available as free downloads at www.ukroadsliasiongroup.org.

- Framework for highway asset management. April 2004.
- Well-lit highways. Code of practice for lighting management. November 2004.
- Well-maintained highways. Code of practice for highway maintenance management. July 2005.
- Asset valuation guide. July 2005.
- Management of highway structures. Code of practice. September 2005.
- Maintaining a vital asset. November 2005.
- Best practice guidelines for surfacing. June 2006.
- Review of transport asset management plans. January 2008.

The political environment in which highway maintenance operates, in the UK at least, must be considered a microcosm of the relationship between central and local government.

1.10.3 Highway maintenance functions
Figure 1.6 sets out the various highway maintenance functions and indicates the contribution they make. The headings provide a reasonable format for monitoring spending and comparing the response of different organisations.

1.11. Pavement management system (PMS)
A pavement management system can be seen to be a major sub-system comprised of an aggregation of several data sets. Experience indicates that, provided the locational referencing system can be properly structured, the various data sets can be established in isolation and used in combination when required. The pavement management system specifically addresses the paved areas comprising both carriageway and footway. In the following discussion, however, only the carriageway will be considered.

The major features of a PMS relating to the carriageway are

(*a*) visual/surface distress condition
(*b*) functional condition
(*c*) roughness
(*d*) rutting
(*e*) safety
  (i) skid resistance
  (ii) texture depth
(*f*) structural condition (bearing capacity)
(*g*) falling weight deflectometer
(*h*) deflectograph
(*i*) construction
  (i) cores
  (ii) trial pits
  (iii) ground radar
(*j*) foundation support (cbr)
(*k*) economics-based prioritisation system
(*l*) continuous performance/condition monitoring process.

The single most important feature in a PMS is common locational referencing. It is described as common because it allows all other modules to be related within the highway management system.

A close relationship exists with the highways laboratory system: this section of the organisation is responsible for sampling and compliance monitoring of materials purchased, and, probably, for carrying out the ongoing monitoring of pavement performance.

What the previous figures do not illustrate is the scale of the management task in delivering such a system, which goes to the roots of what the highways department, or whatever it is called in the organisation being considered, is about. The fundamental issue is organisational development and it has defeated many past attempts at technical progress.

The author's many years of experience of working in large highway organisations confirm that while technical problems can be dealt with, the corporate and organisational challenges involved in successfully implementing a highway asset management system are extremely formidable. The implementation of a comprehensive management system requires serious joined-up thinking by all sections of the organisation, forming a significant and fundamental challenge to the many self-serving local power bases that exist within any large organisation.

1.11.1 Need to secure and manage public funds
It should be clearly understood that maintenance funds don't just come along but must be vigorously competed for by carefully constructed, rational, technically based argument.

There are three pre-conditions to securing and managing public funds, which those in positions of responsibility must be capable of:

Figure 1.6 Highway maintenance functions

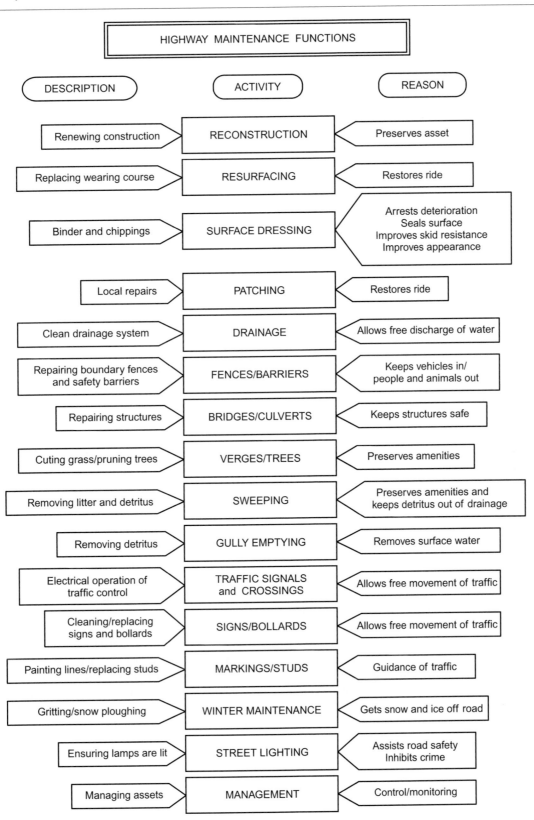

1. The need to argue rationally for the required funds.
2. The need to clearly prioritise where and how the funds are to be spent.
3. The need to demonstrate how effectively the funds were spent.

Those who are unable to fulfil all three of the conditions listed above are not suitable to be in a position to manage public funds. The author makes no excuses for this bluntness.

1.12. Developments in delivery and processes

As local authority funds have become scarcer there has been an increasing move to outsourcing both contracting and client activities.

One of the major benefits of this movement has been the development of and investment in sophisticated plant and operations, examples being

- mechanising potholing with Jet Patch technology, where a cavity is cleared with compressed air before a heated mix of aggregate and emulsion is blown in. This has considerably increased output such that in one day a two-man team can achieve what previously took two men two weeks
- the use of proprietary materials for patching, where the existing pavement is heated in situ first, leading to more robust work
- the increased use of retexturing to reinstate skid resistance
- the increased use of micro-asphalt, made possible due to machinery and materials technology development
- increase in specialist machine-laid surfacing teams employed by major asphalt suppliers, operating to quality-assured procedures
- increased capability of cold planning due to machinery development
- use of indented patterned fine asphalt for demarcation and pedestrian crossings
- increased use of sophisticated mechanised survey techniques, the better to target work
- increased availability of construction data due to ground radar technology.

REFERENCES AND BIBLIOGRAPHY

AASHO (1961) Highway Research Board's Special Report 61A: The AASHO road test: history and description of the project. *National Academy of Sciences*, Washington, DC.

AASHTO (American Association of State Highways and Transportation) (1993) *Guide for Design of Pavement Structures*, 4th edition with 1998 supplement. AASHTO, Washington, DC.

CIPFA (2010) Code of Practice on Transport Infrastructure Assets: Guidance to Support Asset Management and Reporting 2010. Chartered Institute of Public Finance and Accounting, London.

DETR (Department of the Environment, Transport and the Regions) (2001) *Delivering Best Value in Highway Maintenance. Code of Practice for Highway Mainentance.* DETR, Rotherham.

FGSV (Forschungsgesellschaft für Straßen- und Verkehrswesen) (2001) Richtlinien für die Standardisierung des Oberbaues von Verkehrsflächen, RStO 01. FSGV Verlag Gmbh, Köln, Germany.

Frost H (1910) *The Art of Road-making.* Scientific Press, Brooklyn, NY.

Greeman A (2010) M1 widening: The big squeeze. *New Civil Engineer* **2 September**.

Hubner D and Jameson GW (2008) *Guide to Pavement Technology Part 2: Pavement Structural Desig*n. Austroads, Sydney.

LAA (Local Authorities Association) (1989) *Highway Maintenance: A Code of Good Practice.* Association of County Councils, London.

LGPLA (1980) *Local Government, Planning and Land Act 1980.* See www.legislation.gov.uk/ukpga/1980/65/contents for further details (accessed 08/07/2011). HMSO, London.

Marshall AH (1970) Report of the committee on highway maintenance. HMSO, London.

McAdam JL (1820) Report to the London Board of Agriculture, London.

Nicholls JC, McHale MJ and Griffiths RD (2008) Road Note 42: Best practice guide for the durability of asphalt pavements. TRL, Wokingham.

RLG (UK Roads Liason Group) (2005) Well-maintained highways. Code of practice for highway maintenance management. TSO, London. Additions and supplements can be found at www.ukroadsliaisongroup.org (accessed 13/07/11).

Setra and LCPC (Laboratoire Central des Ponts et Chaussées) (1994) Conception et dimensionnement des structures de chaussée: guide technique. Ministère de l'Équipement, des Transports et du Tourisme, Paris. (*French Design Manual for Pavement Structures (Collection Guide Technique)*, 1997).

Smiles S (1862) *Lives of the Engineers.* John Murray, London.

Ullidtz P (1987) *Pavement Analysis.* Elsevier, Amsterdam.

Deterioration and Maintenance of Pavements
ISBN: 978-0-7277-4114-1

ICE Publishing. All rights reserved
http://dx.doi.org/10.1680/dmp.41141.013

Chapter 2
Footways and Walkways

2.1.   Introduction

At this stage, there is merit in clarifying the terms footways and walkways as they are used in this section. In the UK, the generic term 'pavement' is usually applied to the footway, whereas in this text a footway is but a sub-category of the overall family of pavements used exclusively by pedestrians. The term 'walkway' is employed where there is shared use with motor vehicles, and in town centres feature walkways are referred to as pedestrian precincts.

Footways and walkways are a more interesting, complex and challenging entity to design and maintain than carriageways, for a number of reasons which will be explored in detail later in this section.

This chapter should be read in conjunction with Atkinson (1997).

2.2.   Users of the footway and their expectations

Users of the footway are a broad group of people of diverse age and physical ability. There are more people with mobility impairments than one might imagine: the category of people with mobility impairments includes not just those with an ambulatory disability, but also those who push prams, and those who carry shopping. It is this group who provide the greatest challenge both for the provision and the maintenance of the walking surface. Figure 2.1, a photograph of a woman in her eighties carrying a large bag of shopping, may realistically be considered to represent a typical user in the UK.

In Figure 2.1, the woman's shoe has a small heel, which does not assist stability; the shopping that she is carrying also presents a potential impairment to her stability. And in Figure 2.2, neither the young man nor the little boy are wearing structured footwear.

With regard to the walking surface, the user is vulnerable to trips and short undulations, loose surfaces and standing water. It should also be remembered that the walking surface must, in most cases, be capable of sustaining the high stresses resulting from vehicle overrun – both on an isolated and a regular basis.

The design of the highway infrastructure has progressed from the original arrangement of a single joint surface, such as the one depicted in Figure 2.2, to accommodate animals and their accompanying pedestrian minders, and, subsequently, wheeled vehicles of increasing diversity.

From the mid-1700s, separate footways became the norm with vehicles being segregated to the carriageways and pedestrians to the footway. Since the early 1950s there has been progressive

Figure 2.1 A typical UK footway user, for the purpose of design

Figure 2.2 Informal shared surface
Courtesy of Willem Van Herp

Figure 2.3 Typical children's footwear in the early 1900s

encroachment of vehicles onto the footway, which in addition to being dangerous has resulted in many structural problems and a progressive acceptance of the need to provide a greater structural capability in the footway.

In the case of a carriageway, fatigue loading is incremental and is a function of the maximum axle load. Additionally, the loads are transmitted in a generally linear manner by way of a rubber tyre, which has a relatively small range of frictional variance; the tyre itself can cope with a significant variation in surface roughness. With the carriageway there is merit and greater safety in having a surface of the highest possible skid resistance.

Footwear, particularly for women, has varied greatly – from the clog, shown in Figure 2.3, to the stiletto heel, in some cases capable of applying point loads to a surface approaching and in some cases actually exceeding the compressive strength of the materials of construction.

Accidents occur on the walking surface for a number of reasons, the main ones being

- random occurrences
- ambulatory capabilities
- surface type
- pedestrian flow
- surface condition.

At this stage, a brief examination of the walking process is relevant.

Figure 2.4 shows that during the walking phase the foot is lifted then swings through, making an arc centred about the knee. In the swing phase, the toe is generally the lowest part of the foot, and hence it is most often the toe that makes contact with any trip hazard. One of the most important aspects of gait in relation to tripping is the height of the toe above the ground during the swing phase. This is known as toe clearance. A number of studies have investigated minimum toe clearance both during normal walking conditions and in situations where obstacles are negotiated. All of these studies differentiated between the minimum toe clearance of young adults and of elderly people, with the former exhibiting minimum toe clearances of between 10 mm and 20 mm, while the toe clearances of the latter were generally 10 mm or less.

2.3. Objectives of footways and walkways

Since the late 1940s, in England there have been progressively fewer true footways that are not to some greater or lesser extent over-run by vehicles. In these circumstances it is relevant to consider a list of objectives for this class of pavement, whose functionality and maintenance objectives are related predominantly to the needs of pedestrians.

(a) Provides a safe route for pedestrians, cyclists and motor vehicles where appropriate.
(b) Free from:
   (i) obstructions
   (ii) trips
   (iii) standing water
   (iv) loose surfaces
   (v) litter
   (vi) weeds.
(c) Have gradients as gentle as practicable.
(d) Be well lit where necessary.
(e) Have clear markings.

Figure 2.4 Gait analysis
Reproduced from Whittle (2007) with permission from Elsevier

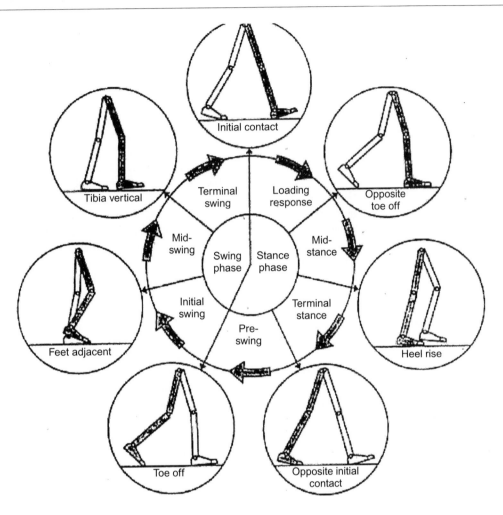

Positions of the legs during a single gait cycle by the right leg (shaded)

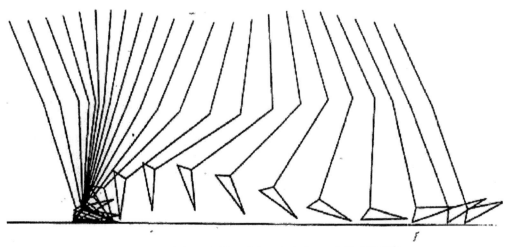

Position of the right leg in the sagittal plane at 40 ms intervals during a single gait cycle

(f) Have non-slip surfaces in wet and dry conditions.

(g) Have a maximum desirable level of slip resistance.

(h) Without gaps to trap:
   (i) wheels
   (ii) walking canes
   (iii) shoe heels.

(i) Compatible with the immediate surroundings.

(j) Permit easy and unhindered usage by all pedestrians and cyclists including those with mobility difficulties.

(k) Designed to minimise the possibility of vehicle overrun.

(l) Capable of supporting overrun where it regularly occurs.

(m) Have minimal maintenance needs consistent with the lowest whole life costs.

(n) Easily reinstated.

There is very little detailed guidance in the literature, which facilitates the quantification of pedestrians' capability or preferences, such that maintenance standards can be developed for the walking surface. Leake *et al.* (1991), however, present a useful starting point; their publication reported on a survey conducted in Sheffield, which had three main objectives

- to obtain pedestrians' reactions to existing footways of differing construction methods and in various states of maintenance condition
- to determine the threshold at which a footway became unacceptable to the user and requires maintenance
- to obtain information on pedestrians' preferred types of footway construction.

Table 2.1 sets out a summary of the findings, which were reported for a variety of surface types.

This can be seen to provide the basis for the development of maintenance objectives.

Trip hazard – the foregoing suggests that a trip hazard of 25 mm would provide a significant obstacle to most pedestrians, particularly the elderly. Leake *et al.* (1991) established that users found difficulties when up-stands exceeded 10 mm. This is consistent with Whittle (2007).

Rocking flags – Leake *et al.* (1991) found that all rocking flags are categorised as dangerous by the user.

Cracks and gaps – Leake *et al.* (1991) found users had difficulties when gaps exceeded 10 mm in width.

Depressions and bumps – Leake *et al.* (1991) found that transverse depressions were more difficult for the user and this was subsequently confirmed by Spong *et al.* (1995).

2.4. The legal position in the UK

In the UK, the fundamental legislation is set out in the Highways Act 1980 and while this covers many aspects of the highway the fundamental principle is to permit safe passage and re-passage within the boundaries of the highway. No guidance, however, is given on acceptable standards of maintenance. This resulted in the development of case law and Figure 2.5 defines what is generally considered acceptable beyond which a claimant may be due to compensation.

The present legal position for all users of an adopted highway (one maintained at public expense) is that if they have an accident they may be able to make a successful claim against the

Table 2.1 Survey findings
Data taken from Leake *et al.*, 1991

Surface	Sex	Undulation: mm	Raised edges ≥5 mm: %	Friction (pendulum value)	Broken pavers: %	Gaps ≥10 mm: %
Block paving	M/F	≤ 10-11	n	≥ 65	≤ 10 (R)	n
Conventional	M	≤ 11	≤ 12	≥ 65	≤ 10	≤ 4
flags	F	≤ 11	≤ 12	≥ 65	≤ 10	≤ 1
Small element	M	≤ 10	≤ 9	≥ 65	≤ 10 (R)	n
flags	F	≤ 10	≤ 9	≥ 65	≤ 10 (R)	n
Asphalt	M/F	≤ 14–15	N/A	≥ 65	N/A	N/A

Key:
n = no standard obtained
N/A = not applicable
M /F = male and female
(R) = recommendation based on conventional flags

Figure 2.5 Walking surface legal benchmarks for surface regularity
Courtesy of the Audit Commission

Highway authorities definition of damage to pavements

Damage is defined as a defect in the footway which impairs the value or usefulness to the footway and provides a safety hazard for pedestrians, a useful guide is as follows:

Trips more than 20 mm.
Rocking flags greater than 20 mm.
Rapid change of footway profile greater than 25 mm and extending in plan dimension less than 600 mm and should be repaired in accordance with individual highway authority reponse times.

Trips greater than 20 mm.

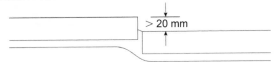

Rocking flags greater than 20 mm.

Rapid change of footway profile greater than 25 mm and extending in plan direction less than 600 mm.

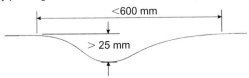

Ref. Audit Commission – The Publication of Information (Standards of Performance) Directive 1994

highway authority for compensation. This is not dealt with in any detail here and the reader is referred to the UK Roads Liaison Group (2005, 2009).

It will be seen that Figure 2.5, which relates to footways and walkways, leads to an unacceptable standard of maintenance when compared with the findings presented in Table 2.1.

The interesting dilemma here is that the general standards of surface compliance seen by users as desirable are considerably more challenging than the legal interpretation of what is reasonable.

2.5.   Design of footways and walkways

This section does not set out to give advice on the conceptual and aesthetic design of footways and walkways, rather it seeks to give some guidance on the structural, construction and maintenance aspects thereof, since this promotes the longevity of the project.

The design of footways and walkways follows highway practices, which are dealt with in detail elsewhere, and can be traced back

to TRL Road Note 29, first published in 1960 (TRL, 1970). While this document relates to asphalt pavement construction, increasingly many areas are constructed in elemental or modular materials. In this text the term elemental construction relates to a range of materials, from concrete to natural stone, in many sizes, from large flagstones to small cobbles.

The greatest challenge for the designer is the urban pedestrian precinct where there is the opportunity for architectural flair to enhance adjacent buildings and follow European practices in the mid to late 1940s with major pedestrian schemes which emerged in the post-World War II rebuilding era. Almost without exception these were of elemental construction.

The synthesis of ideas and requirements of the architect and the engineer has not always been happy, due to the naturally extrovert nature of the former and introvert conservative nature of the latter. Nevertheless, there is a fundamental issue here, which is where the result is viewed from and this is not well understood. The architect is used to drafting elevations to buildings, which can easily be seen by the observer looking with eyes set typically at 1.5 m above ground level. On many occasions photographs of walkways have been taken from adjacent buildings not accessible to the normal user, and the layout and juxtaposition of different materials cannot be fully appreciated from the usual viewing height of 1.5 m above ground level. An example is shown in Figure 2.6.

While there are separate published standards for elemental construction, the general rationale for the determination of overall pavement thickness, especially where wheeled traffic may be expected to use the area, is based on the proposition that the thickness of an element and its bedding provides a structural contribution equivalent to the same thickness of asphalt. This equivalence factor of 1.00 can be found in many international publications, but some UK literature is more conservative.

It is important to consider the usage of a footway. Originally footway design was fairly straightforward but since the 1950s, in the UK, there has been an increasing degree of vehicular encroachment, which must be allowed for, and in the case of a pedestrian precinct full heavy vehicular loading must be considered, as shown in Figure 2.7. At the other extreme the surface must be capable of dealing with concentrated point loads from high-heeled shoes and boots, as seen in Figure 2.8; as the point-load is typically 6 mm × 6 mm, there are potential problems if gaps between adjacent elements are greater than 6 mm.

A 6 mm × 6 mm high heel can impose point loads in excess of the compressive strength of some footway surfacing materials.

Harsh climatic conditions can result in specific design issues. For example, in central Stockholm, where 600 mm of snow can fall overnight, the layout of the precincts is such that snow blowers and 3-axle lorries must be able to manoeuvre to pick up the snow prior to businesses and shops opening in the morning, and in

Figure 2.7 Heavy loading on the walking surface

Figure 2.8 Heavy point loading on the walking surface

Figure 2.6 Nice design but how many people can get this view?

some areas there is 'underfloor' heating from district heating circulating pipes.

2.6. Structural design of footways and walkways

2.6.1 Design considerations

2.6.1.1 Selection of footway category

Catalogue designs, adapted from AG26 (UK Roads Liaison Group, 2003), are given for four categories, the appropriate category being chosen according to the risk and type of vehicle overrun and the amount of pedestrian usage.

A footway in a residential area may be subject to illegal parking by private cars. In a rural area adopting a pedestrian-only design would be sensible as there will be little risk of motor traffic inconvenience to pedestrians.

There are many situations where light vehicle overrun is common, but overrun by heavy vehicles would not be expected to occur more than occasionally. Heavy vehicle overrun is likely where footways are adjacent to roads in areas where deliveries are made to local shops. Where a footway is subjected to regular vehicle overrun from parking the existing structure may require thicker layers, higher quality materials or other strengthening measures.

In many residential areas the most severe loading is from the weekly waste (dustbin) collection.

Shared pedestrian and cyclist facilities should be considered as light vehicle category to allow for cleaning and maintenance vehicles.

2.6.1.2 Assessment of subgrade

A footway must be constructed on an adequate foundation to ensure satisfactory performance. A soft subgrade provides insufficient support for compaction of the layers above, and is likely to cause their rapid deterioration.

When constructing a new footway a CBR (California bearing ratio) assessment can be made. If the bearing capacity of the soil is known, this can be related to CBR by simply dividing the bearing capacity in kPa (kiloPascal), by 140 (UK Roads Liaison Group, 2003). Assessment of bearing capacity is more important if the footway is required to withstand heavy vehicle overrun as this will determine the thickness of construction.

Where reconstruction and upgrading of an existing footway is planned, the accurate determination of bearing capacity is difficult due to the presence of services. In these circumstances it is reasonable to assume a figure greater than 5%.

A rough guide to CBR is set out in Table 2.2.

2.6.1.3 Utility apparatus

In a new footway all utility apparatus must be below formation level (DfT, 2002). The choice of footway surface should have regard to ease of reinstatement.

Table 2.2 Formation CBR basic guidance
Data taken from UK Roads Liaison Group (2003)

Soil condition	CBR
Very soft, exudes between fingers when squeezed	<1%
Can be moulded by light finger pressure	Between 1% and 2%
Can be moulded by strong finger pressure	Between 2% and 3%
Can be indented by a thumbnail but not by a thumb	>6%

Figure 2.9 Urban footway formation – the reality

2.6.1.4 Drainage

Since there should be no standing water on a footway it must be positively drained, consequently adequate falls are necessary and it is suggested that 2.5% is the absolute minimum with a preferred 3.5%. If a consistent cross-fall of 2.5% is not possible, consideration must be given to some form of longitudinal slot or channel drain: great care should be exercised in deciding which, because if incorrectly installed they can present a trip hazard to users. (See Figure 2.10.)

2.6.2 Pedestrian only design

Most pedestrian-only footways are surfaced with asphalt. Typically, this takes the form of a separate 40 mm binder course and a 20 mm surface course on a 100 mm granular sub-base. Some organisations prefer to use a single layer to avoid the problems of compacting thin layers, which cool very quickly. It is more

Figure 2.10 Some functional features can also be hazards

difficult, however, to achieve a good quality surface finish when a separate regulating course is omitted. Typical construction sections are shown in Figure 2.11.

2.6.3 Vehicle-resistant design

2.6.3.1 Light vehicle overrun design

The Figure 2.12 shows the recommended thickness for light vehicle design, where over-run is predominantly from private cars.

2.6.3.2 Occasional heavy vehicle overrun design

Where occasional heavy vehicle overrun is possible such as might occur for delivery vehicles to private houses or where there is a two-weekly cycle of waste collection (where the dustbin lorry is now tending towards a 3-axle design), then consideration should be given to local strengthening at radiuses where overrun is more likely. The constructions in Figure 2.13 are recommended.

2.6.3.3 Heavy vehicle design

The designs for footways to support heavy vehicle over-run are based on the established method of relating the sub-base thickness to the CBR of the subgrade and to the design traffic. Here the design traffic is assumed to be 50 000 standard axles. This allows approximately one vehicle per working day over a design life of 40 years. It is assumed that one heavy vehicle is, on average, equivalent to one standard axle. The number of standard axles is multiplied by three to take channelisation into account (as opposed to normal distribution) and to allow for the effects of dynamic loading due to the vehicle mounting the footway. Because of the impossibility of predicting with any accuracy the type and number of vehicles likely to over-run a footway, a traffic count would be inappropriate. The design figure of 50 000 standard axles should be robust enough subject to over-run. If a higher level of traffic is expected then the structure can no longer be considered a footway (UK Roads Liaison Group, 2003).

Recommended sub-base thickness is set out in Table 2.3 and Figure 2.14.

2.7. Construction of footways and walkways

2.7.1 Introduction

Once the structural design has been completed it is necessary to consider overall aesthetic design, the range of materials to be used and how that will affect the construction process – for example, are all the surfacing elements to be laid in or on sand, or will some of them have a stabilised bed? If clay pavers are included as features have they to be laid on a wet bed. The following examines some of the issues and considerations that must be taken into account.

Figure 2.11 Recommended design thickness – pedestrian-only footway

Reproduced from UK Roads Liaison Group (2003) © TRL

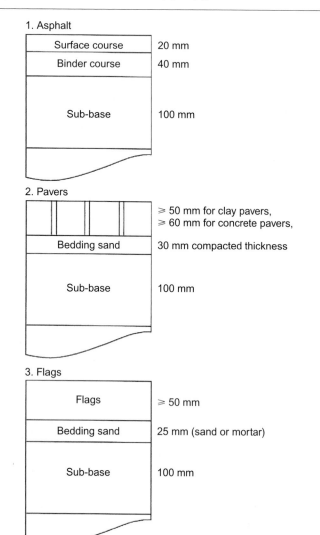

Table 2.3 CBR plotted against sub-base relationship
Data taken from UK Roads Liaison Group (2003)

CBR %	Type 1 sub-base: mm
2	365
3	270
4	210
5	165
>5	150

Figure 2.12 Recommended design thickness – light vehicle overrun footway
Reproduced from UK Roads Liaison Group (2003) © TRL

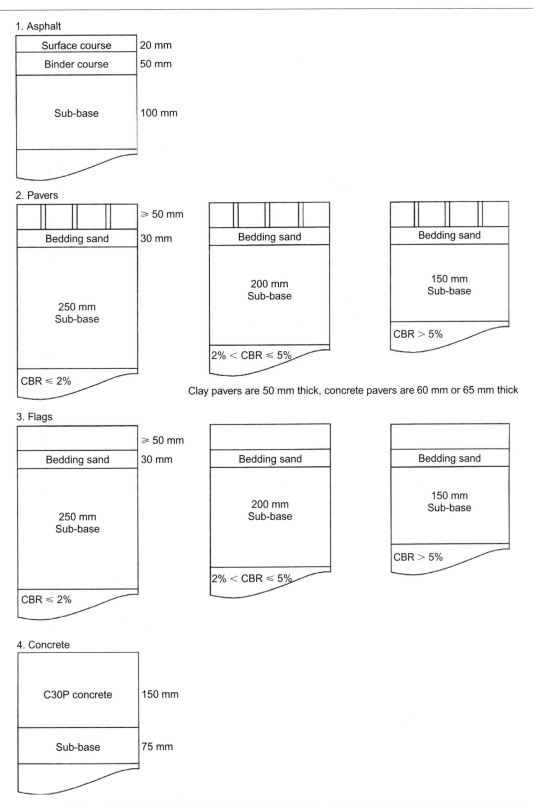

1. Asphalt

Surface course	20 mm
Binder course	50 mm
Sub-base	100 mm

2. Pavers

	≥ 50 mm
Bedding sand	30 mm
250 mm Sub-base	
CBR ≤ 2%	

Bedding sand	
200 mm Sub-base	
2% < CBR ≤ 5%	

Bedding sand	
150 mm Sub-base	
CBR > 5%	

Clay pavers are 50 mm thick, concrete pavers are 60 mm or 65 mm thick

3. Flags

	≥ 50 mm
Bedding sand	30 mm
250 mm Sub-base	
CBR ≤ 2%	

Bedding sand	
200 mm Sub-base	
2% < CBR ≤ 5%	

Bedding sand	
150 mm Sub-base	
CBR > 5%	

4. Concrete

C30P concrete	150 mm
Sub-base	75 mm

Figure 2.13 Recommended design thickness for footway subject to occasional HGV overrun

Reproduced from UK Roads Liaison Group (2003) © TRL

Figure 2.14 Recommended design thickness – footway subject to HGV overrun

Reproduced from UK Roads Liaison Group (2003) © TRL

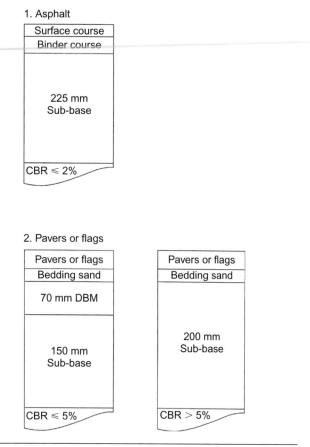

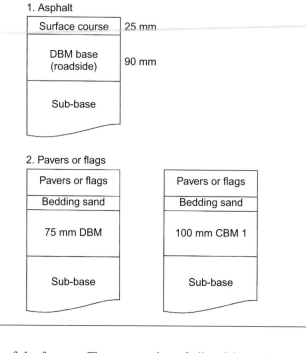

back of the footway. The construction of all walking surfaces is similar to that shown in Figures 2.15 and 2.16.

2.7.2 Slip resistance

The functional requirements of the surface layer must be considered. There has been previous discussion in this chapter regarding user preferences but at this stage it is appropriate to consider the required slip resistance. This is examined in greater detail in the Chapter 9.

Unlike those pavements designed for wheeled traffic, the greater

2.7.1.1 Typical cross-sections

The typical width of 2 m is instated to ensure that two prams can safely pass. It is important to ensure there is a positive drainage provision and that there is robust edge support at the front and

Figure 2.15 Footway with asphalt surface

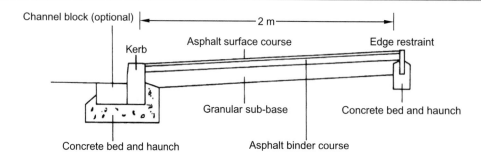

Layer thickness depends on foundation support and loading

Figure 2.16 Footway with elemental of paver surface

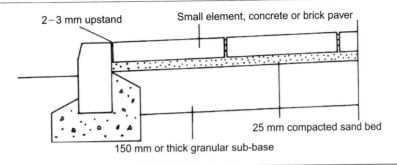

2—3 mm upstand
Small element, concrete or brick paver
25 mm compacted sand bed
150 mm or thick granular sub-base

the skid resistance the safer the surface. In the case of the walking surface, the procedure is similar in that the British Pendulum Tester is used, and the term slip is used. With the walking surface, however, there is a maximum slip resistance value (SRV) which if exceeded makes the process of walking progressively more difficult for the user.

There has been considerable debate about how the slip resistance of the walking surface should be measured. This is principally related to the exact material specification of the slider, the part of the British Pendulum Tester arm that comes into contact with the floor when the test is carried out.

The Health and Safety Laboratory (HSL) uses the pendulum skid resistance tester to determine the dynamic coefficient of friction (CoF) of a floor surface. This test correctly models the interaction between the pedestrian heel and the floor during normal pedestrian gait (HSE, 2004).

Based on guidance set out in HSE (2006), the information in Table 2.4 is relevant at this point.

As is apparent in Table 2.4, an SRV in the range 35–75 is considered to be appropriate.

The footway surface must not become slippery and difficult to walk on when wet. It is unlikely that this will be a problem with asphalt or concrete materials, but care should be taken when

specifying clay pavers or natural stone. The slip resistance of clay pavers is expressed as a polished paver value (PPV). A PPV of 45 is adequate for general use (UK Roads Liaison Group, 2003, paragraph 4.7).

The recommended slip resistance value within BS 6717 (BSI, 2001) for pre-cast pavers is a minimum of 35 for pedestrian-only areas and 45 for use within trafficked areas. These values may also be applied to pavers in natural stone.

Where the slope is >5% the above values should be increased by ten.

Locations near fast food outlets where grease/cooking oil may be dropped may require additional cleaning to maintain an acceptable slip resistance.

2.7.3 Surfacing materials

A broad range of surfacing materials can be used on footways and walkways, and consideration of which is most suitable is related, initially, to the extent to which there will be vehicle overrun. In central urban locations it is usual for there to be a mix of materials and colours as part of the overall scheme's aesthetic design (Table 2.5).

Before choosing a surface one should consider a range of issues recommended by IHT (2000), some of which are

- type and use: traffic (volume and mix) pedestrians, movement patterns
- initial and ongoing maintenance cost
- strength and durability, for anticipated loading
- construction: whether rigid or flexible and ease of construction
- pre-formed or in situ
- maintenance, including ease of cleaning and repair
- visual appearance: colour, widths, joints and bonds
- protection of tree roots
- appropriateness: vernacular/regional style, style of adjacent buildings, availability.

Table 2.4 Slip resistance plotted against risk of slipping
Data taken from HSE (2006)

TRL pendulum value (SRV)	Potential for slip
19 and below	high
20–39	moderate
40–74	low
>75	extremely low

Table 2.5 Footway surfacing materials
Data taken from IHT (Institution of Highways and Transportation, 2000)

Pedestrian-only	Vehicle over-run	Shared (precinct)
Earth		
Gravel		
Natural stone cobbles		Natural stone setts
Natural stone flags	Stone flags	Natural stone small flags
Concrete flags	Concrete flags	Concrete small element
Concrete – in situ	Concrete small element	Concrete block paving
Asphalt	Concrete – in situ	Brick paving
	Asphalt	Mixture of above
		Mastic asphalt
		Hot rolled asphalt

2.7.3.1 Earth and gravel

No comment need be made in this chapter relating either to earth or to gravel footways. In the UK, they tend to be used exclusively for recreational footways and the materials used are those available locally.

2.7.3.2 Cobbles

Natural stone cobbles (Figure 2.17), typically large river gravel of about 75–100 mm diameter, are generally laid in a locally sourced soil or sand-lime mortar. They tend to present a pleasing aesthetic impression rather than a functional walking surface and this form of construction is usually confined to local areas and may be used as a deterrent surface. A recurring problem is disfigurement by weeds.

2.7.3.3 Natural stone flags/slabs

Natural stone flags are not usually of consistent dimensions, either in plan or thickness, due to the vagaries of geological bedding, whereas the development of pre-cast concrete flags led to a progressive standardisation of 3 ft (900 mm) × 2 ft (600 mm) and 600 mm × 600 mm with thickness being either 50 mm or 65 mm.

Figure 2.18 shows the use of large elements during a recent refurbishment of Trafalgar Square, London. The flags (slabs) were up to 100 mm thick and 3 m × 3 m in size, clearly needing specialist skills and laying equipment.

2.7.3.4 Stone setts

In many of the Baltic countries most footways are an interesting and attractive mix of natural stone setts and concrete or natural stone flags (Figures 2.19 and 2.20). Distinct advantages of this format include the possibility of laying flags without cutting, and of using stone cubes by the kerb to cope with vehicles parking with one wheel on the footway, and others to line up with the

Figure 2.17 Cobbles surface

Figure 2.18 Natural stone flags being laid in the refurbishment of Trafalgar Square, London

Figure 2.19 Typical footway, Copenhagen, Denmark

Figure 2.21 A good example of small element paving

Figure 2.20 Typical footway, Tallinn, Estonia

Figure 2.22 Small element paving mixed with concrete block paving and cobbles

varying front face of adjacent buildings. The bedding course is always unbound granular material.

2.7.3.5 Small element concrete paving

The advent of pedestrianisation schemes, from the late 1940s in Europe and the late 1960s in the UK, led to the use of reinforced concrete flags up to 100 mm in thickness (Figure 2.21).

The concept of small element paving (Figure 2.22), typically 450 mm × 450 mm × 50–65 mm thick, was first used in Germany and introduced into the UK in the early 1980s in Birmingham, proving to grow progressively more popular, because a properly constructed bed has the capability to resist traffic.

2.7.3.6 Concrete block and brick paving

For many years brick paving was popular in Europe, where it was generally laid in a fairly low-bearing capacity formation and had the advantage that when localised settlement occurred the bricks could easily be lifted and relaid with the addition of further sand bedding. Bricks tended to be 300 mm × 100 mm × 50 mm to 65 mm in thickness and can be laid either 300 mm × 100 mm or 300 mm × 50 mm in plan. There are a number of interesting brick-paved precincts in the UK, particular examples being Centenary Square in Birmingham and the Cathedral Precinct in Wakefield (Figure 2.23). With 'artistic' arrangements such as these the regularity and consistency of the bedding course is of vital importance.

Figure 2.23 Wakefield Cathedral Precinct

2.7.4 Bedding materials

2.7.4.1 Flags and small element paving

From the early 1800s, in the UK, bedding for stone flags, which formed the predominant surface on footways at the time, was generally clinker ash. Clinker ash was the waste residue of the many coal-powered boilers, which provided the steam to run the industrial machinery of the day. From the early 1900s, in the UK, there was a progressive move to use sand for bedding, as clinker ash became more difficult to obtain. Where there is only pedestrian access to the walking surface these beddings have proved quite adequate. Pre-cast concrete flags, typically 900 mm × 600 mm, first became available in about 1900.

Since the mid 1950s, in the UK, there has been progressive encroachment onto the footway by vehicular traffic. In the urban centre streets with terraced housing and in the roads serving the major estates of social housing, which began to emerge at about that time, there was generally no provision for parking of private motor vehicles; consequently encroachment onto the footways increased and a lot of damage was fairly normal. Where vehicles were allowed to cross the footway it was normal for a sand/cement bed to be used with a thicker 65 mm flag.

The availability of the small element flag from the mid 1970s followed European practice and the use of sand bedding continued. Later, in a misguided attempt to strengthen the pavement, the sand was stabilised with cement.

The problem with a cement-stabilised bed is that a stiff surface element is laid on a stiff base; for the pavement to function properly a bond needs to develop between them. The likelihood of any bond developing in these circumstances is extremely low, consequently any movement of the element will destroy any tenuous bond which may have developed.

It is argued that for any elemental surface to be successful it must be placed on a sand or fine granular bed with some degree of resilience. In the UK, the preference is to use sand, whereas in some parts of Europe and the Scandinavian countries a 3–5 mm crushed granite bed is preferred. This has been examined in detail by Dowson (2001).

Figure 2.24 shows the construction of an exceptional precinct in Stockholm where a 3–5 mm crushed granite bedding was used with hot water 'underfloor' heating to ensure a safe walking surface in the harsh winter conditions. What is particularly interesting is that the picture shows how the mason is placing the three different-coloured small element pavers where the designer specified.

In many cases in Europe small element paving is laid in conjunction with small natural stone cubes to break up the overall surface into irregular shaped areas.

The Stureplan precinct in Stockholm is a good example of this and Figure 2.25 is a copy of the designer's layout, which because of the extremely high quality of work has delivered exceptional results.

The case of Fargate, one of the major pedestrian precincts in Sheffield, constructed in 1972 and one of the early UK pedestrianisation projects. is pertinent here. A sand/cement bed was used and the surface comprised 500 mm × 500 mm × 100 mm thick reinforced concrete flags. By the mid 1980s, an increasing number of flags were cracking and progressively became hazardous to pedestrians. Replacement of the flag with like for like proved unsuccessful, consequently the damaged slabs were removed and the resulting cavity was filled with asphalt. As the number of black infills grew (think tooth fillings!); the areas

Figure 2.24 Laying small element paving for Stureplan precinct, Stockholm, Sweden

became progressively larger and more noticeable, consequently generating increasingly vocal complaints from both the public and the local press. As a short term palliative, concrete blocks of a matching colour were placed in the cavities, which proved more acceptable than asphalt; nevertheless the problem was how to refurbish a major precinct with an attractive long-lasting solution.

At this point it is appropriate to briefly consider the 'design' or service life of the paving in a precinct. From a highway perspective this would typically be 20+ years. The interesting dilemma here is that the precinct is an integral part of the fabric of the commercial area, ideally facilitating unimpeded access by goods and purchasers to the 'sales' areas. As part of the continuing striving for trade and turnover it is not unusual for commercial premises to be refurbished on a ten-year cycle. This leads to the question 'Is the use of a 20+ years design life for the walking surface appropriate?'

2.7.4.2 Natural stone setts and pavers

Many pedestrian pavements are currently constructed on a stabilised bed, particularly where natural stone setts are used and the joints subsequently filled (grouted) with cement mortar slurry, effectively forming a continuous stiff surface layer. If one were to construct a concrete slab it would be split into bays with regular joints to accommodate thermal movement – both positive and negative. Most of the grouting mortar used is of proprietary brands where the exact ingredients are not declared and it is argued by each manufacturer that its product contains a degree of elasticity not normally associated with a cement mortar.

Figure 2.26 shows the construction of a new pedestrianised area in Blackpool, adjacent to the Winter Gardens, which seems to be designed to cope with a considerable traffic load. There is an asphalt layer under the sett layer, which appears to be shaping over the original pavement construction. The setts are a fairly constant 125 mm deep and of varying size; they are laid on/in a semi-dry cement stabilised bedding in a typical fan pattern. There is no evidence of any expansion joints nor any formal edge restraints.

Figure 2.27 shows the construction of a new pedestrianised street within the bounds of the University of Leeds. The existing road has been removed and a concrete slab placed, along with robust edge restraints. The paving elements are all machine cut prior to delivery and are laid on a thin bed of cement bound sharp 6–10 mm crushed stone, prior to the joints being filled with a flowable grout. No evidence of expansion joints is apparent.

What is particularly noticeable elsewhere in Europe and in the Mediterranean countries is the almost universal use of unbound

Figure 2.26 Natural stone setts – Blackpool, 2009

Figure 2.27 Natural stone paving – Leeds, 2010

granular bedding and joint filling, which has the significant advantage that when an area settles or becomes damaged the surface can easily be lifted and relaid using the existing setts with the addition of further material, costing little more than the labour charges involved.

2.7.4.3 Concrete block paving (CBP)

In the UK, concrete block paving tends to have a standard plan size of 200 mm × 100 mm, with a range of thicknesses up to 100 mm being available depending on the usage. CBP is laid on sand bedding which should have a constant thickness of 30–50 mm supported by robust construction.

In all town centre pedestrianisations there is an inevitable amount of variable depth (thickness) adjustment layer to harmonise original and new levels and in some early projects bedding sand was used as a shaping layer. Subsequent experience has demonstrated that this is not sound practice as the degree of settlement in the sand is directly related to its thickness and this has led to a progressively uneven surface developing.

In this situation either lean mix concrete or, ideally, asphalt should be used to harmonise levels. The problem with lean mix concrete is that shrinkage is inevitable, leading to cracking, which can result in the loss of fine bedding sand into the crack, leading to localised surface settlement. Asphalt is preferred as a base, since it does not require a curing period and can be used as a temporary walking surface prior to placing the sand bedding and CBP surface layer.

The appropriateness and specification of bedding sand is a function of both its grading and petrological background, as was demonstrated by Dowson (2001). This is less of a problem for lightly loaded surfaces but it can be critical where there is continuous heavy channelised traffic.

2.7.4.4 Brick paving

2.7.4.4.1 FLEXIBLE PAVING WITH CLAY PAVERS

Initially, brick paving was laid on a sand bed in a similar manner to CBP and gained a share of the market because of the range and fastness of the available colours. Guidance relating to laying was set out by Smith (1988). Essentially, clean sharp sand is used for the 30–50 mm bedding and fine sand, typically 100% passing a 1 mm sieve with <10% passing a 75 µm sieve. Joints between adjacent elements should be in the range 2–5 mm wide.

2.7.4.4.2 RIGID PAVING WITH CLAY PAVERS

Hammett and Smith (1995) set out guidance on the use of rigid paving with clay pavers. To ensure continuity of service the concrete base on which the pavers are to be laid should be sufficiently thick to resist ground movement, otherwise there may be noticeable stepped cracks in the surface. Elements should be laid in a stiff plastic mortar of 1 : 0.25 : 3 (cement, lime, sand) 15–20 mm thick, with a similar mix being used for grouting between adjacent elements.

An alternative to this is to use a semi-dry process where a 20 mm thick bed of 1 : 3 (cement, sand) is laid and the individual elements are coated on the underside with a slurry of 1 : 1 (cement : fine sand) 1 mm–3 mm thick immediately prior to laying.

When using the rigid paving method the movement joint should be incorporated around the edges of the bed and also at 4.5–6 m centres.

2.7.5   Asphalt

Asphalt on footways is generally laid by hand, although the use of mini-pavers is increasing. Ideally, it should be laid in two courses: a surface course on a binder course, typically 25 mm and 65 mm respectively. The major problem is to ensure that the base, which is usually granular, provides sufficient support to permit full compaction of the binder course to be achieved or the service life will be reduced. This compaction is important as the binder course provides the main structural contribution of the structure. Recent practice in a number of areas where the surface course has eroded and the binder course is distressed is to remove all old asphalt and replace it with a single asphalt course. Experience indicates there to be problems with achieving full compaction and maintaining a consistent cross-fall.

Asphalt is available in a limited number of colours, which can be used to delineate a particular usage, for example, to differentiate a cycleway from the footway.

In Europe, there are many examples where the quality of work is much higher than that seen in the UK, and if done properly there is no reason for the surface to be a boring expanse of featureless asphalt. Figure 2.28 shows a pavement in Tenerife with indentations which were obviously made while the asphalt was still hot, in a design which was used in an area comprising many streets. The patterns did not present any difficulties to users and resulted in an attractive addition to an otherwise normally featureless asphalt surface.

Twin drum vibrating rollers are preferred for compaction; special care should be taken to ensure good compaction around street furniture and adjacent to walls and buildings. There are a number of asphalt mixes which may be used.

Figure 2.28 Patterns in asphalt surface, Tenerife

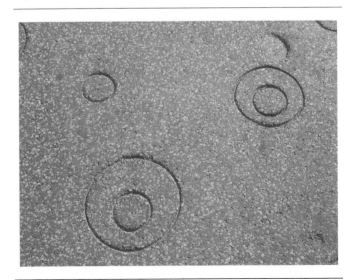

Typically asphalt used on footways contains a higher penetration bitumen binder, characteristically 100 or 200 penetration.

For the surface course a 6 mm aggregate size to BS 594987 (BSI, 2010) is usual and a dense grading is to be preferred. The use of a limestone aggregate is to be preferred as in addition to being a hard stone with good weathering capabilities and it is less aggressive on broken skin in the event of a fall. This is particularly relevant for use in school playgrounds, as limestone has antiseptic properties compared with some other aggregates.

For specialist applications where a high degree of impermeability is required the use of mastic asphalt can be considered. This may be found useful where there are cellars, which project under the footway in urban areas. It is usual for mastic asphalt to be laid hot, by hand, as a skilled operation. Compaction is usually by a relatively light hand roller, which typically leaves a dimpled surface.

2.7.6   Concrete

The use of poured concrete is not widespread in the UK as there is a need for it to achieve a reasonable degree of set before it can be used: otherwise there is the likelihood that third parties will damage the surface. Surface finish is typically tamped, providing a somewhat hostile walking surface. By comparison, in the USA many footways are formed from concrete where the surface finish is lightly brushed and the standard of finish and regularity of colour is considerably better than is usually achieved in the UK.

2.8.   Whole life cost

One of the issues raised by the author when drafting the footways chapter for the second edition of the *Highway Maintenance Handbook* (Atkinson, 1997) was that of whole life costing (WLC) and the development of a consistent standard of surface maintenance for the benefit of the user. In many areas of infrastructure provision WLC is used to justify the first cost of the structure on the assumption of a consistent standard of maintenance.

A major factor in WLC is the user cost, which means that in the case of footways and walkways the proxy accident costs can be used.

The first edition of the *Highway Maintenance Handbook* (Atkinson, 1990) first indicated there was very little factual information relating to the cost of pedestrian accidents. The development of a culture of claiming damages for injury resulting from trips and so on within the highway has drawn attention to the very considerable cost involved. At the present time (2012) there is still little hard information about these costs available in the public domain.

To illustrate the scale of costs involved the following information

Table 2.6 Footway personal injury accident data

Authority	Cost of claims paid in 5 years: £000	Carriageway length: km	Footway length: km	Cost £/km/yr: £	Relative ranking
Sheffield	930	2096	3563	52	1.2
Barnsley	497	965	1640	61	1.4
Rotherham	235	1084	1843	43	1.0
Doncaster	182	1463	2487	15	*
Leeds	10 030	2510	4267	470	10.9
Birmingham	7600	2195	3732	407	9.5
Liverpool	5500	1166	1982	555	12.9
Average cost £/km/yr				229	

* Figure appeared unreasonably low so is omitted in comparison

was taken from an article in the *Sheffield Star* dated 26 August 2009, the base information having been gained under a Freedom of Information request made to the local highway authorities by the Liberal Democrats party.

In an attempt to make the information understandable in a comparative format, Table 2.6 uses the highway length in each authority for which figures were published as a normalising factor. Previous work by the author concluded that in a large urban authority the length of footway was about 1.7 times the carriageway centreline length. It will be seen that there is considerable variation in the accident cost per km.

It can be seen from Table 2.6, which contains only a small number of large urban authorities, that the average cost of claim per km of footway is £229/km/yr.

It should be noted that the above figures only relate to the cost of claims paid; they do not include the cost the National Health Service, legal costs and cost to society.

Spong and Cooper (1996) estimated the average cost of a claim to be £1370 and the average cost of claim per km of footway to be £200 and estimated the economic evaluation of the cost of measures for preventing footway falls to be £5000 per accident.

On the basis of Table 2.6, supported by Spong and Cooper (1996), and making the following assumptions,

Overall length non-national roads	382 274 km
Multiplier between centreline length and footway length	1.4
Average accident claim	£215

The overall annual cost of footway personal injury accident claims in the UK is estimated to be £115 × 10^6.

REFERENCES AND BIBLIOGRAPHY

Atkinson K (ed.) (1990) *Highway Maintenance Handbook*, 1st edn. Thomas Telford, London.

Atkinson K (ed.) (1997) *Highway Maintenance Handbook*, 2nd edn. Thomas Telford, London.

BSI (British Standards Institution) (2001) BS 6717:2001: Precast, unreinforced concrete paving blocks. Requirements and test methods. BSI, Milton Keynes.

BSI (British Standards Institution) (2003) BS EN 1338:2003: Concrete paving blocks. Requirements and test methods. BSI, Milton Keynes.

BSI (British Standards Institution) (2010) BS 594987:2010: Asphalt for roads and other paved areas. Specification for transport, laying, compaction and type testing protocols. BSI, London.

DfT (Department for Transport) (2002) Specification for reinstatement of openings in highways. TSO (The Stationery Office), London.

Dowson AJ (2001) Investigation into the performance and suitability of sand laying course and jointing material in modular pavements. PhD thesis, University of Newcastle, Newcastle upon Tyne.

Griffiths R and Scorey V (2007) UPR/IE/038/07 – Contract 2/462: Footway risk model software operational document. Unpublished report. TRL, Crowthorne.

Hammett M and Smith RA (1995) Rigid paving with clay pavers – design note 8. Brick Development Association, Windsor.

HSE (Health and Safety Executive) (2004) The assessment of pedestrian slip resistance: the HSE approach. See http://www.hse.gov.uk/pubns/web/slips01.pdf for further details (accessed 13/07/2011). HSE, Stoneleigh.

HSE (Health and Safety Executive) (2006) HSL/2006/65: Evaluation of Kirchberg rolling slider and slip alert slip resistance meters. See http://www.hse.gov.uk/pubns for further details (accessed 13/07/2011). HSE, Stoneleigh.

IHT (2000) Guidelines for providing journeys on foot. CIHT,

London.

Leake GR, May AD and Pearson DI (1991) Pedestrians' preferences for footway maintenance and design. *Highways & Transportation* **38(7)**: 5–10.

Lilley AA (1991) *A Handbook of Segmental Paving*. E & FN Spon, London.

Pearson DI (1989) Design, construction and maintenance of walkways and pedestrian areas – a whole life approach. In *Conference Proceedings – Pedestrianisation – Design, Operation and Maintenance* (Pratt CJ (ed.)). Coventry Polytechnic, Coventry.

Pearson DI (1990) A whole life approach to elemental construction in footways UK experience. *Concrete Precast Plant and Technology*, London, issue 12 from BIBM Conference, London.

Pearson DI (1990) Elemental renaissance. *Concrete Quarterly* **Winter**: 18–22.

Pearson DI (1991) Footways inspection, maintenance and the development of a whole life cost framework. Seminar for the British Cement Association: *Towards Better Footways*. TRL, Crowthorne.

Pearson DI (1991) History and development of the physical requirements of footways. Seminar for the British Cement Association: *Towards Better Footways*. TRL, Crowthorne.

Pearson DI (1995) The design of pedestrian facilities. *Proceedings of a Conference on Area-wide Pedestrian and Shared Facilities*. PTRC (Planning and Transport, Research and Computation), London.

Pearson DI (1996) Footway condition assessment. *Proceedings of the Footway Focus Conference Nottingham 1996. The Surveyor Magazine*.

Pratt CJ (ed.) (1980) *Proceedings of the Second Conference on Pedestrianisation, Design, Operation and Maintenance*. Trent Polytechnic, Nottingham.

Pratt CJ (ed.) (1991) *Proceedings of a Conference on Developments in Town and City Centres towards the 21st Century*. Coventry Polytechnic, Coventry.

Shackel B (1996) *Design and Construction of Interlocking Concrete Block Pavements*. Elsevier, Barking.

Smith RA (1988) Design note 9: Flexible paving with clay pavers. Brick Development Association, Windsor.

Spong CC (1993) TRL Project PR/H/43/93: Footway maintenance: A review of profile monitoring techniques. TRL, Crowthorne.

Spong CC and Cooper DR (1994) Project report PR/H/66/94: footway maintenance: An assessment of profile monitoring equipment. TRL, Crowthorne.

Spong CC and Cooper DR (1994) Project Report PR/H/85/94: Footway maintenance: Footway profilometer end product/performance specification. TRL, Crowthorne.

Spong CC and Cooper DR (1996) TRL Unpublished report PR/CE/186/96: Condition assessment of footways: interim report. TRL, Crowthorne.

Spong CC, Cooper DR, Leake GR and Pearson DI (1995) The measurement of footway profiles. *Highways & Transportation*. Institution of Highways and Transportation **42(10)**: 22–24.

TRL (Transport Research Laboratory) (1970) Road note 29: Road pavement design, 3rd edn. TRL, Wokingham.

UK Roads Liaison Group (2003) Application guide AG26 (Version 2): Footways and cycle route design, construction and maintenance guide. TRL, Crowthorne.

UKRLG (UK Roads Liaison Group) (2005) Well-maintained Highways. Code of practice for highway maintenance management. TSO: London.

UKRLG (UK Roads Liaison Group) (2009) Highway risk and liability claims. A practical guide to appendix C of the UK roads board report. London, TSO.

Whittle MW (2007) *Gait Analysis: An introduction*, 4th edn. Elsevier, Kidlington.

Deterioration and Maintenance of Pavements
ISBN: 978-0-7277-4114-1

ICE Publishing. All rights reserved
http://dx.doi.org/10.1680/dmp.41141.033

Chapter 3
Generic Pavement Types

3.1. Introduction

Prior to examining the deterioration process of pavements it is relevant to look briefly at the history and development of pavements. This is appropriate as in many pavements there are examples of past construction and very few fit into idealised types. Understanding the constructions of the past is relevant, for while they may not relate closely to modern thinking they have stood the test of time due principally to excellent workmanship.

This chapter sets out to examine the various common genetic pavement types. The list is not exhaustive as there are many local variations, which have developed over time depending on culture and the ready availability of materials.

3.2. Generic pavement types

While the following list is broad in coverage it is derived from consideration of historical development of pavements in the UK and other countries. Experience suggests that this is a reasonable model to follow, since the early pavements may be aligned to unpaved roads and some of the existing pavements in the UK, are among the most heavily trafficked in the modern world. The list does not set out to be definitive. Some of the broader generic types will have variants, which have been developed locally due to cultural issues, specific problems and materials availability.

The generic pavement types may be listed as follows

(*a*)   prehistoric trackways
(*b*)   Roman roads
(*c*)   unpaved roads
(*d*)   stone causeways
(*e*)   Macadam type roads
(*f*)   Telford type roads
(*g*)   sett paved roads
(*h*)   evolved pavements
(*i*)   flexible pavements
(*j*)   flexible composite pavements
(*k*)   concrete slab pavements
(*l*)   continuously reinforced pavements
(*m*)   block paved roads.

The terms road and pavement are used interchangeably in the following discussion.

The developed world has become used to the continuing and continuous availability of roads as a free and unhindered mode of transport to facilitate trade, commerce and general travel. It is only when this facility is withdrawn, periodically, for whatever reason, that the importance of roads becomes appreciated. In developed countries there is usually another, albeit very circuitous, route to one's destination. In developing countries, however, this may not be the case.

3.3. Prehistoric trackways

One of the most important steps in human history occurred when man changed from being a hunter-gatherer to becoming a farmer. As farmers established their settlements in clearings in forests, paths would be beaten to the adjoining fields, to the nearest streams for water, to the forest for firewood, and to the nearby settlements for barter and social exchange, in a process that in many ways is not dissimilar to the current situation in developing countries.

As the tracks became well used, the topsoil would have worn giving way to a firmer subsoil beneath giving a better surface where the ground was firm and more durable; in other cases when swamps and bogs had to be crossed it was normal for some form of trackway or causeway to be built. Figure 3.1 shows the

Figure 3.1 Timber track from 3800 BC in Somerset, England

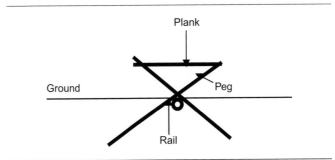

cross-section of such a trackway discovered in 1989 in a Somerset peat bog. This is over 1 mile (1625 m) in length and has been dated at 3800 BC. Similar tracks have been found in Merseyside near Southport.

3.4. Roman roads

The Romans had grasped a fact known to the Hittites in the fourteenth century BC and to the Chinese much later, in the third century BC, that the key to controlling an empire was a good system of roads, and drainage was fundamental to success.

The Romans first came to England in AD 43 and by AD 78 they had conquered both England and Wales. Their method of consolidating their new conquest was to plan and construct a system of military roads for the whole island.

Roman roads may be classified roughly into three categories: first, the strategic military network; second, a series of later roads built for general economic purposes; and, third, purely local roads. Roman roads are notable for their straightness.

The Romans' design for their primary UK roads generally consisted of four layers (top to bottom) as follows (Collins and Hart, 1936)

- *summa crusta* (surfacing): smooth polygonal blocks bedded in underlying layer
- *nucleus:* a kind of base layer composed of gravel and sand with lime cement
- *rudus:* the third layer was composed of rubble masonry and smaller stones set in lime mortar
- *stratum:* two or three courses of flat stones set in lime mortar.

The total thickness was as much as 0.9 m and road widths were 4.5 m or less. An illustration of a Roman pavement structure near Radstock, England is shown in the Figure 3.2. Roman

Figure 3.2 Roman pavement structure near Radstock, England
From Collins and Hart (1936).

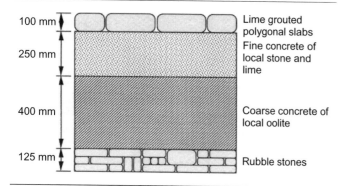

roads up to 2.4 m thick have been found in some countries. The structures had crowned (sloped) surfaces to enhance drainage and often incorporated ditches and /or underground drains. As one might expect, Roman road building was varied to suit local conditions and materials – not unlike road building today, actually. The Romans left the UK in about AD 407. Road design and construction languished for about 1200 years thereafter.

This construction was not used for roads outside cities and towns other than for prestigious projects, and only then when the appropriate materials were available. In Britain, far simpler road construction was practised using locally available material.

The idealised and pragmatic cross-section of a Roman road is shown in Figure 3.3.

It is interesting to note that the US system of interstate roads, and many of the major roads in Scotland, were originally substantially funded from defence budgets to ensure the rapid movement of military resources.

3.5. Unpaved roads

Unpaved roads are common in many parts of the world and may be earth tracks, earth roads or gravel roads. Extensive networks of unpaved roads can be found in both the developing and developed countries and they form the majority of the length of roads in the world. Because they are encountered less in developed countries their need for maintenance is more critical than is that of some paved roads. In some developing countries the temporary closure of a road in rural areas can have a very significant and disastrous effect on the local population and economy.

The primary deterioration of unpaved roads relates to wet weather. Longitudinal gradient, transverse shaping and cross-fall are critical for shedding water into some form of controlled drainage. In many cases this controlled drainage is not provided: consequently wet weather can soon destroy an unpaved road.

Figure 3.3 Roman road – practical cross-section

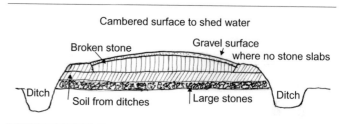

3.5.1   Earth tracks

Earth tracks are the earliest roads and were (are) usually ad-hoc tracks formed as the result of walking between settlements and through rural areas, probably accompanied by carts drawn by draught animals. Earth tracks generally consist of parallel ruts separated by vegetation, and they rapidly become impassable in wet weather.

3.5.2   Earth roads

Earth roads (Figure 3.4) are those where there is no imported gravel or other metalling but the material is cleared of vegetation and lightly compacted, generally by passing traffic. They are often shaped by excavated material taken from the side drains. In developing countries they may be constructed either by a road authority or by the local community, and they are important for the economic and social development of the area.

In England in the period 1400–1600, almost all roads were constructed from available earth and became impassable in wet weather. This accounts for the informal routes taken, with diversions around impassable areas. During this period roads were generally narrow, with passage being either on foot, with a single horse or with groups of pack-horses. In some cases large stones were laid in the form of a causeway. In some parts of England, where there was a significant movement of cattle, roads were much wider. These were known as drove roads, where flocks of animals were driven by a group of professional drovers, who walked and lived with the animals and saw that they came to no harm.

From about 1650, carts were used, and this led to many and various problems, not the least of which was the imposed load from the wheels, which in many cases exceeded the bearing capacity of the soil. This is dealt with in detail in Chapter 4, section 4.3.

3.5.3   Gravel roads

In areas where the economic cost of paved roads cannot be justified, they may have a designed layer of imported material, which is typically constructed to a specified standard and width and provides an all-weather surface (see Figure 3.5). Maintenance needs to be carried out on a regular and systematic basis. Roughness varies with time and traffic and depends significantly on the maintenance activity.

This practice was the essential starting point for the development of the first properly constructed pavements in the 1700s, dealt with in Chapter 15.

3.6.   Stone causeways

The images in Figures 3.6 and 3.7 have been taken from a nineteenth-century text – *Lives of the Engineers* (Smiles, 1862) – and are useful because in addition to illustrating stone causeways, they indicate some modes of travel at that time.

3.7.   Macadam type construction

Unpaved roads were common in Britain until about 1787, when John Loudon McAdam began his method of construction, an example of which is shown in Figure 3.8.

McAdam was one of the first people in Britain, since the demise of the Romans in AD 407, to properly appreciate the importance

Figure 3.5 Typical gravel road
Courtesy of Cyrus Swebato

Figure 3.4 Typical earth road
Courtesy of Cyrus Swebato

Figure 3.6 Ancient causeway in Cock Mill Wood, near Whitby, England
From Smiles, 1862

Figure 3.7 Typical traffic late 1700s, England
From Smiles, 1862

The Pack Horse Convoy

The Basket Coach 1780

Figure 3.8 Typical Macadam construction

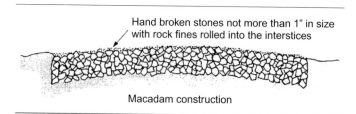

Macadam construction

of drainage. This was allowed for by cambering the formation to encourage positive drainage of surface water to the side ditches. In many of McAdam's roads, transverse drainage ditches can be found below the formation.

McAdam was active in road construction during the period 1787–1827, along with various members of his family, and his designs can be found in many parts of the UK and internationally.

The first step was to prepare the formation and dig drainage ditches along both sides. The formation was finished to a camber on which was placed a layer of broken stone, the individual pieces of which were not more than 1 inch (25 mm) in diameter. The layer of stones was rammed flat with wooden rammers, known as beetles. On this foundation was placed a layer of finer stones, which in the course of time became cemented with stone dust. The stone dust was produced by the grinding action of the iron-tyred traffic running on the road, and rainfall washed the dust into the crevices between the stone particles, binding them together.

The surface of the road was finished with a camber of 3 inches (75 mm) at the centre of an 18 ft (5.5 m) carriageway. Total

pavement thickness was typically 9–10 inches (225–250 mm). Great care was taken to ensure the maximum stone size was 1 inch (25 mm). These stones were produced on site by hand from larger stones, either found on-site or delivered to the site from neighbouring quarries.

McAdam liked to 'make a road in 3 times' by which he meant he liked to lay about 3 inches (75 mm) of metalling at a time and allow the passing traffic to compact each layer, with the ruts being raked smooth periodically. The advent of rollers in 1820 meant that proper compaction could be provided as the construction proceeded.

3.8. Telford type construction

Roads constructed by Thomas Telford, during the period 1787–1821, were also of dry stone but it can be seen in Figure 3.9 that they are fundamentally different to Macadam's in having a flat formation and a robust bottom layer. Telford, having started life as a stonemason, devised a form of construction which comprised large hand-pitched stones.

A thin layer of sand or broken rock fines was laid on a prepared foundation and the main structural layer consisted of large (up to 10 inches high (250 mm)) stones which were hand-pitched on edge, with the broad end of each stone placed downwards; the upward pointed tips of the stones were then knocked off and the chips hammered down into the crevices between the stones to form a dense mass and ensure interlock to form friction. This process was known as 'nidging'.

Next, a layer of smaller stones broken – to be not larger than a hen's egg, was laid. On some jobs Telford provided ring gauges of 2.5 inches (62.5 mm) in diameter for grading the maximum size of the stone in this layer. This layer was 5 inches (125 mm) thick at the edges and 7 inches (175 mm) thick at the crown so as to provide the required camber. It was usual for this to be placed in two layers. Finally, a 1.5 inch (40 mm) layer of even finer broken stone or gravel was laid to form the road surface, giving a total thickness of between 13 and 15 inches (330–375 mm).

The action of the iron tyres running on the upper layer soon produced grit and dust, which, assisted by rain, packed down between the stones and produced a smooth running surface. The final profile was finished to a camber of 2 inches (50 mm) rise on an 18 foot (5.5 m) carriageway.

An inevitability of both Macadam and Telford constructions was

the dust, which resulted from the grinding of the small stones by the iron tyres on carts and coaches. This made them not the preferred surfaces in towns, where regular watering was necessary to minimise the dust.

3.9. Sett paved construction

In urban areas in the UK, especially where heavy loads were generated from adjacent industry and especially from ports, the use of stone sett paving became normal (Figure 3.10). Setts had two major advantages, first, they were resistant to the imposed stresses from the iron tyres of carts and, second, they provided some grip for the feet of the horses pulling the carts, which were the principal means of transporting goods at the time.

In some areas local hard stone was used where it was available and these tended to be rectangular sections 6 × 10 inches deep (150 mm × 250 mm) in plan and typically 8 inches (200 mm) deep, with the larger dimension laid across the road. In many port areas the use of smaller granite setts 150 mm or 200 mm cube was the norm. These setts having usually arrived as ballast in returning trading ships.

Experience indicates there are two different constructions found with setts, which it is convenient to refer to as normal and heavy. In the latter case a concrete supporting layer will be found under the setts. The typical cross-section of heavy construction is shown

Figure 3.10 Typical heavy sett construction c. 1900

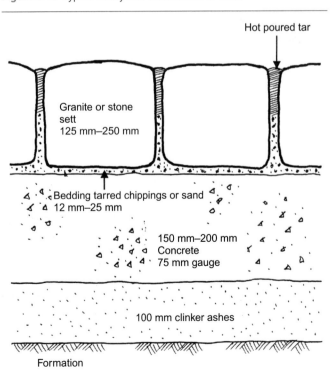

Hot poured tar

Granite or stone sett 125 mm–250 mm

Bedding tarred chippings or sand 12 mm–25 mm

150 mm–200 mm Concrete 75 mm gauge

100 mm clinker ashes

Formation

Figure 3.9 Typical Telford construction

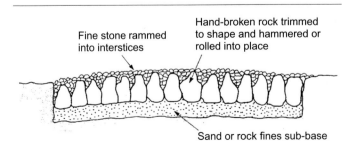

Fine stone rammed into interstices

Hand-broken rock trimmed to shape and hammered or rolled into place

Sand or rock fines sub-base

in Figure 3.10 and it should be noted that the sett is not laid directly onto the concrete, rather onto a 12–20 mm thick bed of tarred chippings. When laid, the sett construction was sealed with poured tar for the top half of the sett. This ensured a degree of flexibility and a very high resistance to moisture penetration, the latter being important in the days of horse-drawn traffic.

Clinker ashes can be found in the lowest layer. They are the product of coal-fired boilers and furnaces. From about 1850 onwards, most industrial processes needed steam-driven motive power requiring coal-powered boilers and furnaces.

Consequently, furnace clinker ashes were in ready supply and in many cases could be obtained at no cost, as the factory owners were very happy to have somebody take them away. For this reason many highway constructions between 1800 and 1920 contained ashes. In some cases, they were stabilised by the use of about 5% of cement, which in the Manchester area was found to be especially suitable in reinstatements (utility cuts), because they ensured no settlement and were not too hard to excavate.

Setts are still widely used in Scandinavia, Germany and most Mediterranean countries, although it is normal for the top half of the sett to be filled with 3–6 mm nominal size crushed granite. Filling with a granular material has the great advantage that relaying is a straightforward affair, with very limited materials cost.

Figures 3.11 and 3.12 show the installation of tram tracks and associated sett paving in Barnsley *c.* 1900.

It can be seen that the setts are bedded in a granular material and are laid to a camber between the rails. An indication of the size of the setts can be seen in comparison with the man looking directly into the camera in Figure 3.11.

Figure 3.11 Sett paving construction, Barnsley, England, *c.* 1900
Courtesy of Tasker Trust

Figure 3.12 Sealing sett paved construction, Barnsley, England, *c.* 1900
Courtesy of Tasker Trust

The dress code of the day demanded that the labourers wore flat caps and the foreman a bowler hat. On larger jobs it would not have been usual to find a more senior person denoted by his top hat.

In Figure 3.12, the foreman can be seen using a 'beetle', which is a heavy wooden tamping tool used for settling the sett into the granular bed prior to the filling of the joints with liquid tar which was heated on site in the boiler – can be seen in the right of the picture. In the situation seen here, the tram lines clearly act as a robust edge restraint.

As an illustration of the general method of compaction the contemporary print in Figure 3.13 shows work in the Strand in London in 1851. Previously, reference was made to the 'beetle', a hand compaction tool. Figure 3.13 shows the gang of workmen being 'conducted' by the foreman (in the top hat) during the compaction phase of the sett-laying process in the late 1800s.

A similar reference to this practice, albeit relating to Macadam construction, can be found in Lay (1986): 'As the macadamising process spread, compaction with 1.5 m wooden stumplike hand rammers became a trade art as it was key to a successful road surface. In 1846 a foreman introduced batteries of tradesmen (paviors) working in unison to him beating time in with a rod.'

3.10. Evolved pavements

An evolved pavement is one which can contain either Macadam, Telford or sett construction, or even some combination, that has subsequently been overlaid, usually, by an asphalt layer(s) –

Figure 3.13 Sett paving of the Strand *c.* 1850

sometimes several times to provide a more acceptable riding surface and/or to improve the vertical alignment.

The asphalt thickness, when on setts, will typically be 50 mm or ideally 100 mm on heavily trafficked routes. In the latter case a very robust pavement is the result. In a number of cases evolved pavements have been found which consist of several discrete pavements one on top of the other, as shown Figure 3.14.

In most urban areas, particularly where industry is to be found, evolved pavements, which have been constructed incrementally, will be the norm. These pavements will be found to be very robust, except where they have been breached by utility or other excavations and not correctly reinstated.

Figure 3.14 Examples of urban evolved pavements

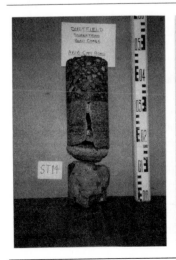

3.11. Flexible pavements

In the countryside, Macadam construction was greeted with great joy as it provided passable all-weather roads. Its main problem was with the dust it created. Coach travellers and motorists often wore goggles and linen dust scarves to protect themselves.

In the urban area, although Macadam surfaces were a great improvement on their predecessors, they were frequently abraded, dusty in summer, muddy in winter, slippery, slimy and malodorous. In dry weather, regular watering was required to allay the dust and in winter regular shovelling was needed to remove the mud. In urban areas, people made a living as 'sweepers' preparing paths for pedestrians wishing to cross the road without soiling their clothes and shoes.

A very significant alternative binder source to water arose as tar increasingly became available as a by-product of the growing nineteenth century production of 'town gas' from coal. Given the concurrent increase in the use of Macadam it was natural but still an innovative step to try the surplus tar as a replacement for the sand, stone, dust and soil then in use as binders for the surface. Tar was first used as a binder in this manner in 1832 in the English town of Gloucester for footpath construction. A subsequent major step was to pre-coat each particle of stone with a thin film of binder before placing it in the pavement. Such products are called precoated (or coated) Macadams. Tarred heated gravel was first used in this manner in a trial in Nottingham in England in 1840 (Lay, 1986).

With the advent of a regular economical source of crushed rock, which became available in the early 1950s, hand pitching as in generic Telford construction became a thing of the past, and flexible pavements of a generic Macadam form became the norm, especially in urban and suburban areas. Additionally, most of the early motorways in the UK were built using flexible constructions with an asphalt surface. The major advantage of this method was that the construction process could be mechanised; consequently considerably less labour was required. Typically, a flexible construction consists of three layers as shown in Table 3.1.

In rural areas, a flexible construction will generally be found to be a Macadam type base surmounted by several layers of surface dressing to provide a dust-free impervious surface.

While many of the early flexible roads were 'designed empirically', based on incremental practical experience of what had

Table 3.1 Typical layer structure – flexible pavement

Asphalt (usually more than 1 layer)
Crushed rock granular sub-base
Formation (existing ground)

performed successfully in the past there has been a progressive desire to undertake some form of analytical design in an attempt to make more economical use of materials, especially the asphalt layer which is the most expensive.

3.12. Flexible composite pavements

A flexible composite pavement is similar to a flexible one, except cement or otherwise stabilised layer replaces the granular layer to provide a significantly enhanced bearing capacity platform to support the asphalt surfacing layers.

The early use of cement-bound granular base (CBGB) material was an attempt to construct a thinner and more economic pavement effectively using stabilised gravel. With the more recent use of other binders, which have lower early age performance properties, this class of supporting layer is now generally referred to as a hydraulically bound material (HBM).

This CBGB form of construction was used extensively in some of the early UK motorways but was not entirely successful due to thermal movement of the cement bound layer, which resulted in reflection cracks migrating to the surface, leading to progressive failure, initially of the surface course and subsequently the CBGB layer.

There has been a progressive movement away from the use solely of cement as a binder, experience of the use of fly ash, slags and lime mixtures as a partial replacement for the cement have been reported, Cabrera and Zoorob (1999), where substantial economies have been noted, without significant loss of strength.

Current thinking with HBM is to pre-crack the layer such that the location of potential reflection cracking can be controlled.

At an early stage in the life of the flexible composite pavement, the various environmental distress types present are similar to those found where there is an with an asphalt surface course on a flexible construction.

3.13. Concrete slab pavements

Concrete slab pavements were originally thought to be the panacea for many problems, particularly as it was believed they would not need any maintenance. This aspiration proved to be incorrect as there is a continuing need to maintain the joint filler and sealer between adjacent slabs. Surfaces with cement concrete slab pavements are no longer permitted on the UK national road network due to problems of traffic generated noise. Individual slabs, typically between 4 m and 5 m in length and a lane width of 3.65 m and up to 300 mm thick, have been used extensively, both with and without reinforcement and with and without load transfer dowels between adjacent slabs.

3.14. Continuously reinforced concrete pavements

In the UK, at the present time there are two options due to the requirement that concrete is not acceptable as a running surface on the national road network. These options are shown in Table 3.2.

The need for maintenance is usually related to degradation of the asphalt surface course, resulting from materials failure exacerbated by thermal stresses. The replacement of the asphalt layer is relatively straightforward thanks to the continuing development of large planning machines.

Continuous construction is not widely used in the UK since there must be a certain critical mass of work before setting up the necessary paving train, which restricts it to very large projects. Because road projects on some of the US interstate network were very large, its use is more normal in the US.

It should be noted that in the USA there are two standards for surface roughness: one for asphalt surfaces and one for concrete, the latter being less exacting.

Problems have been experienced with continuous concrete pavements in Belgium, where the running surface is concrete. There are reports of localised 'blow out' failures where a section of the concrete surface fails over a very short period of time. There is little in the literature but it is believed to be a harmonic frequency problem. It is suggested that passing traffic can excite the slab leading to changes in its harmonic frequency causing stresses which, when they are concentrated, the concrete cannot cope with. It is believed that the remedy is likely to be some form of damping.

Table 3.2 Typical construction of continuously reinforced concrete pavements

Continuously reinforced concrete roadbase	Continuously reinforced concrete pavement
Asphalt 100 mm thick Continuously reinforced pavement quality concrete with reinforcing steel equal to 0.4% of cross-sectional area of the concrete Hydraulically bound base	Thin surface course 30 mm thick Continuously reinforced pavement quality concrete with reinforcing steel equal to 0.6% of cross-sectional area of the concrete Hydraulically bound base

3.15. Block paving

Block paving (Figures 3.15 and 3.16), which comprises a surface course of either concrete or brick elements, typically 200 mm × 100 mm in plan, has progressively become the preferred option for lightly trafficked streets in domestic housing developments.

Additionally it is extensively used in many commercial developments because of its capability to visually enhance the environment by a combination of colour and texture.

Figure 3.15 Typical construction for block paving

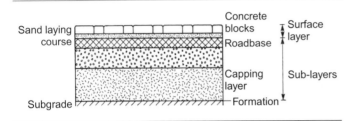

Figure 3.16 Block paving in shared surface precinct

It is also used extensively in port container yards and heavy industrial areas where its resistance to abrasion has many advantages.

It is listed here to complete the list of pavements and is dealt with in detail in Chapter 16.

REFERENCES AND BIBLIOGRAPHY

Cabrera JG and Zoorob SE (eds) (1999) *Proceedings of the Third European Symposium on Performance and Durability of Bituminous Materials and Hydraulic Stabilised Composites.* Aedificatio, Zurich.

Collins HJ and Hart CA (1936) *Principles of Road Engineering.* Edward Arnold, London.

Cudworth DM (1997) An improved method for evaluating the condition of jointed concrete pavements base on deflection testing. MSc dissertation. University of Nottingham, Nottingham.

Interpave (2005) Concrete block paving: guide to the properties, design, construction, reinstatement and maintenance of concrete block pavements. Downloadable (for subscribers) from www.paving.org.uk/concrete_block_paving_DACI.php (accessed 13/07/2011). Interpave, Precast Concrete Paving and Kerb Association, Leicester.

Knapton J (1976) Technical report 42.515: The design of concrete block roads. Cement and Concrete Association, Slough.

Lay MG (1986) *Handbook of Road Technology. Vol. 1: Planning and Pavements.* Gordon and Breach, New York.

Nicholls JC, McHale MJ and Griffiths RD (2008) Road note 42: Best practice guide for the durability of asphalt pavements. TRL, Wokingham.

Nunn ME, Brown A, Weston A and Nicholls JC (1997) TRL 250: Design of long-life flexible pavements for heavy traffic. TRL, Crowthorne.

Smiles S (1862) *Lives of the Engineers, Volume 1.* John Murry, London.

Tillson GW (1900) *Street Pavements and Paving Materials.* Wiley, New York.

West G (2000) *The Technical Development of Roads in Britain.* Ashgate, Aldershot.

Deterioration and Maintenance of Pavements
ISBN: 978-0-7277-4114-1

ICE Publishing. All rights reserved
http://dx.doi.org/10.1680/dmp.41141.043

Chapter 4
Deterioration of Pavements

4.1. Purpose of a pavement

The principal purposes of a pavement are

(a) to facilitate unhindered and free passage to all forms of traffic, by providing a smooth, skid resistant, drained and unhindered surface

(b) to transmit the stresses imposed on it, by a broad range of loading, to the formation in such a manner that the latter does not become overloaded

(c) to minimise fatigue in the various layers due to repeated imposed loading of the pavement and reduce the rate of deterioration of the constituent materials

(d) to ensure water falling on its surface can drain away rapidly and does not hinder free passage.

4.2. Modes of failure

There are essentially five fundamental modes of failure relating to pavements, with a degree of interdependence.

4.2.1 Inadequate bearing capacity of formation

Where the effect of the applied load overstresses the formation. It depends on both the bearing capacity of the formation and its equilibrium moisture content.

4.2.2 Failure due to frost damage

Where moisture gets into the pavement, either as the result of it being permeable due to lack of maintenance or as the result of suction forces drawing moisture from the foundations.

4.2.3 Failure of the constituent materials due to fatigue

Due to the incremental effects of very small strains, some of which are elastic by nature such that the pavement deforms and returns to its original state after the load is removed. Plastic strains, however, progressively cause a residual and increasingly permanent deformation.

4.2.4 Failure of the constituent materials due to environmental exposure

Due to the effect of ultra-violet radiation and oxygenation and the effects of moisture within the pavement in non-freezing conditions.

4.2.5 Inadequate quality of construction

Pavements are designed to operate in all weathers but the time of year when construction takes place can have a significant effect on quality and hence longevity. As with all pavements there is the need for skilled and experienced artisans to deliver them in a manner appropriate to the weather conditions.

4.3. Bearing capacity of the formation – why a pavement?

The following simple example is convenient to illustrate the concept of overstressing the formation (West, 2000).

The pejorative effect of water on the foundation of a road is well understood and is demonstrated in some detail in Chapter 11. If the basic assumption is made that water is kept away from the foundation then the carrying capacity of the road is directly related to the bearing capacity of the foundation. Typical bearing capacities for various soils types are as follows.

Gravel	600 kN/m^2
Sand	300 kN/m^2
Clay	150 kN/m^2

In the UK, between the demise of the Romans and the early 1500s the process of road-building deteriorated and effectively became non-existent. Initially, this may not have been too much of a problem since land was plentiful and in the event of a road becoming impassable a local detour was usually possible. Most of the traffic between areas of population involved walking or driving herds of animals, with the more affluent travelling by horse.

The advent of the mail coach in the early 1600s brought a new dimension to the road, whereby a heavily loaded wheel was in contact with the ground and in many cases its applied loading exceeded the bearing capacity of the ground. While reference to Figures 3.2 and 3.3 shows that this problem had been understood by the Romans, the realisation was lost for about 1000 years after their demise.

43

The problem can be illustrated by the following modest calculations.

Typically, a mail coach and its occupants would have weighed about 3 tonne or 3000 Kg and it may be assumed that this was distributed evenly over the four wheels (Figure 4.1). Each wheel was about 50 mm wide and while constructed of timber had a metal tyre to protect it. Assuming each of the 4 wheels had a load of 750 Kg the following calculations can be made:

Mass in contact with ground is

$$750 \times 9.81 \times 10^3 = 7357 \text{ N} \tag{4.1}$$

Assuming contact area is 50 mm × 50 mm

Pressure at ground level is

$$\frac{7357}{1000 \times \frac{50}{1000} \times \frac{50}{1000}} = 2942 \text{ kN/m}^2 \tag{4.2}$$

Pressure at foundation level is

$$\frac{7357}{1000 \times \frac{250}{1000} \times \frac{250}{1000}} = 118 \text{ kN/m}^2 \tag{4.3}$$

It can be seen that the imposed load at the foundation level is only just lower than the bearing capacity of clay (the predominant UK soil) – assuming that the clay is dry!

To achieve a factor of safety of 2.0 it can be shown that the crushed stone would need to be increased in thickness to greater than 250 mm (10 inches).

The above example uses only a light load compared with present-day commercial vehicles, which can have up to an 11.5 t axle in the UK.

Figure 4.1 Distribution of load under coach wheel

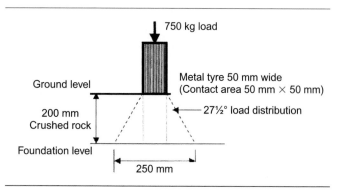

Ground level

200 mm Crushed rock

Foundation level

750 kg load

Metal tyre 50 mm wide (Contact area 50 mm × 50 mm)

27½° load distribution

250 mm

Although it is dealt with in greater detail elsewhere in this book, the influence and importance of drainage should not be under-estimated since the bearing capacity of the formation is directly related to its moisture content.

4.4. Frost damage to pavements

After traffic and water, the next greatest enemy of the road-maker in the UK is frost, as water expands by 9% on freezing. In the days before bound materials were used in roads this was particularly true, but it remains so to some extent up to the present time. The severity of frost is measured by a parameter known as the frost index.

The frost index is simply the number of days on which the temperature is continually below zero degrees Celsius multiplied by the number of degrees Celsius below zero on each day. For example, a frost index of 20 degree days could have resulted from the following:

$$[5 \text{ days at } -2°\text{C}] \text{ followed by } [10 \text{ days at } -1°\text{C}] \tag{4.4}$$

$$(5 \times 2) + (10 \times 1) = 20 \text{ degree days} \tag{4.5}$$

The yearly frost index is the sum of the frost indices for a particular site for a single year, and the mean frost index is the mean value of the yearly frost index for a particular site from data calculated from a period extending over a number of years.

The frost index is a measure of the severity of a single cold spell While the yearly frost index is a measure of the severity of a single year. The mean yearly frost index is a measure of the average severity of yearly frost at a site, and can be used to categorise the frost severity of a particular site, and to compare the frost severity of different sites.

The depth of frost penetration into the ground, and into the road pavement – where this has replaced the natural ground – measured in millimetres, is given by multiplying the square root of the frost index by 50.

For example, at a site with a frost index of 50 degree days, frost penetration can be expected to be at least 350 mm into the pavement, as follows:

$$\sqrt{50} \times 50 = 350 \text{ mm} \tag{4.6}$$

In the UK at the present time, if the mean frost index is 50 or more, all material used within the top 450 mm of the pavement should be non-frost-susceptible. If, however, the index is less than 50, this thickness can be relaxed to 350 mm.

Frost damage to roads arises in three ways.

First, if there are any porous stones in the pavement structure, the water in the pores of the stones will freeze and the resulting 9% volumetric expansion when the water changes to ice can break down the stones into smaller pieces. This is referred to as *frost shattering*. This leads to loose aggregate on the surface, which acts as a destructive abrasive under the action of vehicle tyres. Additionally if there are cracks on the surface this abrasive acts on the edges of the cracks causing them to widen initially at the surface then subsequently at depth, leading to possible local compression failure of the asphalt as temperatures rise.

Second, similar expansion in the voids between the stones will loosen the pavement structure itself. Typically, this may occur when a bituminous surfacing is nearing the end of its useful life and must have been commonplace in the days before roads had impermeable surfaces. This is referred to as *frost loosening*.

Frost shattering can be prevented by the use of non-porous aggregates. Frost loosening can be prevented by the use of an impermeable surface.

Third, and more importantly, frost damage to pavements can occur from the process known as *frost heave,* and for current road constructions this is the most widely seen cause. Frost heave occurs because of the high suction produced at the freezing front when frost penetrates down into the pavement. This suction draws water up from the underlying water table into the zone where freezing is taking place. This leads to the formation of a thick ice lens at the freezing front, as is shown in Figure 4.2. The magnitude of the suction is given by the expression:

$$s = 4.1 \ \log_{10} t \tag{4.7}$$

where:
  s is the suction measured on the pF scale
  t is the number of degrees Celsius below freezing point

To give some idea of the severity of the suction forces involved: if t is only 1°C, then s is just over pF 4, which is 10^4 cm of water or 1 MN/m^2, which is suction equivalent to a negative pressure of 10 atmospheres.

Figure 4.2 shows the principal cause of frost heave in the largely granular roadbases in lightly constructed pavements.

The growth of this ice lens causes the pavement structure to expand upwards or heave – hence the term *frost heave*. While the ice lens remains frozen, the pavement can carry the normal traffic load because the ice is adequately strong. Once the ice thaws, however, the water subsides into the pavement, which becomes saturated so it can no longer carry the traffic loads. For frost heave to occur as well as frost penetration there must be water within the construction and/or a water table near formation level, and the sub-base and roadbase materials must have capillaries of the right size to enable water to be drawn up.

Figure 4.2 Frost heave in a pavement
Conditions (a) before freezing (b) during freezing

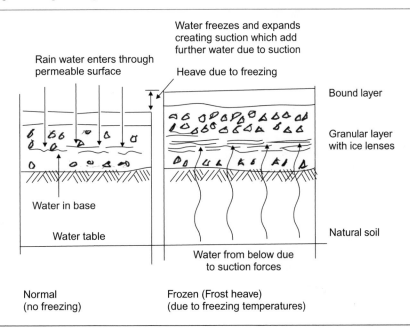

One of the major precautions to be taken with pavement design is to ensure that subgrade drains keep the water table ideally 1 m below the road formation, in order to minimise the likelihood of frost heave. The author experienced serious problems with frost heave in the winter of 1986–1987, when damage estimated at over £1.5 million was noted in Sheffield. Interestingly, this also affected a section of the central pedestrian precinct, which was constructed from thick, traffic-resistant concrete slabs. To maintain safety, areas were fenced off, but after several days most of the surface subsided to its original level.

Figures 4.3 and 4.4 illustrate two examples of frost action which occurred rapidly. Figure 4.3 shows disintegration of a surface layer from above due to its porous surface. Figure 4.4 is an example of inadequate interlayer bonding between an older construction and a newer surface course causing serious loss of

Figure 4.3 Typical frost damage to porous surface Sheffield, 1987

Figure 4.4 Frost damage, South Yorkshire, December 2010

surface in temperatures down to −15°C in early January 2010 where water had been running on the interface. A length of 500 m lost a substantial proportion of its 40 mm surface course over a 3-day period causing a serious safety hazard on a rural derestricted road.

4.5. Failure of constituent materials due to fatigue

The formation can be overstressed as the result of fatigue due to incremental plastic strain. As a simplification to analyse the behaviour of pavements it is usually assumed that the structure is a linear elastic, isotropic, semi-infinite half space. Unfortunately very few of the assumptions made are correct, or even reasonably correct, when it comes to real pavement structures and materials. No pavement material, for example, complies with Hooke's law. When a bituminous pavement material deforms under load, the deformations are not only elastic, but also plastic, viscous or visco-elastic, they are often anisotropic and in many cases the relationship between stress and strain is non-linear.

Under the influence of time, load and climatic effect pavement materials will deteriorate and the pavement will deform (Figures 4.5 to 4.8).

It will be seen that cracking starts within the tension zones, and that as the wheel moves cracking develops in both the top and bottom of the pavement.

The stresses caused by heavy loads may result in micro cracking in bituminous or cement-bound materials, and may also cause permanent deformation in the pavement layers and the formation. Aggregate in the pavement surface can be polished by tyre wear

Figure 4.5 Spread of wheel load pressure through pavement structure

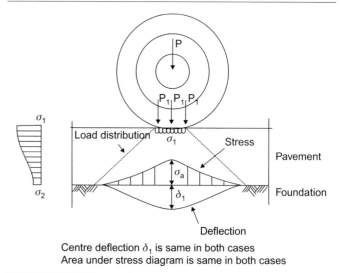

Centre deflection δ_1 is same in both cases
Area under stress diagram is same in both cases

Figure 4.6 Effect of stresses from wheel load on pavement

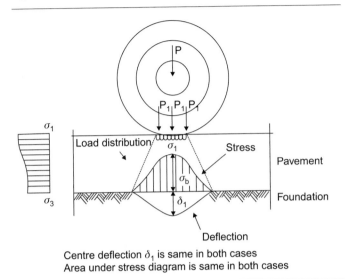

Centre deflection δ_1 is same in both cases
Area under stress diagram is same in both cases

Figure 4.7 Classic fatigue cracking

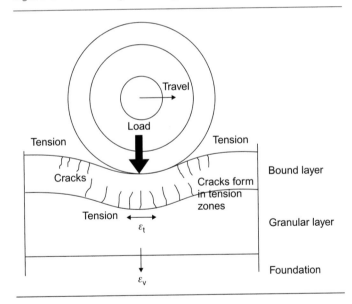

Figure 4.8 Progressive increase in residual strain

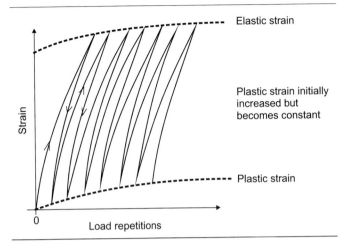

Nunn *et al.* (1997) state, this has become a major issue recently, and while this publication reported on the phenomenon no causal factors were given at the time. It has subsequently been demonstrated to be a function of super-single radial tyres, the treads from which generate large horizontal stresses on the pavement surface, which Croll (2009) describes as 'interactions between the tyres and the asphalt produce, in addition to the high normal compressive stress, and significant levels of shear associated with the restraint to the Poisson bulging of the compliant tyres' (Figure 4.9).

Figure 4.9 Tensile strain in asphalt due to Poisson bulging of tyre (basis of longitudinal top-down cracking)

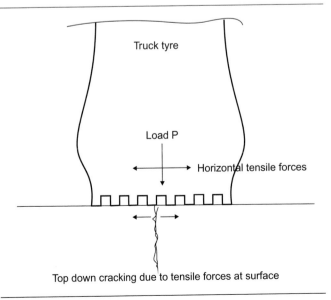

and the texture may be changed by depression of aggregate into the surface or by bleeding, all of which may decrease the skid resistance.

This process of material deterioration and development of permanent deformation is quite complex and difficult to model using analytical tools. From an analytical point of view, it is probably true to say that pavement structures are among the most complicated engineering structures (Ullidtz, 1987).

Reference has been made to longitudinal top-down cracking. As

4.6. Failure of constituent materials due to poor construction and environmental exposure

The designer has little or no control over many assumptions which are made in the design process. Probably the most significant of these assumptions is weather. A competent design delivered on a cold, wet, windy day has less chance of delivering the assumptions made than if it is constructed on a calm, hot day. The principal difference here is the reduction in the degree of compaction achieved in all the asphalt layers. Many years ago it was part of the design guidance of the day that if a pavement was to be constructed in the colder part of the year it needed to be thicker by up to 10% to reflect the potential reduction in compaction.

4.6.1   Compaction

The degree of compaction of the bound layers is directly related to the service life of the pavement, as may be deduced from Figure 4.10.

Compaction is the process by which the volume of air in an asphalt mix is reduced using external forces to reorient the constituent aggregate particles into a more closely spaced arrangement. This reduction in air volume produces a corresponding increase in the asphalt weight or density. Inadequate compaction results in a pavement with reduced stiffness, fatigue

life, accelerated ageing and decreased durability, and increased susceptibility to rutting, fretting and moisture damage.

The volume of air in an asphalt pavement is important because it has a profound effect on long-term pavement performance. An approximate 'rule of thumb' is that for every 1% increase in air voids above 8%, about 10% of the pavement life may be lost. There is also evidence that in addition to asphalt mixes not exceeding 8% they should not fall below 3% air voids during the service life of the pavement.

4.6.2   Environmental factors

Environmental exposure leads to ageing and weathering of the bitumen and is primarily the result of accumulated ultra-violet radiation and subsequent rainfall erosion. Additionally, oxidation of the bitumen and binder hardening assists the process. This is particularly so if there is a high air void content (>8%).

Bitumen and tar age from the moment that they are incorporated into the mix, due to oxidation, which hardens the binder and causes it to become progressively brittle. In pavement mixes, as a rule of thumb, bitumen with a binder penetration of 20 is at the end of its useful life. Loss of binder efficiency and brittleness prevent the material from containing the stresses imposed by traffic, leading to the development of micro-cracking. This process is most obvious in the surface course, where it is exposed to sunlight (UV radiation). The condition can be assessed during inspection by noting changes in the colour of the bituminous binder, from the initial black to a light grey; also chippings will be more prominently exposed and many will have been plucked out. If handled, pieces of the surface will probably disintegrate and individual stones can be dislodged due to loss of the adhesive properties in the binder.

Stripping of the binder from the aggregate will also lead to surface deterioration. Stripping may also occur because the bitumen has become brittle with age, because insufficient bitumen was used in the mix, or because absorption of bitumen into the aggregate has taken place. The process of stripping is hastened by the presence of water in the voids. Stripping which occurs soon after construction may be due to insufficient bitumen in the mix, poor adhesion of bitumen to stone due to wet or dusty aggregate, or to cold or wet weather at the time of construction.

The surface will probably look tired and dry, and it can most effectively be treated using surface dressing, slurry seal or micro-surfacing. If a surface dressing is used the chipping size and binder spread rate will depend on the traffic using the road, the hardness of the road and other external factors. With harder surfaces smaller chippings will be used, as embedment will be less than it would be with a softer surface.

Once fretting (exfoliation of small aggregate) has started, it

Figure 4.10 Void content plotted against dynamic stiffness
Reproduced from Whiteoak (1990) with permission

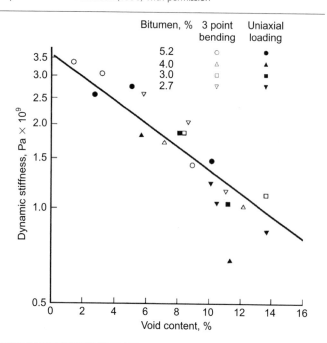

continues and gets progressively worse as the loose materials act as an abrasive under the action of traffic, either foot or wheeled, further damaging the surface. Where there are cracks this loose material is particularly damaging to the edges of the crack and leads to progressive widening, consequently enhancing the ability of water to penetrate.

Cracking of the asphalt surfacing may be a result of ageing of the surface or may indicate structural problems. Longitudinal cracks may result from insufficient edge restraint allowing a footway to spread or from shrinkage of clay subgrades. Cracks can also arise at joints, leading to ingress of water and deterioration. Reflective cracking resulting from thermal movement can occur on pavements with a lean concrete base.

Croll (2009) suggests the relevance of thermal ratcheting in the formation of surface cracking of asphalt has been underestimated and observes that where the pavement is in shade cracking is generally absent. He also suggests the thermo-chemical processes associated with the eventual evaporation of puddle water could result in an accelerated ageing of the bituminous binders and a leaching away of certain volatile substances responsible for asphalt retaining its ductile properties.

Strain or work-hardening arising from repeated wheel loading is clearly another source of localised asphalt embrittlement. Contraction-induced tensile stressing in such locally embrittled areas may be expected to produce selective cracking.

4.6.3 Moisture in and under the pavement

In a bituminous pavement, performance, classically, has been related to fatigue failure of the bound layers and a deformation failure of the foundation. While these parameters are load-related the action of moisture below, within or passing through the pavement can have a very significant effect.

The previous section indicates the likely presence of micro-cracking in the surface of all pavements, leading to a degree of permeability. If the surface is maintained in a sealed condition the pavement life can generally be related to the number of load applications.

If, however the surface is permeable – which to a certain degree all pavements are – the life of the asphalt layer(s) can be significantly reduced by the action of water within the matrix. This progressively causes the bitumen to strip from the aggregate and lose its binding effect and capability to resist tensile stresses, in exceptional cases leaving a 'dry' stone with no tensile strength.

The presence of moisture in the interface between layers leads to a debonding of the layers and an associated reduction in the bearing capacity of the pavement.

Moisture in the subgrade significantly reduces its bearing capacity. As the shear strength of the support is reduced so the pavement life is also reduced.

In addition to moisture percolating through the pavement, water can also get into the subgrade from inadequate or malfunctioning drainage or leaking utility mains.

4.7. Pavements with lean mix concrete

In theory, at least, lean concrete roadbase is the ultimate platform on which to build a pavement since due to its stiffness it will distribute the load to the foundation better than bituminous or granular layers, which are inherently less stiff. There are, however, a number of problems, which cause concern as they have occurred on almost all sites where lean concrete has been used.

While the term 'lean concrete' is used in the UK, and it may be considered to be a 'stabilised gravel', this should not be confused with a broad range of stabilised materials found internationally which generally do not achieve the levels of layer stiffness required of a lean concrete in the UK. Lean concrete (cement-bound material or CBM) has been used for many years in the UK and has been made to a series of specifications set out in previous editions of the *Manual of Contract Documents for Highway Works* (MCHW) (DfT, 1992) as follows in Table 4.1.

Typically CBM 3 would be found in the heavily trafficked sections of the UK network. Cracking occurs in lean concrete roadbase due to thermal movement.

Transverse shrinkage cracking, or primary cracking as it is often called, is one of the most common forms of distress observed in pavements with lean concrete roadbases, especially if the surfacing is thin. Sometimes cracks can extend over the entire width of the carriageway at longitudinal intervals greater than 4 m. The most common cause of this type of cracking is drying shrinkage

Table 4.1 Strength of cement-bound materials (6.9 MPa = 1000 psi)

Type	Cube strength MPa	
	Mean of 5	Minimum
CBM 1	4.5	2.5
CBM 2	7.0	4.5
CBM 3	10.0	6.5
CBM 4	15.0	10.0

While MCHW is concerned primarily with the evaluation of existing pavements rather than the design of new ones, past editions of the various standards may generally be found to be more relevant than current ones or thermal contraction of the lean concrete, which can occur even before trafficking. When the lean concrete is strong (higher cement content), the crack spacing is wider and the movement is concentrated at fewer cracks, therefore the likelihood of reflective cracking is greater.

Secondary cracking, which is generally longitudinal in the wheel-paths, often begins at transverse cracks (primary cracking), and is associated with traffic loading. As the lean concrete deteriorates further under loading, surface cracking or crazing appears, and this can allow the entry of rainwater causing further deterioration and even premature failure of the foundation.

The current edition of MCHW (Volume 1) permits the use of a range of binders, which are referred to generically as hydraulically bound materials (HBM). The principal binders are pulverised fly ash (PFA), lime and ground blast furnace slag.

4.7.1 Prevention of reflective cracking in the bituminous layer

There are several ways to inhibit cracking in the bituminous layer.

If the bituminous layer is very thick then it will take time for the reflective cracking to appear on the surface. Current thinking is that a minimum of 190 mm of asphalt material should be used over an HBM layer as it appears that the rate of vertical crack propagation is about 20 mm/year.

An alternative is to attempt to minimise the shrinkage of the lean concrete (CBM) layer. Research indicates that if up to 30% of the cement is replaced by fly ash there is little or no loss in the strength of the concrete but a virtual absence of shrinkage. This is used extensively in France and the USA.

A further alternative is to accept that transverse (primary) shrinkage (cracking) is going to take place and assist it to happen by the use of transverse segmentation by various means. While this is argued to be successful it is much less elegant than inhibiting the shrinkage to start with.

The literature contains many reports of the use of stress-absorbing membrane interlayers (SAMIs) between CBM and asphalt, to prevent upward crack migration. Geotextiles of varying kinds have been used extensively in this research and while the concept of providing a tensile capable layer is sensible there seems to be some way to go in developing and demonstrating the validity of the process. Nevertheless, there are various reports, based on informed visual assessment, of this method resulting in extended pavement life prior to the appearance of surface cracking. One such report noted that 'we can't actually quantify the benefit in design terms but it does appear to work'.

When examining deterioration in bituminous surfaces supported by a lean concrete roadbase, the following levels of stiffness have been found to be typical in the roadbase (Table 4.2).

4.7.2 Primary failure modes

With a flexible composite construction which, has a cement-bound layer overlaid by an asphalt layer, the failure criteria are tensile strain at the bottom of the asphalt layer and tensile stress in the bottom of the cement-bound layer. Initially, the load distributing capabilities of the CBM layer is such that the bearing capacity of the subgrade is never in doubt.

The development of strain in the asphalt layer is related to the degree of support it gets from the underlying layer – in the case of a CBM layer this is not a problem as the support is initially very high. In these circumstances, the primary failure mode relates to the tensile stress in the CBM and the ruling factor is the strength of the mix, which is governed by the cement content.

Transverse cracking is the result of thermal movement, whereas longitudinal cracking is the result of materials degradation when initially a homogeneous cement-stabilised composite progressively tends towards a granular layer.

As the cement-bound material progressively converts into smaller blocks resulting from thermal and traffic-generated stresses there is a concentration of strain in the asphalt layer at the cracks in the underlying layer, and this leads to reflective cracks appearing on the surface of the asphalt layer. With primary cracking this is typically a narrow transverse crack between 4 m and 6 m centres, depending on the cement content in the CBM.

As the CBM blocks become smaller and progressively tend towards being granular, the primary failure mode changes to one that is normally associated with a flexible pavement. The level of support for the asphalt layer reduces and the tensile strain in the bottom of that layer increases until it exceeds permissible levels. In addition the vertical loads imposed on the subgrade increase and the possibility of a bearing capacity failure increases. This is assisted by the introduction of water through the cracked upper layers.

Table 4.2 Typical levels of stiffness of lean concrete roadbase

Pavement visual condition	CBM layer modulus: MPa
Visually sound	>20 000
Transverse cracking	14 000–20 000
Wheeltrack cracking	<14 000
Surface patching	<5000

The concept of a failure mode shift is used creatively when there is serious loss of ride quality with a concrete pavement due to movement of the slabs. In this case the use of crack and seat techniques are normal. In these circumstances the slabs are physically converted with heavy mechanical shearing equipment into smaller sections, typically about 0.5–1 m in length, forming rectangular polygons.

The current UK advice on the problems of assessing flexible composite pavements is set out in Table 4.3, taken from HD30/99 (DfT, 1999), to which the following notes refer.

4.7.2.1 Severity ratings

Severity 1:   Widely spaced cracks. Cracks without fretting, and no evidence of vertical movement.

Severity 2:   Regularly spaced cracks. Cracks fine or medium with some fretting and some evidence of horizontal and vertical movement.

Severity 3:   Regularly and irregularly spaced cracks. Cracks medium or fine without fretting, and evidence of horizontal and vertical movement.

Concrete strength: CBM 28-day strength taken from records, or estimated from cores.

4.7.3   Assessment of treatment of flexible composite pavements

See Table 4.3.

4.8.   Earth and unpaved roads – deterioration

While most developing countries have a predominance of unpaved roads there are also many examples of these in developed countries, the primary difference being the availability of graded granular materials for construction.

Based on a study by the World Bank in Brazil in 1982, earth roads are defined as unpaved roads with a surface of predominantly fine soil materials with more than 35% finer than a 0.075 mm particle size.

They can be considered in 4 categories.

- **Unformed roads or earth roads** have no drainage, cross-fall, added granular material or other features that would ensure all-weather access.
- **Formed roads** have a reasonably well defined cross-section, including drainage. They usually consist of locally available earth material with no added surfacing material.
- **Gravelled roads** are built and designed to certain engineering principles, including the supply, where warranted, of gravel-

wearing course. Construction of these roads also involves a defined cross-section, drainage and structures (bridges, culverts).

- **Sealed roads**: These are all-weather dust-free surfaces. Sealing is done with a wide range of technologies from bitumen seal to thin (not load-bearing) asphalt surfacing.

The deterioration of unpaved roads is governed by the behaviour of the surfacing material and the roadbed under the combined action of traffic and environment. The surfacing is typically 100 mm to 300 mm thick and serves as both the wearing course and the base-course of the pavement, providing sufficient structural strength and cover thickness to distribute the applied traffic loads to the roadbed material.

As the surfacing comprises a natural material, it is usually permeable, although in some cases the permeability may be very low, such as in densely graded plastic gravel or cemented material (which includes self-cementing materials like laterites, ferricretes and calcretes). Consequently, material properties, rainfall and surface drainage influence the behaviour of the surfacing under traffic; similarly, surface water runoff and side drainage usually affect the moisture penetration of the roadbed and thus its bearing capacity.

There are three fundamental mechanisms of deterioration, namely wear and abrasion of the surface material under traffic, deformation of the surface and roadbed material under the stresses induced by traffic loading and moisture condition, and, finally, erosion of the surface by traffic, water and wind. Consequently, the modes of deterioration differ in dry weather and wet weather on the one hand and depend on the strength of the surfacing and roadbed material (which are most critical in wet weather) on the other hand.

4.8.1   Dry weather deterioration

Under dry weather conditions, the most prominent deterioration mechanisms are as follows.

- Wear and abrasion of the surface, which generates loose material and develops ruts, loss of surface homogeneity (tightness) due to speed and/or power of passing traffic.
- Loss of surfacing material by whip off and dust, progressive loss of fines from the surface, blown onto adjacent land or carried along by passing traffic.
- The movement under traffic action of loose material forming corrugations resulting from the dynamic effects of passing vehicles.
- Longitudinal rutting, usually from foundation overload.
- Ravelling of the surface, in cases where there is insufficient cohesion in the material to keep the surface intact. This could be caused either by the abrasive action of vehicle tyres, or by incorrect blading of the surface. At points where ravelling

Table 4.3 Treatment of flexible composite pavements
From DfT (1999) © Crown copyright 1999

	Category 1	Category 2	Category 3	Category 4
Visual observation	Surface cracking not evident or confined to widely spaced minor transverse cracks unless associated with construction joints in CBM. Consistent deflection measurements which are low in relation to foundation stiffness.	Surface transverse cracking confined to left hand lane. No (or very minor) longitudinal cracking in the wheelpath. Measurements peak at regular intervals and the average is as expected in relation to foundation stiffness.	Transverse cracking and longitudinal cracking in the wheelpaths are both evident with a medium or high frequency. Measurements are variable and the average is as expected in relation to foundation stiffness.	Transverse cracking and longitudinal cracking in the wheelpath are both evident with a high frequency. Measurements are high in relation to foundation stiffness.
Deflection				
Crack severity	Transverse generally severity 1	Transverse generally severity 2	Transverse severity 2 longitudinal severity generally 1	Transverse and longitudinal severity generally 3
CBM strength Cores	10 MPa or more Consistent CBM with no wide cracks	10 MPa or more Some distinct cracking in CBM but material generally sound	10 MPa or less Wide longitudinal cracks but material between cracks is sound	10 MPa or less Wide cracks throughout some cores
FWD – mean pavement layer stiffness modulus (<20°C)	Consistent results >10 GPa with few individual results below 7 MPa	>10 GPa with some individual results below 7 GPa	Variable results average >10 GPa with successive below 7 GPa	<7 GPa
Probable CBM condition	Little deterioration beyond initial transverse cracking due to early shrinkage and thermal warping with good load transfer across transverse cracks.	Deterioration has gone beyond initial transverse cracking. CBM slabs are large with movement at transverse cracks. Longitudinal cracking is slight or not present with good load transfer across cracks.	CBM slabs are large with significant movement at transverse cracks. Longitudinal cracking is present.	CBM slabs are small, probably less than 4 m maximum dimension. Multiple transverse and longitudinal cracks with poor load transfer.
Implications for strength	Structure is very little deteriorated and pavement may be indeterminate with potential traffic capacity between 20 and 80 msa. If less than 10 years old and determinate, it may be sensible to overlay to get indeterminate life.	Structure has some deterioration and so cannot be assessed for an indeterminate life. Refer to overlay design procedure. Treat severity 2 cracks by trenching and replacing with bituminous material.	Refer to overlay design procedure. Treat transverse cracks of severity 2 and 3 by trenching and replacing with asphalt. Locally reconstruct areas of badly cracked CBM with asphalt.	Pavement to be removed to top of sub-base, or lower, and reconstructed. CBM will deteriorate towards a granular consistency. Consider retaining the pavement until the estimated amount of patching in one year is unacceptable. Possibly use thick overlay.

occurs the tyre action continues the abrasion process and loose material is removed from abraded areas. This results in depressions and increased roughness.

4.8.2 Wet weather deterioration

Under wet weather conditions the shear strengths of the materials determine the pattern of deterioration. When the shear strengths of the surfacing and roadbed materials are adequate for the stresses induced by traffic, deterioration occurs only at the surface. This is prevalent in regions where either road drainage is good, or good quality materials are found. The major modes of deterioration under these conditions are

- environment and traffic influences on surface erosion longitudinal rutting caused by scour from surface water when gradient >5%
- wear and abrasion of the surface by traffic causing rutting and loss of surfacing material
- the formation of potholes under traffic action. When gradients are <2% free water on the surface accumulates in any depressions, and the passage of a vehicle tyre stirs up the water causing fine material to pass into suspension. Water, with the suspended fine material, is also forced out of the depression. Under the action of many wheel passages and sufficient water, this is a rapidly accelerating phenomenon
- washout when drainage ditches are either inadequately designed or maintained
- if the road is very lightly trafficked, vegetation growth can cause problems: initially some grass in the centre of the lane, developing progressively to inward growth of overhanging vegetation from the sides of the road inhibiting passage of vehicles.

4.9. Deterioration – the effects of materials and construction

4.9.1 Introduction

This section is the result of investigation into several examples of heavy-duty asphalt pavements, containing low penetration (stiff) binders (35 pen or lower), which have shown early signs of longitudinal cracking outside the wheelpaths. These examples have caused serious concern and the problems appear to be part of an ongoing learning process where new unproven materials and construction techniques have been used.

4.9.2 Materials

The use of 35, 25 and 15 pen binders was permitted by the Highways Agency in 1998. At the time there were a considerable number of design, build, finance and operate (DBFO) projects and the availability of stiffer binders appeared to lead to the possible use of thinner pavement sections overall – which was particularly attractive to the private financiers. Initial trials carried out by TRL indicated these stiffer binder mixes were little different, from the point of view of laying, to the 50 pen mixes

previously used on heavier pavements. What was not understood at the time was that there were a number of issues that made these mixes significantly different from mixes which had been used successfully previously, the principal differences being

- durability
- bond
- compaction
- joints.

4.9.3 Durability

The problems of durability have come into focus as the result of using mixes with stiffer binders. These stiffer mixes tended to use less binder than did earlier mixes, and experience indicates there is a greater tendency for the stiffer binder to be stripped from the aggregate by the action of moisture when it has gained access to the lower layers of the pavement. The subject is dealt with in depth in Road note 42 (Nicholls *et al.*, 2008), from which the following definition has been adapted.

Pavement durability is defined as:

The retention over the structure's expected service-life of a satisfactory level of performance without major maintenance for all properties that are required for the particular road situation in addition to asphalt durability.

The main steps that lead to durability are

- the control of water (getting it away from the structure if not actually stopping it ever entering)
- limiting the number of sealing joints (both vertical and horizontal)
- adequate compaction (particularly at the joints).

Asphalt durability is defined as maintenance of the structural integrity of compacted material over the expected service life when exposed to the effects of the environment (water, oxygen, sunlight) and traffic loading.

Notes on the definition of durability:

Asphalt durability is dependent on

- the component materials used
- the weather conditions during laying
- the mixture, both the generic type and the job mix design
- the workmanship during mixing, transport, laying and compaction
- the site conditions, including geometry, subsequent local weather conditions, drainage and (possibly) traffic.

Pavement durability is dependent on

- the asphalt durability
- the traffic and site conditions
- the performance requirements set
- the asphalt performance requirements set.

The performance requirements could include any or all of the following

- stiffness
- resistance to fatigue
- texture depth
- transverse rutting
- longitudinal ride quality
- skid resistance
- noise level
- colour.

4.9.4 Bond
As pavement layers have become thinner there has developed a greater need to ensure that the several layers have acted compositely by being firmly bonded together. The need to ensure that this has happened was not, until recently, generally well understood, and little attention has been given to the issue as it was generally found to be neglected as just another site process that could be skimped on.

4.9.5 Compaction
In France, where stiffer binders were first used, compaction of the roadbase layer employs pneumatic tyred rollers (PTR) far heavier than the steel wheeled rollers that have traditionally been used in the UK. The PTR effectively kneads the asphalt to a higher level of compaction. Coupled with a much higher binder content than that used in the UK the French system involves compaction almost to refusal but leaves a very low air void content to accommodate any subsequent binder movement. The consequence of this has been to ensure the materials have a much greater durability than have those used in the UK.

4.9.6 Joints
When a new pavement is being constructed it is invariably laid in a series of parallel passes by the paving machine (rips). This process is then repeated for successive layers. Current practice is to ensure that the longitudinal joint of a higher layer is not on top of those in a lower layer. In the case of a surface course there is the requirement to cut back the edge of the newly laid rip before the adjacent rip is laid. This is to ensure there is a high degree of compaction adjacent to the joint. Figure 4.11 attempts to illustrate the problem.

Typically, each lower layer is thicker than the one above it.

For example, the usual typical thickness of the various layers may be:

Figure 4.11 Achieving compaction at joints in asphalt

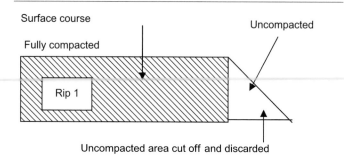

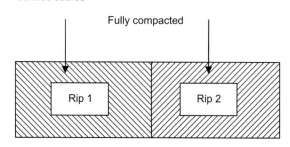

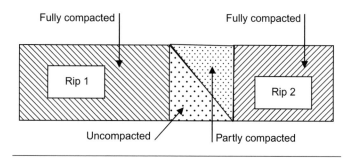

- Surface course 30 mm
- Binder course 60 mm
- Roadbase 120 mm or greater

The thickness of the roadbase depends on traffic load, whereas the surface course and the binder course thickness are fairly standard.

In these circumstances it can be seen that the width of the 'weak' area is related to the layer thickness and may well be as wide as it is thick. Thermally generated movements in this weak area lead to the formation of a vertical crack in the layer above it, which progressively reaches the surface and provides a ready access for water into the lower layer. It will be recalled that the stiffer mixes have been found to be less durable: as with the previous 50 pen mixes used in heavy duty pavements, consequently the failure process has been found to be much more rapid.

The lesson here is that ideally all layers should be cut back and painted as and when the surface course requires it.

Clearly, there is a cost penalty in doing so – nevertheless in whole life cost terms this would seem to be an overall good investment as it significantly reduces the risk of failure of the pavement.

As the design process calls for an increasingly higher level of technical discrimination, so must more attention be paid to the construction process, remembering that the product is not being delivered in controlled factory conditions, rather outside in widely varying weather conditions and temperatures.

While it may be argued that an analytical design should be undertaken – with all the assumptions that entails – it may well be that the current standards of delivery have some way to go to ensure these assumptions are realistic and can be delivered.

It is interesting to note that the *French Design Manual* (Centre de la sécurité et des techniques routières, 1997) has a factor in the design procedure, which contains a series of adjustment factors related to the conditions of execution, including the explicit assumption that all interfaces are bonded.

4.10. Deterioration resulting from expanding sub-base materials

A specific pavement deterioration problem, which can be found in the South and West Yorkshire areas of the UK and other steel making areas of the world, is that of expanding steel slag sub-base, the typical consequences of which are shown in Figure 4.12, which is a photograph of one of the major roads in Barnsley.

Figure 4.12 Effects on pavement surface of expanding sub-base

Typically, melting scrap metal and monitoring and adjusting the chemical constitution of the molten mix, which can be altered by the addition of secondary chemical materials, makes steel. Steel slag is the waste product of this process, which results from impurities in the original scrap and residuals from the secondary materials introduced as part of the culturing process of the molten metal within the furnace.

The potential problems of expansion of this slag material have been known for some considerable time, and result from the effect of moisture on the free lime in the slag, causing swelling of the material – which can have devastating consequences on the functional condition of the pavement.

During the melting process once the molten steel is demonstrated to be of the appropriate chemical constitution the furnace is tapped and the molten charge allowed to run into a large ladle from which the 'pure' steel can be decanted into moulds to form billets prior to rolling, which alters its microstructure and hence its physical properties. What remained in the ladle is in a semi-molten state and is regarded as slag and this has to be removed from the ladle prior to it solidifying. This waste material is usually tipped onto slag banks and allowed to cool prior to being crushed to form a granular material which is allowed to mature, typically for a period of several years. In some cases where the banks are well managed the material is physically turned over and watered to hasten any possible expansive effects and consequently reduce the maturing period.

The amount of free lime in individual banks varies depending on the constituents of the original melt. The presence of unmatured lime in the slag results in expansion of the granular mass when moisture is able to access it. While this had been known for many years, the effects were largely minimised by careful maturing of the slag materials before they were used in pavement construction. This was generally found to be successful and latterly few problems were found in the use of matured granular steel slag.

Unfortunately, in the early 1980s the Aldwarke steel works in Rotherham, which generated most of the slag used locally in pavement construction, changed the source and specification of the refractory bricks used in the furnaces and ladles. Refractory bricks were normally disposed of on the slag banks and are subsequently crushed, along with the slag, eventually becoming part of the granular sub-base used in pavements.

What was not understood at that time was that the various sources and specifications of refractory bricks had significantly different expansion profiles when wetted, although this has taken several years to become apparent. The consequence of this being that while it was generally believed the problems of expanding steel slag used in pavements had been controlled by careful maturing, a significant latent problem existed, relating to previously unidentified problems with contamination by waste refractory material, which has been very slow to show itself – typically taking up to 20 years to become apparent (Cartwright, 2000).

The consequence of this is that a number of roads, which have provided satisfactory functional conditions, for a lengthy period, typically greater than 20 years, have been rapidly becoming unsatisfactory due to rapid local expansion of the form shown in Figure 4.12.

4.11. Pavements – overall deterioration factors

Figure 4.13 attempts to illustrate the many and varied factors which affect the deterioration of a pavement.

Figure 4.13 Overall deterioration factors affecting an asphalt pavement

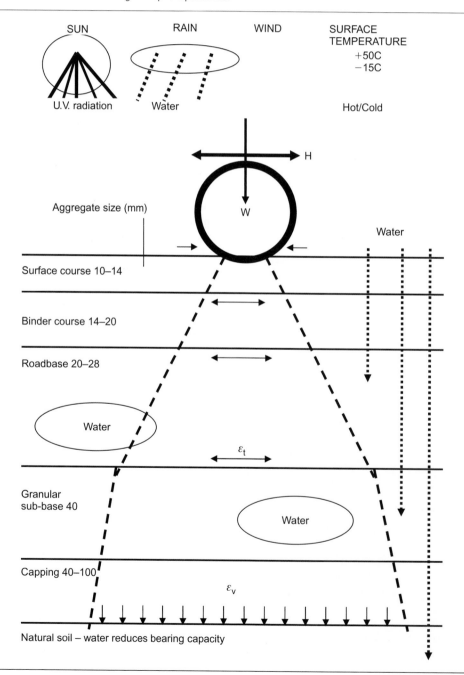

4.12. Factors affecting the deterioration of pavements

There follows a comprehensive list of the factors contributing to the deterioration of a pavement

- **stone (aggregate)**
  aggregate shape
  aggregate strength
    impact (aiv)
    crushing (tfv)
  abrasion (aav)
  weathering history (geological)
  cleanliness
  binder affinity
  moisture content
  contamination by moisture susceptible softer inclusions
- **binder**
  mix proportions
  mix temperatures
    too cold/too hot/burnt
    moisture content of stone in mix
  sand incompatibility
  binder penetration
  binder chemistry/source incompatibility
  binder rehology (flow characteristics)
- **laying**
  delivery temperatures
  laying temperatures
  rolling temperature
  windchill
  rolling pattern
  thickness variation
  joints
    cutting
    painting
- **loading/structural**
  axle load (maximum and equivalent standard axles)
  traffic flows
  traffic speed
  design life
  channelisation
  formation bearing capacity
  formation moisture content
- **usage/environmental**
  sun (uv radiation)
  temperature range
  wetting/drying cycle
  freeze/thaw cycle
  chemical
  surface condition
    cracked – permeable/impermeable
  maintenance regime
  subgrade moisture regime

REFERENCES AND BIBLIOGRAPHY

Asphalt Institute (1991) *Thickness Design: Asphalt Pavements for Highways & Streets. Manual series no. 1 (MS-1)*. Asphalt Institute, Lexington, KY.

Cabrera JG and Zoorob SE (eds) (1999) *Proceedings of the Third European Symposium on Performance and Durability of Bituminous Materials and Hydraulic Stabilised Composites.* Aedificatio, Zurich.

Cartwright M (2000) Private communication.

Centre de la sécurité et des techniques routières (1997) *French Design Manual for Pavement Structures* (Translation of Setra and LCPC (1994) *Conception et dimensionnement des structures de chausée – Guide Technique*, Ministère de l'Équipement, des Transports et du Tourisme, Paris). LCPC/Setra, Paris.

Collins HJ and Hart CA (1936) *Principles of Road Engineering.* Edward Arnold, London.

Croll JGA (2009) The role of thermal ratcheting in pavement failures. *Proceedings of the Institution of Civil Engineers, Transport* **162(3)**: 127–140. doi:10.1680/tran.2009.162.3.127.

Cudworth DM (1997) An improved method for evaluating the condition of jointed concrete pavements based on deflection testing. MSc dissertation. University of Nottingham, Nottingham.

DfT (Department for Transport) (1992) MCHW: *Manual of Contract Documents for Highways*. DFT, London. http://www.dft.gov.uk/ha/standards/mchw for further details (accessed 14/07/2011).

DfT (Department for Transport) (1999) HD30/99: *Design Manual for Roads and Bridges*, Vol. 7: Pavement design and maintenance, section 3: Pavement maintenance assessment, part 3: Maintenance assessment procedure. DfT, London.

Knapton J (1976) Technical Report 42.515: The design of concrete block roads. Cement and Concrete Association, Slough.

Nicholls JC, McHale MJ and Griffiths RD (2008) – Road note 42: Best practice guide for the durability of asphalt pavements. TRL, Wokingham.

Nunn ME, Brown A, Weston A and Nicholls JC (1997) TRL 250: Design of long-life flexible pavements for heavy traffic. TRL, Crowthorne.

Sayers MW, Gillespie TD and Queiroz CAV (1986) The International Road Roughness Experiment, Establishing Correlation and Calibration Standard for Measurements, World Bank Technical Paper number 45. The World Bank, Washington, DC, USA.

Tillson GW (1900) *Street Pavements and Paving Materials.* Wiley, New York.

UKRLG (UK Road Liaison Group) (2006) Best practice guidelines for modern negative texture surfaces of local authority highways. TSO, London. For more information see: http://www.ukroadsliaisongroup.org (accessed 13/07/11).

Ullidtz P (1987) Pavement analysis. In *Developments in Civil Engineering*, Vol. 19. Elsevier Science, Amsterdam.

Walsh ID (1997) Surface characteristics of thin surfacings. *Proceedings of the European Symposium on Performance and Durability of Bituminous Materials*. University of Leeds, Leeds, pp 605–616.

West G (2000) *The Technical Development of Roads in Britain*. Ashgate, Aldershot.

Whiteoak D (1990) *The Shell Bitumen Handbook*, 4th edn. Shell Bitumen UK, Chertsey.

Deterioration and Maintenance of Pavements
ISBN: 978-0-7277-4114-1

ICE Publishing. All rights reserved
http://dx.doi.org/10.1680/dmp.41141.059

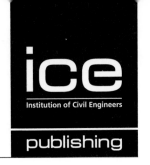

Chapter 5
Pavement Evaluation and Data Collection

5.1. Introduction

While the majority of the maintenance work referred to in Chapter 13, 'Repair and maintenance – asphalt pavements', can be identified by a visual survey, when more substantial works are considered it is necessary to undertakes a comprehensive pavement evaluation. Figure 5.1 gives an overview of the various issues relating to pavement evaluation. The specific issues shown in Figure 5.1 are dealt with individually in Chapters 6–12, and a detailed consideration of the options relating to strengthening of pavements is dealt with in Chapter 21.

Various data are required to ensure that the money spent maintaining pavements is used effectively and maximises the possible contribution to the existing asset. In some cases these data are common to both levels, for example the locational referencing framework; in others a particular sub-set may be relevant only to a particular level. Generally with project level surveys there is a greater need for detail and locational accuracy.

While this section deals primarily on the needs of project level rehabilitation, for completeness the broader issues related to network level management are discussed where relevant.

Figure 5.1 sets out the various data that are required, besides the topographical details of the site, in the preparation of an optimal rehabilitation proposal.

5.2. Locational referencing

The single most important feature of a pavement evaluation is the locational referencing of the various data to be collected. It is also necessary in database management systems to have a common locational referencing system such that the various data can easily be combined. The increasing development of computer processing power linked to geographic information systems makes accurate GPS digital referencing a practical and economical option. Equipment is now commercially available that can be carried by a surveyor or fixed to data collection equipment to spatially fix position in the x–y–z planes. This generates a string of digital data, which can be incorporated into existing databases and as such provide a universal reference. In this manner it is

Figure 5.1 Data requirements for comprehensive pavement evaluation

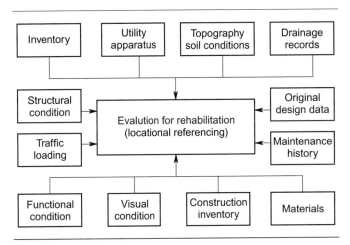

possible to access and combine all data in a map format with different data being regarded as separate layers.

The highway network can be symbolised in a skeletal diagram, and, at the crudest level, can be represented by a system of straight lines joining junctions. The spatial coordinates of these junctions (nodes) can readily be established, either from existing Ordnance Survey maps or by direct on-site measurement. Existing technology allows for the digitisation of discrete points within a highway network to facilitate the plotting of an accurate map rather than an idealised straight line skeletal representation. The overall concept is set out in the Figure 5.2.

Many data collection contractors utilise GPS locational referencing as a matter of course to manage their own operations.

Figure 5.3 shows a simple example where the point of interest can be defined as a distance from Node 178 towards Node 201 of X metres and a left offset of Y metres. An alternative is to use distance together with the concept of cross-sectional positions, for example

Figure 5.2 Digitised locational referencing

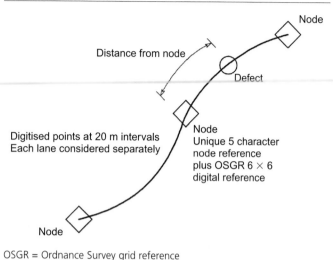

OSGR = Ordnance Survey grid reference

Figure 5.3 Localised locational referencing

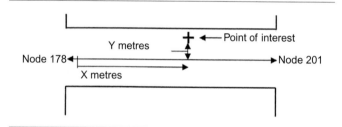

■ left verge
■ left footway
■ left lane or L1, L2 etc. if more than one lane
■ right lane
■ right footway
■ right verge.

In this system, left and right are controlled by node precedence such that if the description was Node 201 towards Node 178 then the offset used in Figure 5.3 would be right rather than left.

5.3. Inventory

The inventory is a catalogue listing of what is to be maintained, and ranges from coarse details such as road classification and length, to gullies and their location.

An inventory is the starting point for a comprehensive management system – in the old cliché 'if you cannot quantify it you cannot manage it'. For many years highway maintenance managers have operated with surprisingly little information – in some cases there may not even be a comprehensive listing of streets and their lengths. At the other extreme an inventory can be a self-

satisfying system where the detail is both very fine and complex. In any management system an early decision must be made about the level of inventory information to collect. The test should be 'what are we going to use it for, how and with what benefit?'

5.4. Utility apparatus

Most highways are a conduit for utility apparatus (Figure 5.4), with the managers having inadequate control over the utility, and a study of international highway maintenance literature will show the worldwide problems associated with utility apparatus. The legal position varies in different countries, but in the UK a utility must register to become a statutory undertaker, which means agreement to compliance with various legislation. Nobody, unless they are a registered utility, or third party by licence agreement with the local highway authority, can legally open the fabric of the highway. The utilities staff, both manual and management, must be certificated to approved training standards. Before the utility can open the highway, notice must be served on all other utilities to facilitate coordination. In the case of an emergency, however, the utility can open the highway and provide the paperwork after the event. This facility has been, and to a certain extent is, abused and is the cause of many debates.

Figure 5.4 What lies under the surface?
Courtesy of Rex Features

The author recalls many years ago laying a new asphalt carpet through an out-of-town shopping area. The project was scheduled to last for three days and on day two a utility begun to open the road within the area of work completed on day one.

In many urban situations, the need to rehabilitate sections of carriageway is primarily due to poor ride, some of which may be caused by failure at the location of utility apparatus, rather than due to a general structural inadequacy of the pavement. For example, hot laid asphalt materials in a reinstatement generally have a shorter life than the parent material due to inadequate laying temperature or lack of proper compaction – or both.

As part of the collection of data prior to undertaking on-site testing a detailed record of the utility apparatus should be assembled. Ideally, this should be plotted on a map, which also shows the location of the visual distress. Visual distress is dealt with in detail in a later section. An experienced engineer should be able to develop an understanding of the overall situation by making a site inspection, paying particular attention to ironwork (access chambers, etc.) in the carriageway. For example, a series of large Telecom access chambers will indicate that a major installation is present. In the case of trunk water mains these might not be so easy to see, unless there are under-bridges where the water mains may be found fixed to the side of the bridge. Alternatively, the location of a service reservoir adjacent to the road in an urban area would suggest the presence of water mains. A detailed site reconnaissance by the engineer is, therefore, the first step in familiarising himself or herself with the problems of the site.

5.5.   Topography, geology and soil conditions

As part of the general familiarisation process there is the need to consider topography. Is the section under consideration on an embankment, or in a cutting, or in an area of side-hung land? In the latter two cases there may be problems with water in the foundations of the pavement, which is likely to cause local loss of bearing capacity. Equally, it is not unknown for the water to have come from a water main leaking slowly from a joint(s). This can be identified by testing for chlorine traces in the groundwater, since chlorine is universally used at some stage in the purification of drinking water. Similarly, testing for traces of ammonia in the groundwater can identify a leaking sewer.

There is a need to understand the geology and soil conditions under the site, both as part of an evaluation of the foundation-bearing capacity and in estimating the sensitivity of the ground to moisture changes.

5.6.   Drainage records

The importance of drainage cannot be overstated and this is dealt with more fully in the Chapter 11. One of the most usual reasons for local foundation soft spots is due to inadequately functioning drainage.

What is relevant here is the need for a comprehensive understanding of the drainage provision and knowledge of its condition. A detailed drainage survey should be made from the gullies through to the outfall, or at least the main carrier to the outfall. Sizes and gradients should be measured and recorded. A combination of flushing and CCTV will be needed to demonstrate that the pipes are free from detritus and breakages. If there are no existing records then time and effort must be spent in proving the drainage system.

5.7.   Original design data

If possible the original design data should be considered, especially if the pavement design was likely to be based on Road note 29 (TRL, 1970) and forms the background and basis of the current UK methodology.

In the case of one major urban road, built in the early 1970s on a substantially greenfield site examined by the author, the pavement was showing serious distress, necessitating a reconstruction. During the evaluation it was found that when the original traffic loading was considered the pavement had carried well over three times its original design load. The original 150 mm asphalt on granular sub-base construction was replaced by partial reconstruction employing 300 mm asphalt on a thinner granular layer.

5.8.   Maintenance history

To assist understanding of the mechanics of failure on any one site it is helpful if the maintenance history can be found. Some highway authorities do have comprehensive records, but unfortunately most do not. Nevertheless there is some merit in trying to find what was done, even if that means finding and talking to the older employees or even retired members of the department, the latter usually being very happy to help.

As the concept of asset management develops, there is an increasing need to have reliable maintenance history information from which deterioration profiles can be deduced.

5.9.   Materials

Knowledge of the materials used can usually be found from a comprehensive logging of cores or trial pits. The use of cores is adequate for the upper bound layers but trial pits are required to examine the pavement at depth. When cores of bound materials are available consideration should be given to undertaking laboratory tests to characterise what has been found. This will usually include, grading, binder content, recovered binder penetration and NAT (Nottingham Asphalt Tester) stiffness.

A careful examination of the aggregate should be made to consider any possible materials incompatibilities, which might be a reason for unsatisfactory performance. For example, while granite is a hard durable aggregate it is known in some cases to have poor binder affinity.

The substantial demise of many highway authority soils and materials laboratories can now be seen clearly to have been a retrograde step as it has resulted in the loss of much valuable local data, which can no longer be found elsewhere.

5.10. Remaining attributes

The overall format of a comprehensive pavement evaluation was shown in Figure 5.1. Items not considered here are dealt with in detail in other chapters.

The aspects considered above are principally desk studies, with a limited amount of on-site investigation. The remaining aspects are the subject of a detailed on-site study, employing both invasive and non-destructive testing. Because of their scale and nature they are dealt with separately in individual chapters.

REFERENCE

TRL (Transport Road Laboratory) (1970) Road note 29: Road pavement design, 3rd edn. TRL, Wokingham.

Deterioration and Maintenance of Pavements
ISBN: 978-0-7277-4114-1

ICE Publishing. All rights reserved
http://dx.doi.org/10.1680/dmp.41141.063

Chapter 6
Visual Distress on Pavement Surfaces

6.1.   Introduction

In Chapter 3 the range of pavements types and constructions has been set out and with any of these a first indication of existing or latent maintenance problems can be found by a detailed examination of the surface.

For guidance a separate diagrammatic representation of the various distresses as they affect different pavement types is set out in the following major groups

- asphalt flexible pavements
- jointed unreinforced concrete pavements
- continuously reinforced concrete pavements.

It should be noted that in the UK, particularly on the national road network (motorways and trunk roads), most if not all have asphalt running surfaces. Progressively, this surface is of a common type formulated to minimise traffic noise and is generally referred to as a 'quieter surface'. Nevertheless, cracks as they appear on the surface may have a different meaning compared with the more traditional surfaces depending on the nature of the structural base.

When viewed by an experienced engineer a crack in an asphalt surface may indicate the onset of future problems, whereas in a concrete slab, especially an unreinforced one, it would indicate a structural failure. For that reason the various types of pavement must be considered separately, although to the inexperienced the defect(s) may appear identical.

There are two other major issues, which for the sake of brevity are not dealt with here.

Firstly, defect severity. In simple terms with a crack, in an asphalt surface, the distinction between minor and major is when the crack width is less than or greater than 2 mm in width. With distress, which affects the homogeneity of the surface, the description of severities is more complex and can best be done photographically using an extensive manual as an instruction guide to a comprehensive training course.

Secondly, defect incidence (% per unit length or area) is not as straightforward as it may at first appear.

These apparently simple issues must be defined clearly, especially if the data is to be used in a pavement management system such as United Kingdom Pavement Management System (UKPMS), where all the input elements must comply with strict quality assurance rules.

To minimise the size of this section of the book, the various figures in the present chapter are photographs whose subject matter is confined to asphalt surfaces; these photos are set out to assist an understanding of generic defects in flexible pavements – which are the most common (FHWA, 2003; UKPMS, 2007).

6.2.   Generic defects on an asphalt surface

Figure 6.1 sets out the generic defects that may be found on an asphalt surface.

6.2.1   Loss of surface integrity

Loss of surface integrity results from a number of reasons, some of which are

- mix laid out of specified temperature limits
- incomplete rolling due to mat outside temperature limits
- inadequate binder in mix
- poor binder affinity with aggregate.

Fretting is the name usually given to loss of surface integrity, and is shown in Figures 6.2 and 6.3. Typically, temperature problems tend to affect the edges and ends of a lay, whereas inadequate binder and poor binder/aggregate affinity tend to show as isolated or general surface deterioration in the body of the surface.

Ravelling may be considered to be serious fretting, although as shown in Figure 6.3 the lack/absence of a tack bond coat ensuring the surface course is homogeneously bonded to its substrate may well be a contributory factor.

Figure 6.1 Asphalt pavement generic distress patterns

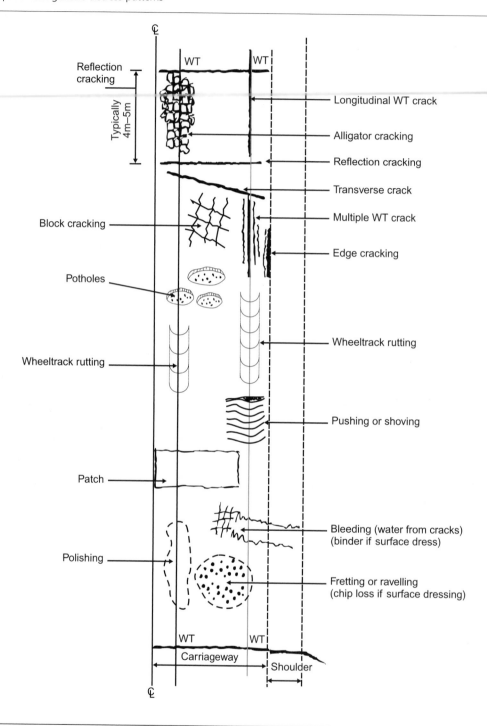

WT = wheel track

6.2.2   Rutting

Non-structural rutting (as shown in Figure 6.4) is usually confined to the surface courses and results either from general pavement usage temperatures approaching or in excess of the binder softening point, or from an incorrectly designed mix. Serious problems have also been found since the introduction in the UK of 'super single' tyres, were previously more common in Europe.

Figure 6.2 Fretting of hot rolled asphalt on main road

Courtesy of Iain McGregor

Figure 6.3 Ravelling of asphalt concrete on a minor urban road

Figure 6.4 Non-structural rutting

Courtesy of Iain McGregor

6.2.2.1 Structural rutting

Usually the result of deformation of the lower layers of the pavement, typically due to inadequate design or increased moisture in the formation reducing its bearing capacity. In Figure 6.5, multiple longitudinal wheeltrack cracking can also be seen.

6.2.3 Cracking

Cracking is likely to be the first indication of possible structural problems and may be the result of two generic routes of formation. Thermal and structural cracks and their development are shown in Figures 6.6 and 6.7. In an advanced stage, they may look almost identical when they present as crocodile cracking in the wheelpaths.

Figure 6.5 Structural rutting

Figure 6.6 Development of thermal cracking

Reproduced from Transport Research Laboratory 1999 ©TRL

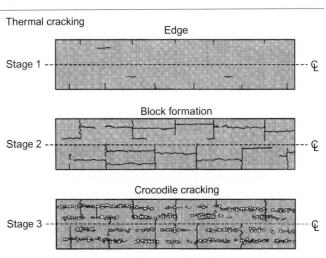

Figure 6.7 Development of fatigue cracking
Reproduced from Transport Research Laboratory 1999 © TRL

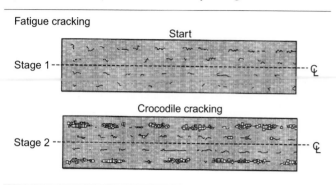

Fatigue cracking

Figure 6.9 Block cracking
Reproduced from FHWA, 2003. In the public domain

Figure 6.8 Map cracking
Reproduced from FHWA, 2003. In the public domain

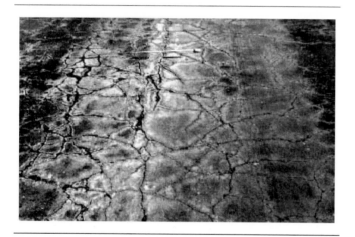

Stage 2 thermal cracking is described as map cracking or block cracking, and is shown in Figures 6.8 and 6.9.

6.2.3.1 Map cracking
See Figure 6.8.

6.2.3.2 Block cracking
See Figure 6.9.

6.2.3.3 Wheeltrack cracking plus mud pumping
When vertical deformation and wheeltrack cracking occur, due, initially, to an inadequate pavement construction, subsequently this permits access of water to the body of the pavement, which then permeates to the foundation, resulting in the evacuation of fine fractions of the underlying soil up through the pavement leaving a characteristic deposit on the surface, providing a clear indication of failure (as shown in Figure 6.10).

Figure 6.10 Wheeltrack cracking plus mud pumping

Figure 6.11 Crocodile cracking plus mud pumping

Figure 6.13 General loss of surface

Figure 6.12 Pothole

Figure 6.14 Ironwork

6.2.3.4 Crocodile cracking plus mud pumping
Crocodile cracking is a progression of single and subsequent wheeltrack cracking. When structural failure results, this is indicated by mud pumping (Figure 6.11).

6.2.4 Potholes and general loss of surface
As deterioration progresses a loss of surface results, which initially presents as potholes (Figure 6.12) and subsequent more general loss of integrity (Figure 6.13), which results in damage to vehicles and a reduction in travelling speed. In exceptional cases, the road may become impassable.

6.2.4.1 Pothole
See Figure 6.12.

6.2.4.2 General loss of surface
See Figure 6.13.

6.2.5 Miscellaneous
6.2.5.1 Ironwork
As shown in Figure 6.14, ironwork within a pavement has long been a point of weakness, particularly so with the reduction in the use of hot rolled asphalt (HRA) and the increase of 'quieter surfacing', which has a layer stiffness of about half that of HRA.

6.2.5.2 Foreign bodies
Foreign bodies, in this case a piece of rubber in the surface of a motorway, are more typically pieces of timber typically 50 mm × 25 mm × 150 mm in lower classification roads. These

Figure 6.15 Foreign body

Figure 6.16 Edge deterioration

inevitably lead, over time, to the development of a pothole (as shown in Figure 6.15).

6.2.5.3   Edge deterioration

Edge deterioration (Figure 6.16) is common in rural areas, where roads are relatively narrow and commercial vehicles,

Figure 6.17 Spring under pavement

particularly those associated with agriculture, are getting larger. In most of these roads, the fabric is crushed stone sealed with several layers of binder and chip dressings.

6.2.5.4   Spring under pavement

This problem is more usually, but not exclusively, found in rural areas and leads to a progressive break-up of the pavement (see Figure 6.17), especially in winter during freeze–thaw conditions.

6.2.5.5   Bleeding

Bleeding (Figure 6.18) typically occurs with chip seal in hot weather when the binder is mobilised by heat and bubbles through the surface.

6.2.5.6   Expanding sub-base

Expanding sub-base (as shown in Figure 6.19) is a problem in the Yorkshire area where steel slag has been used extensively as sub-base. This used to be a serious problem some 30 years ago and had been believed to have been cured. Recent experience with a number of major urban roads, however, indicates otherwise. The only known long-term remedy is replacement of the sub-base.

6.2.5.7   Frost damage

While frost damage can be found in the UK, which has the greatest number of freeze–thaw cycles of anywhere in Europe, in its extreme form it occurs where serious freezing conditions can be found, such as Scandinavia and parts of the USA and Canada. In these circumstances in conditions of permafrost the pavement foundation is frozen – sometimes to a considerable depth – and when frozen the road has a high bearing capacity. During the spring thaw, this bearing capacity reduces considerably to the extent that the pavement can become easily damaged. Figure 6.20 shows surface distress typical of frost damage.

Figure 6.18 Bleeding
Courtesy of J.J. Farrington

Figure 6.20 Frost damage
Courtesy of Road Scanners Oy

condition should correlate with several of the other aspects of the investigation, if a properly balanced project is to result. In some cases, it may be that the structural investigation will indicate the need for a substantial overlay and this can only be supported if there is obvious distress in the surface course. Conversely, if there is no surface distress – regardless of what the structural investigation might indicate – it would be inappropriate to undertake any significant works.

6.4.   Visual survey for rehabilitation

It will be seen that great complexity can be introduced into visual rating systems. As this chapter is primarily concerned about the relevance of visual defects as they relate to the preparation of rehabilitation proposals, the five defects set out in the list below are of the greatest relevance, and these should be correlated with the deflection survey. If there is not a correlation then further investigation is needed to find out why

- wheeltrack cracking – single
- wheeltrack cracking – multiple
- wheeltrack rutting > 20 mm
- random cracking
- fretting.

A format used successfully by the author for visual defect collection, together with a companion map format used in the interpretation of the various data, is set out in the following pages.

Figure 6.21 sets out a graphical format for recording the various distresses and their location, and Figure 6.22 sets out a map format which has been found useful when considering various datasets in parallel; for example, visual, deflection and construction.

Figure 6.19 Expanding sub-base

6.3.   Visual condition of the surface

One of the more important parameters in the process of assembling the relevant data for a rehabilitation investigation is that of the visual condition of the pavement since, among other things, the credibility of what is being done will be judged by the general public. Nevertheless, it is important that the visual

Figure 6.21 Distress data collection format

Pavement visual condition survey

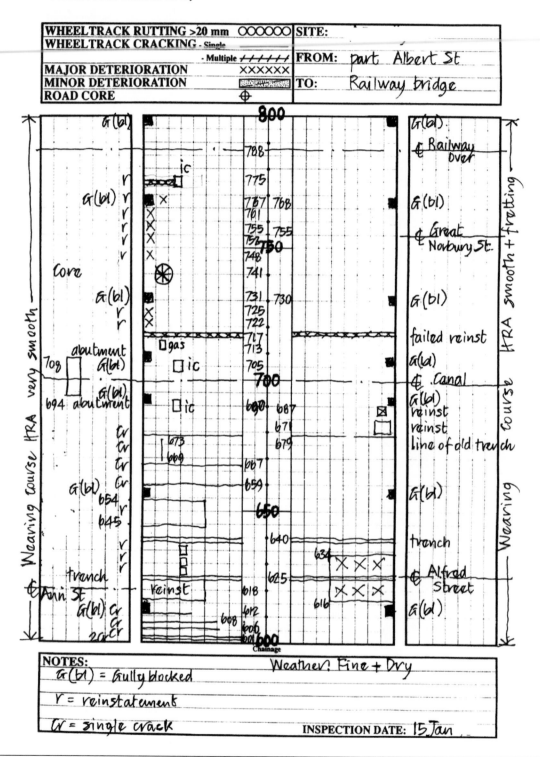

Figure 6.22 Map format distress data

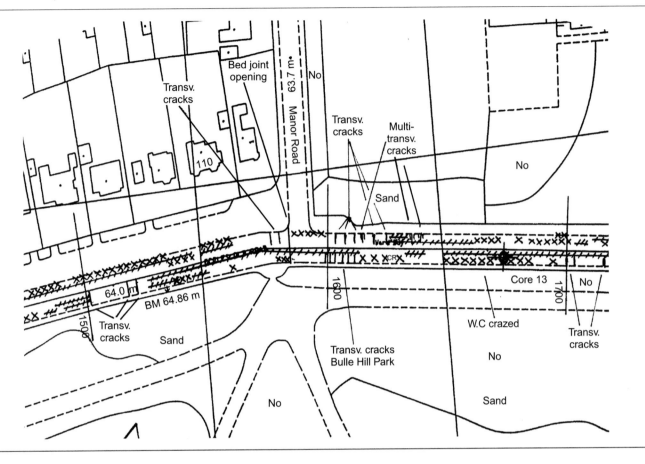

6.5. PAVER

PAVER (Shahin and Walther, 1990) is a well-used system in the USA and was developed by the US Army, Corps of Engineers, who are responsible for maintaining more than 560 million square yards of pavement on US military facilities throughout the world. As the result of its progressive development and implementation from the early 1980s there is a considerable volume of research data supporting the methodology used.

In concept, PAVER is quite different from the UK systems. It is based on the concept of a pavement classification index (PCI) and sample survey. A pavement is assumed to have a PCI of 100 when it is in perfect condition, decreasing to a value between 0 and 10 when it is considered to have failed. A considerable list of defects are defined and each defect is ascribed a 'deduct value' such that, depending on the defect and its incidence within a section, the 'rating' it generates is subtracted from 100.

The PAVER manual sets out a diagram (Figure 6.23), which is considered useful in developing an understanding in the minds of non-technical colleagues.

Figure 6.23 Typical pavement condition life cycle
Shahin and Walther (1990). In the public domain

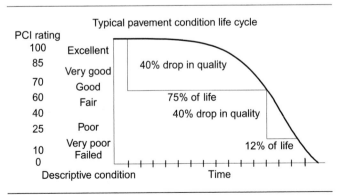

The PAVER manual also gives, in some detail, a comprehensive list of defects – which it helpfully describes, relating not only what they look like, but what may have caused them and whether they are related to structural, climatic or environmental effects.

While the Paver system is impressive, partly due to the consider-able amount of research that has gone into its development, it is very strange to see that it does not appear to consider wheeltrack cracking as a greater contributor to pavement deterioration.

6.6. A graphical approach to describing distress

In section 6.2, above, a graphical approach was presented illustrating distress patterns on asphalt pavements and it is

Figure 6.24 Distress types on jointed concrete pavements
Adapted from FHWA, 2003. In the public domain

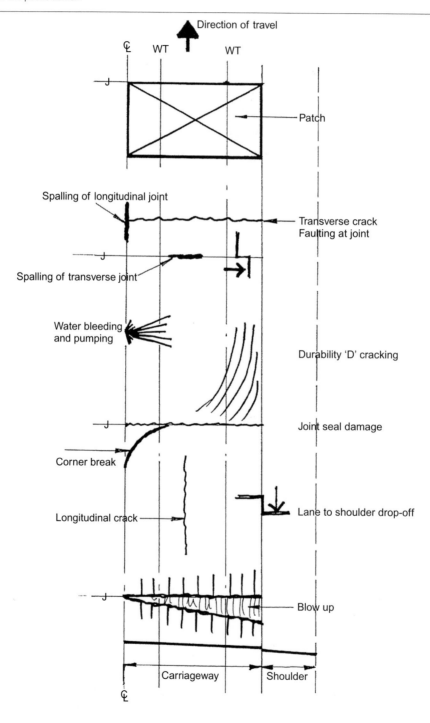

J = joint

convenient to use the same concept with the other two generic pavement types set out in that section, namely

■   jointed unreinforced concrete pavements

■   continuously reinforced concrete pavements.

To try and assist the learning process for those not familiar with pavements and in the interest of brevity the illustrative diagrams

Figure 6.25 Distress types on continuously reinforced concrete pavements
Adapted from FHWA 2003. In the public domain

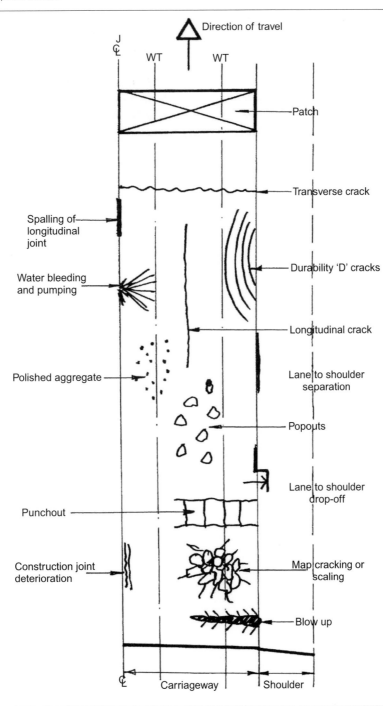

have been prepared by the author adapted from FHWA (2003) and personal experience.

Experience indicates that this approach is helpful with in-experienced personnel in looking for and recognising the different forms of distress most common in pavements.

REFERENCES AND BIBLIOGRAPHY

Dinesen PG (1981) National Road Laboratory report no. 50A-1981. Technical-economical guidelines to road maintenance: minor roads with asphalt pavement. Danish Road Directorate, Roskilde, Denmark.

FHWA (Federal Highways Administration) (2003) *Distress identification manual for long term pavement program*, FHWA-RD-03-031, FDHA, Washington, DC. For more information see http://www.fhwa.dot.gov/publications/research/infrastructure/pavements/ltpp/reports/03031/03031.pdf (accessed 15/07/2011).

Shahin MY (1994) *Pavement Management for Airports, Roads, and Parking Lots*. Chapman & Hall, New York.

Shahin MY and Walther JA (1990) USACERL technical report M-90/05: Pavement maintenance management of roads and streets using the PAVER system.

TRL (Transport Research Laboratory) (1999) TRL OSRN 18-1999. A guide to the pavement evaluation of bitumen-surfaced roads in tropical and sub-tropical countries. Transport Research Limited, Crowthorne.

UKPMS (United Kingdom Pavement Management System) (2007) UKPMS *User's Manual – Vol. 2, Visual Data Collection for UKPMS*, Chapter 6: DVI (detailed visual inspection). UKPMS, Guildford. For further details see http://www.ukpms.com/owner_forum/shared_files/UKPMS_Manual_02_06v05.pdf (accessed 15/07/2011).

Deterioration and Maintenance of Pavements
ISBN: 978-0-7277-4114-1

Chapter 7
Traffic Loading

7.1.   Introduction

The loading of traffic over the design life of the pavement is a fundamental input, and is an area that is subject to much debate and inaccuracy.

The basic loading unit is known as an equivalent standard axle (ESA) and is the result of work carried out at the AASHO Road Tests in 1958–1960. This work also proposed a method of relating the damaging effect of different axle weights, which is generally referred to as the 'fourth power law'.

Having developed a method of relating the damaging effect of different axles it is then necessary to know the number of vehicles, number of axles and the axle weights. This can readily be done by counting and classifying vehicles into different types and undertaking axle weighing to assign a damaging effect to the various types. In many countries this may well have to be undertaken from first principles.

In some developed countries, laws have been made to fix maximum axle weights for different vehicles. In the UK, data are also available where the traffic mix can be determined from knowledge of the daily traffic flow, although this is progressively changing due to the development of road transport technology.

The final factor is that of growth and it must be accepted that this is the most difficult to predict over the design life of the pavement, which is progressively being set at 40 years. Look back 40 years and consider the then normal road transport industry and available technology, and compare this with the present situation.

The cumulative traffic load for the traffic lane in question can be calculated using the following equation, with the answer being expressed in units of msa (million standard axles), or as some texts refer to it, as Esal (equivalent standard axles/lane).

$$T = 365 \times F \times Y \times G \times L \times C \times W \times 10^{-6} \text{ msa} \qquad (7.1)$$

where:

T = design load (msa)

F = present traffic flow (AADF (annual average daily flow)) (one-way flow)

Y = design period (years)

G = growth factor

L = lane factor (latest HA publication uses P)

C = channelisation factor

W = wear factor

In the event of traffic data being available as AADT (annual average daily traffic) and no other information being available, then it is reasonable to assume that the directional split is 50:50 (i.e. $F = 0.5 \times \text{AADT}$).

The wear factor used in Equation 7.1 above is an overall damage factor for the traffic flow as a whole, which is typical of UK practice and is dealt with later.

If more detailed traffic data are available, the more discriminating approach also described later is to be preferred.

7.2.   Wear factor (equivalent standard axle)

In 1958–1960, AASHO undertook a large set of full-scale pavement trials in Ottawa, Illinois. Six test tracks were constructed (both flexible and rigid) of different thicknesses. Each track was trafficked 24 hours per day by one of six vehicle types ranging from 2-axle trucks with a maximum weight of 3.6 tons to a 5-axle truck with a maximum weight of 48 tons. A total of about 17 million vehicle-miles were driven in two years. An axle carrying a load of 18 000 lbs (18 kips) (equivalent to 80 kN) was arbitrarily defined as a standard axle and was assigned a damaging effect of unity (AASHO, 1962).

Probably the most important result of the AASHO Road Test was the 'fourth power law'. A regression analysis of the results of the test indicated that the decrease in pavement serviceability caused by a heavy vehicle axle could be related to the fourth power of the static load. Serviceability was assessed by a panel of experts and rated on a scale known as the 'present serviceability index' (PSI). PSI values ranged from 0 to 5 with a 'perfect' road being represented by a score of 5. In the AASHO Road Test it was found that PSI could be expressed in a regression equation relating 'cracking and patching', rutting and surface roughness. This information can be used to convert the loads applied to the pavement in mixed traffic into a number of equivalent standard axles by applying the fourth power to each axle.

The **equivalent standard axle** is related to a static load W by the following:

$$N = \left(\frac{W}{W_0}\right)^4 \qquad (7.2)$$

where W_0 is generally taken to be 80 kN (18 000 lbs) or (8160 kg).

Overseas road note 31 (TRL, 1993) uses an exponent of 4.5, which produces a significantly different answer at high axle overloading such as may be experienced in Asia and Africa.

When using design guides available in various countries, care should be taken to check the reference axle weight in that country. For example, the French *Design Manual for Pavement Structures* (Setra and LCPC, 1994) makes it clear that in France the reference axle is a dual-wheels isolated axle weighing 130 kN. When comparison of the needed asphalt thickness is between the UK and French design guides, Setra and LCPC (1994), it is necessary to remember that the 130 kN axle used there is almost seven times more damaging than the UK standard 80 kN axle.

In Germany, the standard axle load is 100 kN (FGSV, 2001) which is almost 2.5 times more damaging than the UK standard 80 kN axle. In that publication the design is based on a catalogue system of 7 classes. Initially it appears that the equivalent standard axle count is quite low until the relative factor of 2.5 is introduced. Interestingly the class SV, effectively the motorway is the equivalent of 80 msa used in the Highways Agency design chart for the UK, DMRB (Highways Agency, 2006b).

Whereas the traffic engineer is interested in total flow in equivalent passenger car units to design the pavement width, the pavement engineer needs to estimate the number of equivalent standard (80 kN) axles per lane (ESALs) to design the thickness of the pavement. It is important when organising a traffic count to capture the relevant data for both.

For convenience Table 7.1 sets out the relative damaging effect of axles between 750 kg and 30 000 kg based on an ESA of 8160 kg.

A number of things are apparent from Table 7.1: first, how irrelevant is a normal private motor car: if a private motor car has two 750 kg axles it will need almost 13 000 private cars with a 650 kg axle weight to equal the damaging effect of one standard 8160 kg standard axle.

Table 7.1 Axle weight plotted against damaging factor

Axle weight: kg	Damaging factor
650	0.000043
1000	0.0002
2500	0.0088
5000	0.1410
7500	0.7136
8160	1.00
10 000	2.26
11 000	3.31
12 000	4.68
13 000	6.46
14 000	8.66
15 000	11.42
20 000	36.08
25 000	88.10
30 000	182.69

Second, it underlines the great damaging effect of trucks that run illegally with axle weights up to 30 tonne, effectively 50 times heavier than a normal truck, such as is illustrated in Table 7.2.

7.3. Current research

The validity of the fourth power law is being questioned, particularly for current axle loads, axle group configurations, tyre sizes, tyre pressures, pavement constructions and traffic volumes, all of which are significantly different from the conditions in the AASHO Road Tests. Recent research has indicated that the damage exponent 'n' may be in a range from 1.3–3.6 for flexible pavements and as high as 8–33 for composite and rigid pavements. The implications of the latter would be very significant on design loadings. At the present time the use of 4, or a number of that order, is recommended in all circumstances in the UK in DMRB (Highways Agency, 2006b), although Overseas road note 31 (TRL, 1993) recommends 4.5. The difference is significant in that the calculated damage factor for a 25 tonne

Table 7.2 Permitted axle weights in European countries

Country	Max. load on single axle (1000 kg)	Gross vehicle weight: t
France	13	44
Germany	11.5	44
Italy	12	44
Netherlands	9	50
UK	11.5	44

Figure 7.1 Percentage of HGVs in the heaviest loaded lane
Reproduced from Highways Agency, 2006a © Crown copyright 2006

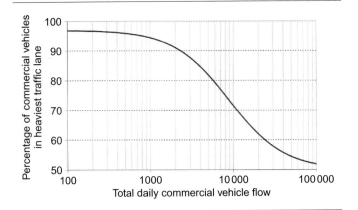

axle increases from 88 (exponent = 4) as in Table 7.1 to a calculated 154 (exponent = 4.5).

7.4. Standard axles per vehicle

This depends on overall axle configuration and weights and theoretically a whole range of other things, from the stiffness of the pavement to the stiffness of the subgrade. The issue is well set out by Huang (1993) but for all practical purposes it is normal to use the fourth power law.

The basis of deriving the effect of a single vehicle is illustrated by the following example. At its simplest consider a 2-axle rigid vehicle of 16 000 kg gross weight with the weight being distributed as shown in Table 7.3.

The principle can be used to calculate an ESA for any vehicle,

Figure 7.2 Growth factor for traffic – overall approach
Reproduced from Highways Agency, 2006a © Crown copyright 2006

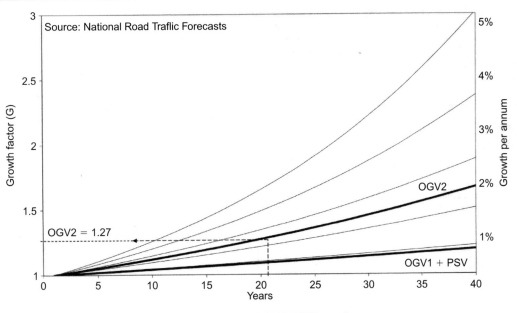

Extracted growth factor (G) values assuming 1997 NRTF growth:

Design period (years)	5	10	15	20	25	30	35	40
OGV1 + PSV	1.02	1.04	1.06	1.09	1.11	1.14	1.17	1.19
OGV2	1.05	1.12	1.19	1.27	1.36	1.45	1.56	1.67

Example

Considering OGV2
Design period   20 years
Growth factor   1.27

Table 7.3 Damaging effect of 2-axle truck

Gross weight 16 000 kg	
Front 30%	Rear 70%
4800 kg	11 200 kg
ESA	ESA
0.12	3.55
Total ESAs 3.67	

and while the gross weight of vehicles is on the increase in Europe, so is the number of axles, which has the effect of reducing the ESA count per vehicle. In practice, however, variations in tyre pressure and poor loading can have the opposite effect.

7.5. Tyre pressure

There is an ongoing conflict between the road haulage industry (RHI) and pavement owners (PO) on the subject of tyre pressure.

Figure 7.3 Calculation of 40-year traffic loading – global approach
Reproduced from Highways Agency (2006a) © Crown copyright 2006

Commercial vehicle classes and categories

Commercial vehicle (cv)	cv class*	cv category
	Buses and coaches	PSV
	2-axle rigid	OGV1
	3-axle rigid	
	3-axle articulated	OGV2
	4-axle rigid	
	4-axle articulated	
	5-axle articulated	
	6 (or more)-axle articulated	

Example

Count data converted to AADF using COBA 11 classification.

Buses and coaches	32	PSV
2-axle rigid	467	OGVI
3-axle rigid	67	"
3- and 4-axle articulated	274	OGV2
4-axle rigid	49	"
5-axle articulated	938	"
6- or more axle	530	"

Total flow	2357	cv/d
Total OGV2 flow	1791	cv/d
Percentage OGV2	76%	

Typical average commercial vehicle flow compositions are given below (Department for Transport, 2003). There is a wide variation in the values for the proportion of commercial vehicles on the trunk road network and the values in the table may be exceeded in many cases.

Typical Commercial Vehicle Flow Compositions

Road Type	Motorway or trunk	Principal
Percentage of commercial vehicles (% cv within AADF)	11	4
% OGV2	65	38

The road haulage industry's position is that higher pressure reduces tyre wear and fuel consumption.

Yoder and Witczak (1975) indicate that the loading from the tyres on a pavement is equal to and cannot be higher than the tyre pressure, consequently the pavement owner's position is that the higher the pressure the greater the damaging effect of the tyre.

During the AASHO Road Tests the tyre pressures were maintained at 465 kPa and recent research indicates the range found in practice to be from 500 kPa to 1500 kPa with a mean of 694 kPa (100 psi).

The annual TRB conference in Washington, DC, in January 1997 reported research by the US Corps of Engineers Cold Regions Research Station that constituted an attempt to negate the need to ban traffic from forest tracks during the spring thaw. The research indicated that if the tyre pressures are kept below 50 psi (345 kPa) then no rutting was found in very unstable thawing constructions.

7.6. Axle weighing

There are three methods available for the measurement of axle loading.

The first consists of stopping a representative sample of commercial vehicles and measuring the load on each axle using some form of load-meter.

The second method is to direct the representative sample to a nearby public weighbridge where the axle weights can be measured individually.

Alternatively, a recording weighbridge can be set into the surface of the road so that all axle loads can be weighed and recorded as the vehicles move at normal speed. All these methods are in use worldwide, but the last is favoured as giving the most complete information. There is some difficulty with the other methods in determining what is a representative sample, and the relatively small number of overloads are likely to be missed.

The isolated effects of some of these overloads can be significant

Table 7.4 Lane distribution for HGV on multi-lane road
From Highways Agency 2006a © Crown copyright 2006

No. of lanes in each direction	% of HGVs in design lane
1	100
2	80–100
3	60–80
4	50–75

as there are examples in the literature in some Asian and Middle East countries where an axle load of 25 000 kg has been measured. This has an equivalent damage factor of 88.

7.7. Direction effect

Traffic surveys are normally conducted on the section of road in question and unless there is some data from the survey that would indicate otherwise, it is usual to assume that 50% of traffic is flowing in each direction.

7.8. Lane factor (*L*)

Having derived the total directional traffic it is necessary to allocate this over the various lanes since the design of the pavement will be based on the flow in the nearside lane, which is normally the heaviest (Figure 7.1).

Various works of guidance are available.

In the case of a two-lane carriageway where the HGV flow is less than 500 cv/day this is of the order of 5%. The effect only becomes significant at flows exceeding 2000 cvpd in one

Table 7.5 Axle factor multipliers

Effect	Multiplier
Traffic islands	2
Parking	2
Traffic signals	1.5
Roundabouts	1.5
Severe bends	1.5
Steep hill	2

Table 7.6 Wear factor for commercial vehicle classes and categories – UK
From Highways Agency, 2006a © Crown copyright 2006

Wear factors	Maintenance Wm	New build Wn
Buses and coaches	2.6	3.9
2-axle rigid	0.4	0.6
3-axle rigid	2.3	3.4
4-axle rigid	3.0	4.6
3- and 4-axle articulated	1.7	2.5
5-axle articulated	2.9	4.4
6-axle articulated	3.7	5.6
OGV 1 + PSV	0.6	1.0
OGV2	3.0	4.4

Figure 7.4 Commercial vehicle classes and categories
Reproduced from Highways Agency, 2006a © Crown copyright 2006

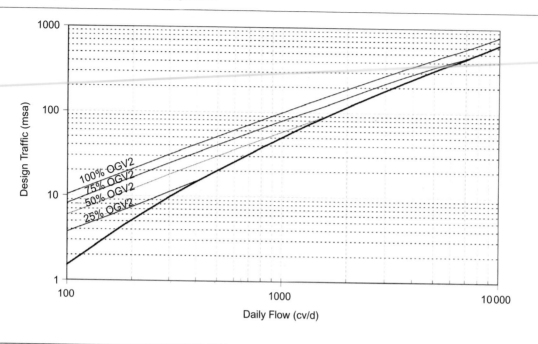

direction. Table 7.4 is recommended for two-lane carriageways, including motorways, to derive the HGV traffic in the near-side lane. At flows greater than 30 000 HGVs/day a proportion of 50% should be taken in lane 1.

In the case of a three-lane carriageway, it should be assumed that HGVs not in the left-hand lane are taken by the middle lane unless specific data indicates otherwise (Highways Agency, 2006a).

For a four-lane carriageway the number of HGVs not in the left-hand lane should be assumed to be evenly distributed between the two middle lanes.

7.9.   Growth factor (G)

Growth (Figure 7.2) is assumed to be compound over the design period, and based on the HGV flow at the start of the period the final flow can be calculated, from which it is possible to determine the mid-period traffic flow.

$$\text{Traffic at end of design period} = \text{Start flow, } X(1 + r)^n \tag{7.5}$$

where r = growth rate (%) and n = design period (yrs)

Huang (1993) suggests that an alternative may be:

$$\text{Growth factor (G)} = 0.5[1 + (1 + r)^n] \tag{7.6}$$

If local estimates of traffic growth are available they should be used. If there are no specific details it has been normal to allow for a 2% compound growth.

7.10.   Channelisation factor (C)

In the urban area it is relevant to consider the effects of vehicle channelisation, which may be caused by various factors. The report 'Vehicle damage factors: present, past and future values' (County Surveyors' Society (CSS), 1983) indicated that where the normal tendency for transverse wander is constrained by, for example, traffic islands, then the damaging effect can be at least twice that normally expected.

In narrow urban streets where on-street parking is permitted there is a tendency for buses and HGVs to use the same wheeltracks when passing in both directions.

An increased axle load factor may also be relevant at bus stops in the urban area, particularly where double-decker buses are used, at traffic signals and at the approach to roundabouts.

In the case of long severe gradients where there are significant HGV flows there is an indication that the normal damaging effect calculations may not be adequate.

Table 7.7 Calculation of traffic loading – worksheet
From Highways Agency, 2006b © Crown copyright 2006

Vehicle class	AADF (vpd)	Design period (yrs)	Growth factor	Wear factor	Cumulative load (msa)
Either					
Buses and coaches (PSV)				2.6	
OGV1					
2-axle rigid				0.4	
3-axle rigid				2.3	
3-axle articulated				2.3	
OGV2					
4-axle rigid				3.0	
4-axle articulated				1.7	
5-axle articulated				2.9	
6-axle articulated				3.7	
subtotal 1					
Or					
OGV1 + PSV				0.6	
OGV2			1.66	3.0	
subtotal 2					
Total cv/d					
Total msa all lanes (highest subtotal 1 or 2)					
% traffic in left-hand lane					
Channelisation effect					
Design traffic loading (msa)					
Required bituminous thickness (mm)					

The overall multipliers set out in Table 7.5 are suggested.

In certain locations and circumstances it may be appropriate to consider the multipliers to be cumulative.

7.11. Wear factor – UK (DMRB)

See Figure 7.3 and Table 7.6.

7.12. Calculation of traffic load

The wear factor for new construction is higher than for maintenance works to reflect the greater risk that arises from the additional uncertainty with traffic predictions for new designs. The format used in Table 7.7 is recommended for use in calculating traffic loading. It has been amended by the author to include a space to enter the required thickness of bituminous material from the relevant section of the source material 7 (Highways Agency, 2006b):

Having regard to the inherent vagaries of predicting traffic flows for a 40-year forward period, Figure 7.4 may be considered to be appropriate.

REFERENCES AND BIBLIOGRAPHY

AASHO (American Association of State Highway Organization) (1962) The AASHO Road Tests, report 5: Pavement research. Special report 61E, publication 954. Highway Research Board, Washington, DC.

Croney D and Croney P (1981) *The Design and Performance of Road Pavements*, 2nd edn. McGraw-Hill, London.

CSS (County Surveyors' Society) (1983) Vehicle damage factors: present past and future values. Kent County Council, Maidstone.

FGSV (Forschungegesellschaft für Straßen und Verkehrswesen) (2001) Richtlinien für die Standardisierung des Oberbaues von Verkehrsflächen, RStO 01. FSGV Verlag Gmbh, Köln.

Highways Agency (2006a) DMRB HD 24/06: *Design Manual for Roads and Bridges*, vol. 7, section 2, part 1: Traffic assessment. TSO, London.

Highways Agency (2006b) DMRB HD 26/06: *Design Manual for Roads and Bridges*, vol. 7, section 2, part 3: Pavement design. TSO, London.

Huang YH (1993) *Pavement Analysis and Design*. Prentice Hall, Englewood Cliffs, NJ.

Nicholls JC, McHale MJ and Griffiths RD (2008) Road note 42: Best practice guide for the durability of asphalt pavements. TRL, Wokingham.

Powell WD, Potter JF, Mayhew HC and Nunn ME (1984) Report LR 1132: The structural design of bituminous roads. TRRL, Wokingham.

Robinson RG (1988) Report RR138: Trends in axle loading and their effect on design of road pavements. TRRL, Wokingham.

Setra and LCPC (Laboratoire Central des Ponts et Chaussées) (1994) Conception et dimensionnement des structures de chaussée: guide technique. Ministère de l'Équipement, des Transports et du Tourisme, Paris. (*French Design Manual for Pavement Structures (Collection Guide Technique)*, 1997). LCPC, Paris.

TRL (Transport Research Laboratory) (1970) Road note 29: A guide to the structural design of pavements for new roads, 3rd edn. HMSO, London.

TRL (Transport Research Laboratory) (1993) Overseas road note 31: A guide to the structural design of bitumen surfaced roads in tropical and sub-tropical countries, 4th edn. TRL, Crowthorne.

Yoder EJ and Witczak MW (1975) *Principles of Pavement Design*. Wiley, New York.

Deterioration and Maintenance of Pavements
ISBN: 978-0-7277-4114-1

ICE Publishing. All rights reserved
http://dx.doi.org/10.1680/dmp.41141.083

Chapter 8
Construction Inventory

8.1. Introduction

This chapter deals with the assembly of the information required for a comprehensive understanding of what comprises the layered system of the pavement structure. An accurate knowledge of this is required if a meaningful assessment is to be made of the strength and likely service life of the pavement.

If a deflectograph is used, it is only necessary to know the thickness of the bound layer and the general characteristics of the supporting layer(s). With the falling weight deflectometer, where estimates are made of the stresses and strains within the pavement, it is necessary to have a more accurate idea of the layer thickness. This accuracy is required since in a mechanistic calculation the thickness of the relevant layer is related directly to the stresses and strains, which are themselves related to the serviceable life of the pavement.

The main problem with pavements is that there is an inevitable (statistical) variation in the thicknesses since no control process is infallible. For example, with the construction of the UK motorway network from about the early 1950s onward, where there were greenfield sites and, presumably, good site control, it was reasonable to assume that layer thicknesses would be extremely uniform. In practice, this has not proved to be the case and in these circumstances the inherent variation in the construction of older road pavements may be seen to present real problems.

In urban areas, the general layout of some of the current major road network has not changed significantly over the last 200–300 years. While the physical arrangement of roads may not have altered, the construction most certainly has and in several cases known to the author as many as five separate layers of construction have been found in a single location. To illustrate this point a summary core log is set out in Table 8.1. It will be seen that the construction comprised five layers of differently dated constructions.

The variation along the road can be judged from Table 8.2, which relates to a section of major urban road some 3 km in length. The summary core log used in Table 8.1 was taken from the project which forms the subject of Tables 8.2 and 8.3.

Table 8.1 Core log from urban road (actual)

Thickness: mm	Description
25	HRA wearing course
40	HRA basecourse
20	HRA wearing Course
80	HRA basecourse
35	HRA wearing course
30	HRA wearing course
40	HRA basecourse
70	Loose stones
140	Granite setts
150	Concrete
150	Ashes
	Clay strata

There can be seen to be several challenges, the primary aspects of which are the following requirements

- the vertical capture of the data
- the development of a realistic interpretation at specific individual locations
- the development of a realistic interpretation along the project length.

It is evident that the theory of pavement evaluation does not solely concern regular consistent layers. In the urban area, not only does the construction vary longitudinally but also transversely, which must be borne in mind.

Several methods of approach are available to capture the data. These are

- trial pits carefully excavated by hand
- rotary cores usually taken using a waterflush method
- dynamic cone penetrometer (DCP)
- ground penetrating radar (GPR)
- ad-hoc records of excavations.

Table 8.2 Eastbound core summary

Core no.	Chainage: m	Bit: mm	Sett: mm	Conc: mm	Loose stone	CBR %
1	20	230	130	155		
3	200	80		300		
5	500	140	145	180		
7	750	165		495	Y	
9	860	95		250		
11	1040	125			Y	
14	1330	150		325		
15	1450	340	140			
17	1705	75	125	290		
19	1900	65	135	250		
21	2200	75	130	205		6
23	2500	270		230		
25	2800	305			Y	
26	3000	180		105		
28	3175	165	140	170		

Table 8.3 Westbound core summary

Core no.	Chainage: m	Bit: mm	Sett: mm	Conc: mm	Loose stone	CBR %
2	50	560		130		
4	400	450			Y	
6	600	315			Y	
8	700	350			Y	
10	920	205	150			
12	1100	200			Y	
13	1285	270			Y	
16	1560	265	150			
18	1800	180			Y	
20	2020	215			Y	
22	2300	265			Y	
24	2700	265			Y	
27	3000	245			Y	
29	3220	290		180	Y	

8.2. Trial pits

Trial pits are a long used and proven method and consist of an excavation 1 m square which progressively steps in as lower layers are reached so that an assessment of the layer interface can be made and accurate measurements taken. The preferred location for trial pits is on the line of the nearside wheel-track.

Excavation is carried out carefully by hand with the excavated material from each layer being kept separate for subsequent examination or testing.

The major advantage with trial pits is that samples of sensible size can be gained for examination and laboratory testing.

They also present the opportunity to inspect the subgrade, which if reconstruction is a possibility is an important attribute. In situ CBR tests can also be carried out using a variety of apparatus.

Samples of the subgrade should be taken for classification, plastic and liquid limit and moisture content evaluation.

Samples of sub-base material should be taken for grading, classification and the determination of moisture content. The density of the sub-base should be taken and the capping material, if present, investigated.

Samples of the asphalt materials can be examined for the constituent aggregate type, aggregate grading, bitumen content and binder penetration. Depending on its condition it may be possible to make indirect tensile stiffness tests.

Trial pits may allow the level of the water table to be established.

While it is possible to take photographs of the excavation the oblique angle of approach does not give a particularly good indication of the layer structure.

The disadvantage with trial pits, besides the considerable expense (approx. £700–£1000) is that the process is invasive and destructive and it is not unusual for there to be subsequent reinstatement problems.

8.2.1   Trial pit log
See Table 8.4.

8.3.   Coring
Coring is much cheaper than trial pits (approx. £100–£150 per core, excluding traffic management and mobilisation) and less invasive. Cores can be drilled in a range of sizes, typically 100 mm and 150 mm diameter, which allows good samples to be recovered. They also provide a clear picture of the layer structure and permit accurate measurement. In some cases it is possible to judge the bonding between bound layers.

Smaller diameter (25 mm to 50 mm) cores can be very cost effective if it is only necessary to get details of thickness. The advantage is that a much greater number can be taken and it will be appreciated from Table 8.4 that the more observations the better.

There is merit in taking cores on two occasions. First, before any structural testing is carried out to get an indication of the pavement structure and by drilling on the location of cracking, if present, it is possible to make a preliminary judgement about which of several problems may be being faced.

Second, when the testing has been carried out the raw deflection data can be examined by calculating the surface modulus and an evaluation made of whether there appears to be any reasonably homogeneous section. If this appears to be the case then cores can be targeted to try to understand the pattern of areas of relatively higher and lower deflections.

It is possible to carry out a hand cone penetrometer test in the core hole using a hand-held probe. While the absolute accuracy of this may be in doubt it is quick and easy to do and as the hole is full of water it may be argued to represent a worst (soaked) condition. It is becoming normal practice to use a dynamic cone penetrometer (DCP) once the bound layer has been removed, to assess the thickness of the granular supporting layer and to get an idea of the foundation support. The DCP is described in detail later and should only be used after a careful utility survey has been undertaken.

Coring is usually carried out using a purpose-made mobile rig, (Figures 8.1 and 8.2) which typically is a towed trailer with its own power source which usually drives a small hydraulic pump to drive the rotating core barrel. Ballast is provided by water in

Figure 8.1 Typical trailer coring rig

Figure 8.2 DCP being used at night on an airfield

Table 8.4 Typical trial pit log
From Highways Agency, 2008 © Crown copyright 2008

TEST PIT LOG

Test pit:	17						Date:	26 July 2006
location:	M1 CH, 113 + 45 Northbound slow lane						Rut Depth (mm):	Near side = 3 mm
								Off side = 0 mm

Material	Depth from surface (mm)		Thickness of layer (mm)		Test sample no.	Required tests	Comments
	N/S	O/S	N/S	O/S			
14 mm slag HRA surface course	35	45	35	45	5678	1. Bitumen content 2. Bitumen properties 3. Grading	Surface condition sound
20 mm limestone HRA overlaid surface course	99	95	64	50	5679	1. Bitumen content 2. Bitumen properties 3. Grading	
28 mm limestone HRA binder course	159	151	60	56	5680	1. Bitumen content 2. Grading	
40 mm limestone DBM base	219	191	60	40	–		
40 mm limestone DBM base	329	306	110	115	–		
Granular sub-base material Type 1 crushed limestone	850	870	521	564	5681	1. Grading	Slight water seepage @ 0.80 m at centre of N/S lane. Terram between sub-base and subgrade
Firm mottled grey & olive brown silty Clay with traces of fine to medium sand and medium gravel	1100	1100	250	230	NS 5682 OS 5683	1. Atterberg limits 2. Field moisture content	
Firm dark grey silty Clay with traces of sand with some medium gravel size ironstone cobbles	1300	1400	200	300	NS 5684 OS 5685	1. Atterberg limits 2. Field moisture content	Trial hole terminated @ 1.30–1.40 m with water seepage @ 0.80 m as above.

saddle tanks, and this water is also used for cooling the diamond tipped core barrel. Depending on the nature of the ground, from setting up to reinstating the hole takes about half an hour. Reinstatement is carried out using a proprietary bituminous mix and is compacted by hand rammer. Cores can be used to

■ determine the thickness of each bound layer and the degree of bonding
■ note the visual condition of each layer, for example, the occurrence of stripping of the binder from the aggregate or the presence of detritus where there is a lack of bond between layers
■ indicate the depth of cracking, providing the cores are suitably located in relation to a pattern of cracking
■ provide representative samples for composition analysis and measurement of properties.

In the case of a concrete pavement cores may be used to

■ determine the thickness of concrete
■ note the visual condition, for example, aggregate type, voiding

- assess the compaction level by measuring density
- examine cracking
- provide representative samples for strength testing.

The cores should be returned to the laboratory, where they are photographed and logged in a standard manner: an example is set out in Figure 8.3.

8.3.1 Typical core log

The following information should be stated on the log sheet for each core:

(a) core reference
(b) section reference and chainage
(c) traffic direction
(d) lane and offset
(e) coring date
(f) pavement condition at core location including presence of cracks and their orientation
(g) thickness of each layer
(h) any missing layers
(i) each layer as appropriate
    (i) type of material present
    (ii) possible presence of tar bound layers (if smell or staining is present)
    (iii) condition of material, for example sound, cracked, friable, etc.
    (iv) stripping of binder from the aggregates (if present)
    (v) condition of bonding between layers

    (vi) presence of detritus where there is a lack of bond between layers
    (vii) voiding and segregation (if present)
    (viii) crack depth and severity, soft or otherwise deleterious aggregate, bleeding and any other peculiarities

Source: Highways Agency, 2008

8.4. Dynamic cone penetrometer

The dynamic cone penetrometer (DCP) is an instrument designed for the rapid in situ measurement of the structural properties of existing road pavements constructed from unbound materials.

The DCP consists of an 8 kg weight dropping through a height of 575 mm onto a 60° cone having a diameter of 20 mm. Readings of penetration are taken after every ten or five blows. A plot of cumulative blows against depth is made from which the change in gradient of the line can be judged. By inspection the change in gradient of the line is used to determine the thickness of a particular layer. By calculating the gradient of the line in mm/blow and using the following equation an estimate of the CBR of the layer under examination can be made.

Correlations have been established so that the results can be interpreted and compared with CBR values. The equation proposed by Jones and Rolt (1991) is shown below:

$$\text{Log}_{10}(\text{CBR}) = 2.48 - 1.057\,\text{Log}_{10}(\text{mm/blow}) \qquad (8.1)$$

A typical test takes only a few minutes and therefore the

Figure 8.3 Typical core log format
Reproduced from Highways Agency, 2008 © Crown copyright 2008

No	Top mm	Btm mm	Thkn mm	Mat'l	Max size mm	Type	Comments
1	0	40	40	HRA	14	GNT	Full depth crack in layer
2	40	120	80	DBM	28	GNT	Full depth crack in layer. De-bonded from layer 3
3	120	225	105	DBM	28	GNT	Sound. De-bonded from layer 4
4	115	353	128	HRA	28	GNT	Sound
							Asphalt resting on crushed limestone sub-base

Pavement condition: Transverse crack
Key: HRA = Hot rolled asphalt; DBM = Dense bituminous macadam; GNT = Granite

CORE LOG	Project area 15	Location/road: A1	Date: 7th August 2006 Ref: A1/L1/WB/10/1
	Section: 2400A1/357	Section chainage: 137 m	
	Mp: 10/1 Lane: 1	Direction: WB Offset: NSWP	

instrument provides a very efficient method of obtaining information, which would normally require the digging of test pits.

Figure 8.4 shows a typical result plot.

In the USA, at the MnRoad test facility in Minnesota, which replicates the original AASHTO test from which much of the current performance data are derived, a considerable amount of money has been spent developing a trailer-mounted automatic DCP in an attempt to calibrate it against a falling weight deflectometer.

Figure 8.5 illustrates the detail of a dynamic cone penetrometer.

8.5. Laboratory tests

Depending on the nature of the materials found and the type of distress recorded on the pavement there are several laboratory tests that can provide useful information to assist the evaluation. Only materials in reasonable condition can be tested and these should be used with care so as not to introduce bias.

The following are the main useful typical tests that may be undertaken.

8.5.1 Bituminous materials

- Receive and log extracted cores.
- Selected cores prepared for mechanical testing.
- Bulk density of all prepared cores measured.

- ITSM (indirect tensile stiffness modulus) stiffness of all prepared cores assessed using Nottingham asphalt tester (NAT).
- Resistance to deformation of upper layers (excluding lower bound layer) of material from selected cores is assessed using the RLAT (repeated load axial test) test in the NAT.
- Fatigue resistance of the lowest bound layer assessed using ITFT (indirect tensile fatigue test) test in the NAT.
- Carry out maximum density (RICE) testing on selected cores of material to enable assessment of air voids to be carried out.

Other optional testing which can be carried out is as follows.

- Determination of particle grading and binder content of selected layers of material.
- Assessment of calculated penetration and softening point of residual binder recovered during determination of binder content using Bohlin DSR (dynamic shear rheometer).
- Recovery of binder from selected materials using a heated centrifuge.
- Assessment of calculated penetration and softening point of residual binder recovered from heated centrifuge using Bohlin DSR.

Carrying out the standard suite of materials tests detailed in the above has the following benefits.

- Provides confirmation of actual overall bituminous material thickness, layer thicknesses and generic material type and nominal aggregate size.

Figure 8.4 Typical plot of DCP results
Reproduced from TRL (1999) © TRL

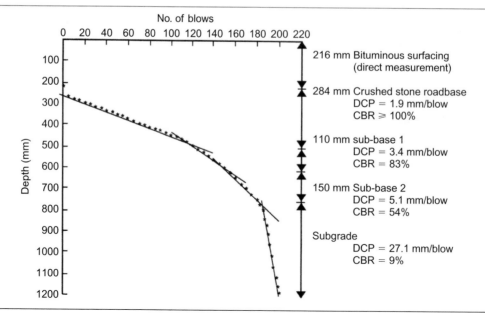

Figure 8.5 Dynamic cone penetrometer

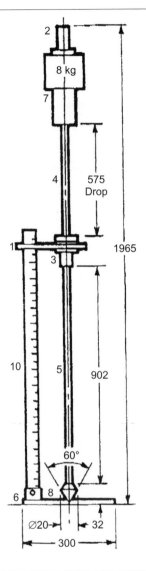

- Density: to assess the degree of compaction if the relative density is available.
- Relative density: of the aggregate to allow estimate of degree of compaction.
- Stiffness modulus.

8.5.3 Unbound materials

- Moisture content.
- Particle size distribution.
- Relative density.
- Absorption.
- Atterberg limits.

In summary, therefore, carrying out a programme of materials investigation provides the pavement assessment engineer with an invaluable resource of test data to help support the assumptions made during analysis of the existing structure and design of any reconstruction or overlays.

8.6. Ground penetrating radar

Radar techniques are well known and were originally developed for the detection of objects in the sky, on land or on sea. These methods have been adapted for the investigation of non-conductive materials, e.g. soils, rocks, concrete etc. in a technique commonly known as ground penetrating (probing) radar (GPR). Applications of GPR are diverse and include surveys relating to structural testing, archaeological investigations, pipe and conduit detection, mapping and object detection.

Figures 8.6 and 8.7 have been taken from HD 29/94 (Highways Agency, 1994 (as amended in February 2001)) to illustrate the concept as applied to pavements.

The reflection of the radar signal from the various interfaces can

- Enables a comparison to be made between back calculated layer stiffnesses and ITSM stiffnesses measured using the NAT.
- The reasons for any areas of observed rutting can be explored through assessment of RLAT data, air void data and determining calculated penetration and softening points of recovered binder.
- A comparison can be made between the strain line measured using the ITFT and the assumed strain line used in the elastic design.

8.5.2 Hydraulically bound materials

- Cube strength: usually undertaken by means of cylinder tests to provide an estimate of the flexural strength.

Figure 8.6 Diagram of radar-energy wave penetrating a pavement

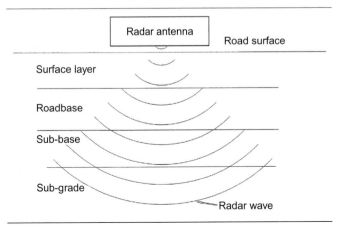

Figure 8.7 Reflection of radar signal at pavement interfaces and signal waveforms
Reproduced from Highways Agency, 1994 © Crown copyright 1994

Figure 8.8 Waveform graph of longitudinal section of road
Reproduced from Highways Agency, 1994 © Crown copyright 1994

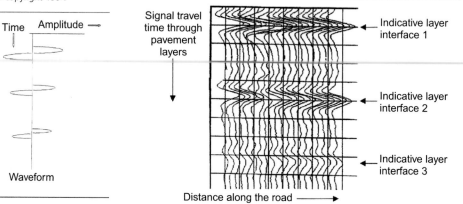

be seen in Figure 8.8 where with the appropriate software and experience it is possible to deduce the position of the indicative layer interface. Having knowledge of the dielectric constant – the speed with which the waves travel through various materials – it is possible to estimate the depth of these various interfaces below the surface. When this is done the thickness and variation in the layer structure can be developed. (See also Figure 8.9.)

It is important to take a number of cores to ensure there is a clear relationship between the cores and the GPR plot. Some years ago the author had great problems on a particular site which contained a section of lean mix concrete where the two systems gave significantly different results. Similarly it is vital to ensure the same locational referencing is used. It is not unknown for the zero chainage to be at different ends of the project length.

Figure 8.9 Example of ground radar slice of major road pavement
Reproduced from Highways Agency, 2008 © Crown copyright 2008

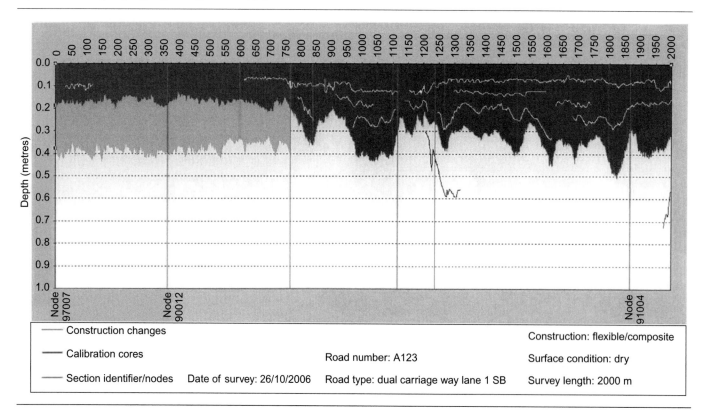

Figure 8.10 Example of GPR plot (idealised) for an airfield runway

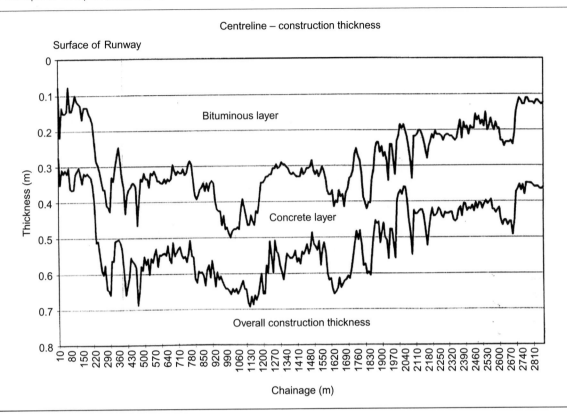

Table 8.5 Penetration and resolution of different types of radar
From Highways Agency, 1994 © Crown copyright 1994

Factors	Radar frequency				
	400/500 MHz	900 MHz	1 GHz	1.5 GHz	2.0–2.5 GHz
Antenna type	Dipole	Dipole	Horn	Dipole	Horn
Coupling: air coupling gives slightly better resolution of the surface layer but slightly less penetration than ground coupling.	Ground	Ground	Air	Ground	Air
Resolution: minimum thickness of surface layer which radar can resolve.	200 mm	100 mm	50 mm	70 mm	25 mm
Penetration: practical depth to which the radar can provide information.	2 m depending on subgrade material and moisture content	800 mm	600 mm	500 mm	300 mm
Sampling rate: effective spacing along road at which radar pulse is fired.	At 80 km/h a sampling rate of 4 measurements every metre is achievable on some radar systems which means that features and defects less than 250 mm long may be missed by the radar scan. At lower survey speeds smaller features and defects will be detected. Sampling rate is dependent on the type of ground radar equipment being used.				

Following discussions with the runway owners it was interesting to understand the manner in which the runway referred to in Figure 8.10 had developed as follows:

Chainage 300–2000   original wartime runway
Chainage 2000–2700   major extension
Chainage 0–300   later runoff extension
Chainage 2700–2900   later runoff extension

The depth of penetration differs with the radar frequency of the aerial used and it is usual for an experienced contractor to run several aerials together to ensure best results. Table 8.5, taken from HD 29/94 (Highways Agency, 1994), summarised current experience:

One of the major advantages of GPR is its ability to demonstrate where there are significant changes in the layer thickness, which it would not be possible to detect with coring. While cores are necessary to correlate and calibrate the radar generated slice, it should be remembered that this construction data would be used in the interpretation of falling weight deflectometer (FWD) – generated deflection data.

In the section of these notes relating to FWD the following guidance is given:

A 15% underestimate in the bound layer thickness results in a 50% overestimate of the bound layer modulus from the FWD deflections.

The author recalls a situation some years ago when his employer was asked to undertake an FWD survey on a road which was to be the subject of a design and build project and they were asked to produce two reports, one for each of two bidders. In one case the thickness data were provided from GPR data and in the other from cores. The base was cement bound, which is not the easiest

Figure 8.11 Typical ground penetrating radar systems
Reproduced from Highways Agency, 2008 © Crown copyright 2008

Radar with ground coupled dipole antenna – surveying at 0.5 km/h

Crack depth investigation at 0.5 km/h

Radar with horn antenna – surveying at 80 km/h

Radar with a pair of air-coupled dipole antennas – surveying at 80 km/h

material for GPR to distinguish from underlying granular material, particularly when it is wet.

The two opinions given about the level of degradation of the CBM were quite different. In the case where GPR generated data were available it suggested they were very poor. One bidder had on his team an engineer who had worked on the original construction and who challenged our findings. Trial holes were dug and the correct thickness given, the calculations re-run and the material was found to be sound and robust which supported the site findings.

The clear message here is that uncorrelated GPR data can be misleading: never accept data from a single source (Figure 8.11).

REFERENCES

Highways Agency (1994) DMRB HD 29/94: Traffic speed conditions survey. *Design Manual for Roads and Bridges*. Highways Agency, London.

Highways Agency (2008) DMRB HD 29/08: Data for pavement assessment. *Design Manual for Roads and Bridges*. Highways Agency, London.

Jones CR and Rolt J (1991) *Operating Instructions for the TRL Dynamic Cone Penetrometer*, 2nd edn. TRL, Crowthorne.

TRL (1999) TRL ORN-18-1999 A guide to the pavement evaluation and maintenance of bitumen-surfaced roads in tropical and sub-tropical countries. Transport Research Laboratory, Crowthorne.

Deterioration and Maintenance of Pavements
ISBN: 978-0-7277-4114-1

Chapter 9
Skid Resistance

9.1.   Introduction

Skid resistance is about friction and the following short note sets out the basic principles.

If a body of weight **P** (mass [M] × acceleration due to gravity [g]) is at rest on a surface all the forces acting on it are vertical. If a horizontal force **F** is applied to try and move the body the magnitude of this force must be sufficient to overcome the resisting effects of friction. If the coefficient of friction is 1.0 then **F = P**.

In the case of a pavement the coefficient of friction **μ** is known as the skid resistance and acts to resist horizontal (uncontrolled) movement of the vehicle (Figure 9.1).

The highway engineer has no direct influence on the force **F** but needs to ensure that **μ** is as large as possible by ensuring competent drainage to minimise surface lubrication and that the coefficient of friction of the surface aggregate is as high as possible – or within certain limits depending on location. This characteristic is known as the polished stone value (PSV).

The interpretation of skid resistance is complicated by various factors some of which are

- tyre size, tread depth, pattern, rubber compound
- slip speed
- vertical load
- quantity (depth) of water on surface
- seasonal variation due to weathering (microtexture)

Figure 9.1 Forces acting on a body at rest

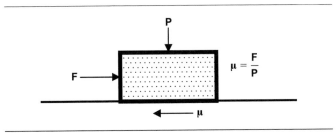

- texture depth (macrotexture)
- temperature and speed of measurement.

Testing is carried out on a wetted pavement using either

- portable skid resistance tester (pendulum)
- sideways force coefficient routine investigation machine (SCRIM) (slip fixed at 20° and 50 kph)
- GripTester
- high-speed locked wheel device.

9.1.1   Terminology
9.1.1.1   Microtexture
Microtexture is the roughness of the surface of the aggregate. It is affected by weathering, achieving its greatest depth during the winter months due to the combined abrading effects of water and detritus. This is the principal determinant of skid resistance on a given site assuming competent drainage to ensure that the tyre is in direct contact with the aggregate.

9.1.1.2   Macrotexture
Macrotexture is the texture depth, which is the height the aggregate sits above the bituminous matrix and is the principal determinant of competent drainage to ensure there is a minimum thickness of water between the aggregate and tyre.

Figure 9.2 is relevant to hot rolled asphalt, which has been used extensively in the UK and is largely credited with the good record of high skid resistance and relatively low skidding accident rate compared with some other European countries.

The terminology has become more complicated with the advent of generic stone mastic asphalt (SMA) mixes where the aggregate does not stand proud of the bituminous matrix, as can be seen in Figure 9.3.

9.1.2   Early developments in the UK
In the first half of the twentieth century, growth of motorised traffic, capable of ever greater speeds, created a pressure to find ways of making road surfaces that could both withstand the

Figure 9.2 Microtexture and macrotexture

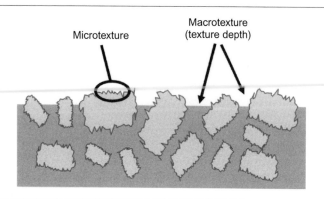

Figure 9.3 Macrotexture – positive and negative

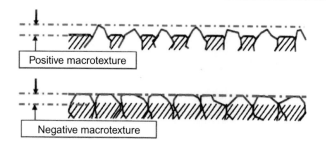

Figure 9.4 Early measuring equipment (1930s)
© TRL

Figure 9.5 Front-wheel drive car with internally mounted wheel (c. 1955)
© TRL

increased loads and provide grip for the tyres of the vehicles using the roads. Surfacings and structures that had been designed for horse-drawn traffic and slow-moving vehicles with steel or solid rubber tyres were no longer suitable. Cobbled streets, wooden blocks between the rails in tramways in cities, and unsealed surfaces in rural areas were inadequate for the demands of modern traffic.

Research to try and understand the problem of providing grip for road vehicle tyres began in Britain in the inter-war years with the development of a device that could be used to measure skid resistance on in-service roads. The motorcycle and sidecar with its angled wheel and mechanical linkage to transfer the frictional forces from the tyre to a chart recorder has become an iconic image in the study of road surface characteristics. A small fleet of these machines was developed and used in the 1930s to establish some fundamental principles that continue to be used to this day (Bird and Scott, 1936) (Figure 9.4).

Developments in measurement techniques continued after World War II, moving to rather safer front-wheel drive cars with an internally mounted angled wheel to measure sideways-force coefficient (SFC) (Figure 9.5) and a towed trailer with a small, lockable wheel to measure the braking force coefficient (BFC) at different speeds. It rapidly became apparent that standardisation

of test conditions was important and so these devices tended to use standard tyres with smooth tread and were operated at controlled speeds.

Other machines were built in that period that allowed the performance of different tyres to be assessed but work on road surfaces depended primarily on the use of the side-force cars and brake-force trailer. As research progressed, important factors – such as the decrease in skid resistance with increasing speed, the microtexture on the aggregate and the influence of surface texture depth – became known and better understood.

To comply with the appropriate protocols any testing for slip (pedestrian surface) or skid (vehicular surface) should be done with the surface wetted. Figure 9.6 clearly indicates the variation

Figure 9.6 Variation in SFC with transition from dry to wet surface
Reproduced from Croney (1977) © Crown copyright 1977

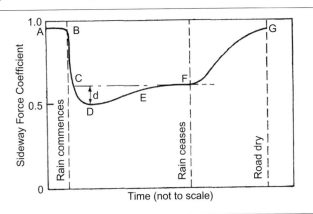

of skid resistance with the onset and cessation of rainfall, returning to a maximum when the surface becomes dry.

Figure 9.7 shows the relationship between slip resistance value (SRV) and (SFC).

As explained below, suggestions for possible skid resistance levels for UK roads were first made in the late 1950s (Giles, 1957). However, at that stage measurement techniques were confined to the specialised SFC cars and BFC trailer plus the portable skid resistance tester – the 'pendulum' (Giles *et al.*, 1964). However, the test vehicles needed support from water

Figure 9.7 Observed correlation between SRV and SFC in 63 tests on rough-looking and medium-textured surfaces
Reproduced from Croney (1977) © Crown copyright 1977

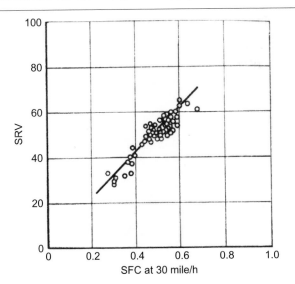

tankers if any length of road was to be measured. The BFC method could only measure very short lengths and both types of equipment recorded their data on paper charts. The pendulum could only make spot checks. These techniques were really only suitable for research use or localised checks. Before national standards could be contemplated, a machine was needed that could make continuous measurements of the skid resistance over long distances, together with a means of processing the large volumes of data that would be collected.

The advent of digital computers in the 1960s provided a solution to the data-processing problem and the SCRIM was developed at TRL (then the Road Research Laboratory) in the late 1960s as a potential network level survey tool. The concept combined the well-established side-force coefficient principle with a large capacity on-board water supply and electronic data recording.

With some development, the prototype proved successful and in the early 1970s the first production machines were introduced, built under licence by WDM Ltd of Bristol who have made them ever since. With the production machines came the direct recording of the data on punched paper tape as an on-board storage medium, which meant an easy transfer of data for computer analysis. At that stage the machine was still primarily used for research but the Department for Transport centrally began to use it to assess portions of its network and one or two county councils purchased machines to monitor their own local networks.

A period of further refinement to improve reproducibility followed (Hosking and Woodford, 1976a, 1976b, 1978) that continued into the 1980s, during which period comparison exercises were carried out that have evolved into an annual accreditation trial in which the whole UK and Ireland fleet of SCRIMs comes to TRL for cross-checking every spring. Fourteen machines attended the 2008 trials.

9.1.3   Influence of traffic (Figure 9.8)

9.1.4   Effects of seasonal variation (Figure 9.9)

Figure 9.8 Example of the influence of traffic on SFC
Reproduced from Highways Agency, 1994 © Crown copyright 1994

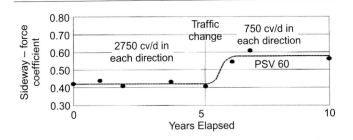

Figure 9.9 Effects of seasonal variation of SFC
Reproduced from Highways Agency, 1994 © Crown copyright 1994

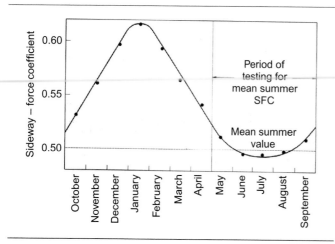

9.1.5 Skid resistance investigatory levels for carriageways (SCRIM and Pendulum GripTester)

Table 9.1 shows both SFC and GN (grip number) for convenience.

A chart showing the same SFC values can be found in HD 28/04 (Highways Agency, 2004).

9.1.6 Slip resistance for footways and walkways

Returning to the subject of footways and slip resistance, dealt with in Chapter 2, the British Pendulum Tester is currently the preferred method of slipperiness assessment of HSL/HSE and the UK Slip Resistance Group.

For use on footways and external areas the use of the standard TRL rubber slider is recommended. RAPRA (Rubber and Plastics Research Association) have developed a standard simulated shoe sole known as Four-S to represent footwear heel materials of moderate slip resistance.

Guidance relating to potential for slip produced (Hallas and Shaw, 2006) is set out in Table 9.2.

9.2. Skid resistance measuring equipment

9.2.1 Portable or pendulum skid resistance tester

In the early 1960s the portable or pendulum skid resistance tester was developed (Giles *et al.*, 1964) that could be taken to a local site to measure the skid resistance of the road (Figure 9.10).

The test procedure is now the subject of a European standard (CEN, 1997). The device is not suitable for network monitoring because the test is time-consuming and requires traffic management to protect the operator. While there are shortcomings, one advantage is that readings can be readily taken at different

Table 9.1 Skid resistance investigatory levels
Reproduced from Highways Agency, 2004 © Crown copyright 2004

Site Category and Definition			Investigatory level at 50 km/h							
		SFC	0.30	0.35	0.40	0.45	0.50	0.55	0.60	0.65
		GN	0.35	0.41	0.47	0.53	0.59	0.65	0.71	0.76
A	Motorway									
B	Dual carriageway – non event									
C	Single carriageway – non event									
Q	Approaches to and across minor and major junctions, approaches to roundabouts									
K	Approaches to pedestrian crossings and other high risk situations									
R	Roundabout									
G1	Gradient 5–10% longer than 50 m									
G2	Gradient > 10% longer than 50 m									
S1	Bend radius < 500 m – dual carriageway									
S2	Bend radius < 500 m single carriageway									

Table 9.2 Recommended levels of pedestrian surface potential for slip
Data taken from HSE (2006)

Potential for slip	British Pendulum Tester value	Four-S pendulum value	Surface roughness: μm [micron]
High	19 and below	25 and below	Below 10
Moderate	20 to 39	25 to 35	Between 10 and 20
Low	40 to 74	35 to 65	> 20 and up to 30
Extremely low	Above 75	Above 65	Above 30

Figure 9.10 Pendulum skid tester
Reproduced from Giles *et al.*, 1964 © Crown copyright 1964

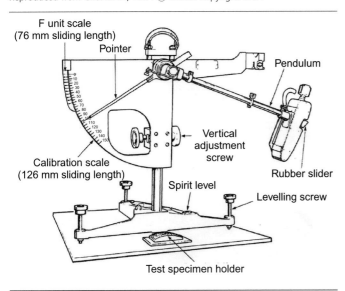

friction (CoF) by simple division by 100, although this simple relationship is not accurate above a slip resistance value of 40.

The conversion set out in BSI 96/104915 [B/208] (Hallas and Shaw, 2006) is as follows:

$$CoF = (3 \times SRV)/(330 - SRV) \qquad (9.1)$$

The correlation between pendulum data and SCRIM (SC) is:

$$SC = SRV/100 - 0.05 \qquad (9.2)$$

9.2.2 SCRIM

The SCRIM is the best-know example of sideways force measurement methods (Figures 9.11 and 9.12). It was developed by TRL in the late 1960s and its rugged construction and large water

Figure 9.11 SCRIM machine
Courtesy of WDM

positions along or across a carriageway, which is useful in detailed investigations such as accident investigations.

The equipment consists of a rubber slider mounted on a 'foot' assembly at the end of a pendulum arm. The slider is angled at approximately 20° to the foot and mounted on a soft spring. Following release from a horizontal position, the foot reaches a speed of approximately 10 kph before the trailing edge of the slider makes contact with the road surface. Contact is maintained for a distance of approximately 125 mm. The work done to overcome frictional forces between the slider and the road surface determines the height the pendulum reaches after leaving contact with the road. The scale is calibrated in units of skid resistance value (SRV), which can, with reference to Giles (1957), be converted to friction coefficients.

As a general rule, SRV values (also known as the British pendulum number [BPN]) may be converted to coefficient of

Figure 9.12 SCRIM machine – diagram
© TRL

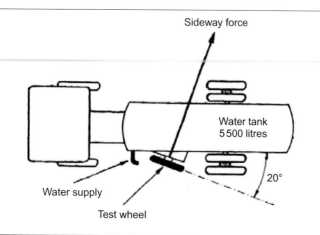

A vertical load of 200 kg was originally applied by means of a dead weight attached to the test assembly. Recent developments have introduced a load cell to monitor the actual load as it can vary if the vehicle tilts during cornering or the surface of the pavement is uneven.

A detailed calibration procedure takes place annually at TRL for all UK SCRIM machines. The recommended survey procedure, in terms of calibration requirements, test speed, tyre conditioning and maximum wear, and flow rate, etc. is set out in BS 7941–1 (BSI, 2006).

The standard test speed is 50 kph, which can lead to problems at roundabouts and in urban areas. In these circumstances it is possible to test at 20 kph.

tank, giving an extended survey range, make it ideal for routine network monitoring.

Each SCRIM chassis is fitted with a test wheel, generally in the nearside wheelpath, which is aligned to the direction of travel (Figure 9.13). The test wheel is free to rotate, but the alignment means it is forced to slip continuously over the road surface, providing a continuous measurement of skid resistance. The slip speed depends on the vehicle speed and the angle of the test wheel. UK SCRIMS have an angle of 20° between the test wheel and the direction of travel and this geometry means that at 50 kph, the standard speed for testing in the UK, the slip speed is 17 kph. The test wheel is fitted with a smooth pneumatic tyre fabricated from natural rubber within a specified resilience range.

9.2.3 GripTester

The GripTester (Figure 9.14, 9.15 and 9.16) is a three-wheeled trailer developed in the mid-1980s by Findlay Irvine in Edinburgh, initially designed to measure the surface friction on helidecks on offshore oil drilling/production platforms, where it was used in push mode. Because of its compactness, it will fit in the back of a Volvo estate car.

The GripTester is an alternative to SCRIM for smaller networks and is used by many local highway authorities. It is also commonly used for friction measurements on airfield pavements, where the International Civil Aviation Organisation (ICAO) regulations are more stringent than those normally used on highway pavements.

In push mode the GripTester is fitted with a small water tank and

Figure 9.13 SCRIM measuring wheel
Courtesy of WDM

Figure 9.14 GripTester
Courtesy of Findlay Irvine Ltd

Figure 9.15 Push mode
Courtesy of Findlay Irvine Ltd

Figure 9.16 Towed mode
Courtesy of Findlay Irvine Ltd

has been used in this manner to test pedestrian footways, as well as the surfaces of aircraft carriers and helicopter landing pads.

In tow mode the payload of the tow vehicle, which restricts the volume of water that can be carried, generally limits the range of the survey.

The test wheel is fitted with a smooth tyre compliant with an American Society for Testing and Materials (ASTM) International specification. It is mounted in the same direction as the other wheels but is geared so that it travels more slowly. It is therefore forced to slip continuously across the surface. The slip speed is a fixed 14.5% of the vehicle speed: a slip speed of 7 kph if the test speed is 50 kph. While the GripTester can be operated at a maximum speed of 130 kph, high speeds are not recommended because of the oscillation in wheel loading that could occur, leading to dangerous instability.

Trials were undertaken by Jacobs Babtie in 2004 to establish a correlation with SCRIM with the following results:

Mark 1 GripTester data and SCRIM

$$SC = 0.789 \times GripNumber - 0.049 \qquad (9.3)$$

Mark 2 GripTester data and SCRIM

$$SC = 0.85 \times GripNumber \qquad (9.4)$$

9.2.4 High-speed locked wheel friction tester

The methods described previously are low-speed techniques, in that the slip speeds between the rubber material and road surface are relatively low. This is a direct consequence of the test methods used but it can be argued that the speeds are not representative of the speed of majority of the vehicles. Other methods are required to measure skid at high slip speeds, but these are not suitable for continuous monitoring because of the high rate of wear of the test tyres.

One example is the ASTM trailer, where the wheel on the trailer is locked for a period of a few seconds during a test. The slip speed is equal to the vehicle speed once the wheel is locked and tests can be carried out at up to 130 kph. Since the load and traction forces are measured throughout the test, it also provides information on the peak friction force, which is reached when the test wheel is beginning to slide. The Dynatest T1290 is shown in Figure 9.17. The typical output from the device is also shown (Figure 9.18). This and similar methods are likely to remain as research techniques only because the methods are not practical for network monitoring.

One must, however, wonder about the inherent safety and stability of a trailer with a single axle with two wheels, one of which is momentarily locked.

9.3. Practical issues

9.3.1 Identifying problem sites

See Figure 9.19.

Figure 9.17 Dynatest T1290 high speed pavement friction tester
Courtesy of Dynatest International A/S

Spraying of water during a friction test

Figure 9.18 Dynatest T1290 pavement friction tester – example of typical output
Courtesy of Dynatest International A/S

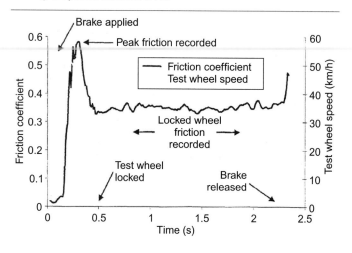

There is therefore a new challenge to establish appropriate criteria for their use. To this end, collaborative research (supported by the Highways Agency, Quarry Products Association and Refined Bitumen Association) is in hand that is studying the performance of modern asphalt surfaces using different sizes of coarse aggregate (including 0/6, 0/10 and 0/14 mm mixtures) in relation to their texture depth and skid resistance at higher speeds (Roe et al., 2008). Texture depth requirements for these types of materials in some situations are currently being revised.

9.3.3 Polished stone value (PSV)
Simply put, polished stone value is a measure of the resistance of the aggregate to wear.

Samples of aggregate are set in a curved mould and after conditioning for a standard time with an abrasive compound the polished stone value is measured using a standard pendulum test.

PSV is regarded as one of the most useful tests undertaken on the components of an asphalt mix.

9.3.3.1 Typical values of PSV (Table 9.3)

9.3.4 Selection of aggregate minimum PSV
See Table 9.4.

9.3.5 Maximum aggregate abrasion value (AAV)
See Table 9.5.

9.3.6 Road deaths in western Europe in 2008
See Table 9.6.

9.3.2 New surfacing technology
The specifications that support the UK skidding standards are essentially based on the hot rolled asphalt (HRA) with pre-coated chippings and surface dressing materials that were traditionally used on the network. In recent years, however, different types of asphalt mixtures – the so-called 'thin surfacings' – have become more widely used in the UK and are the first choice for new surfacings on trunk roads where their qualities of reduced tyre/ road noise and speed of laying bring advantages.

It is less easy, however, to make these materials comply with current specifications, particularly in relation to texture depth. Also, the shape and form of the texture could mean that these materials develop better skid resistance for a given level of polishing resistance. This raises the possibility of greater flexibility of aggregate choice in some situations.

Figure 9.19 Procedure to identify and treat sites with skidding resistance problems
Reproduced from Highways Agency, 2004 © Crown copyright 2004

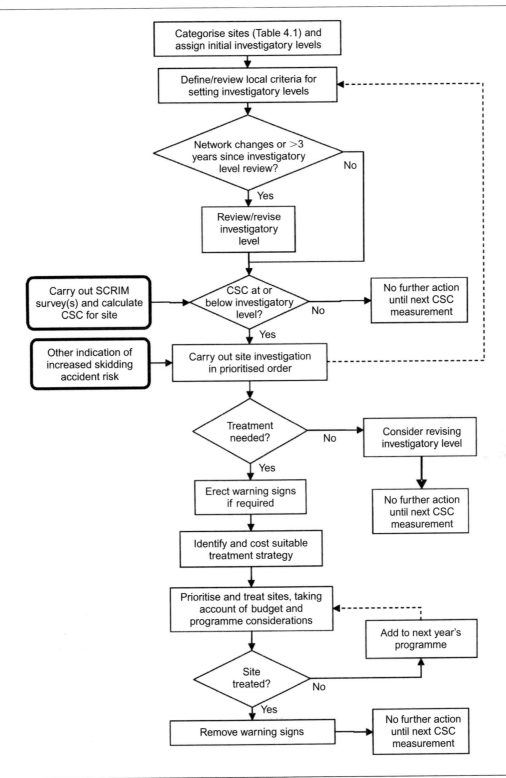

Table 9.3 Typical values of PSV

Group of roadstone	PSV
Crushed rock aggregates	
Dolerite	57
Granite	56
Sandstones	66
Limestones	56
Natural gravel aggregates	
Flint gravel	41
Quartzite gravels	40

9.3.7 Effects of winter conditions

The following information sets out some interesting relative figures relating, among other things, to skid resistance in icy conditions (Wallman and Åström, 2001).

A number of surveys of friction for different road conditions can be summarised in Table 9.7.

The friction numbers were obtained by skiddometer measurements with 17% slip.

The numbers should be considered as relative to one another and must not be compared with SCRIM output.

Table 9.4 Minimum PSV of chippings or coarse aggregate in unchipped surfaces of new surface courses
From DfT, 2006 © Crown copyright 2006

Site category	Site description	IL	Minimum PSV required for given IL, traffic level and type of site									
			Traffic (cv/lane/day) at design life									
			0–250	251–500	501–750	751–1000	1001–2000	2001–3000	3001–4000	4001–5000	5001–6000	Over 6000
A1	Motorways where traffic is generally free-flowing on a relatively straight line	0.30	50	50	50	50	50	55	55	60	65	65
		0.35	50	50	50	50	50	60	60	60	65	65
A2	Motorways where some braking regularly occurs (e.g. on 300 m approach to an off-slip)	0.35	50	50	50	55	55	60	60	65	65	65
B1	Dual carriageways where traffic is generally free-flowing on a relatively straight line	0.3	50	50	50	50	50	55	55	60	65	65
		0.35	50	50	50	50	50	60	60	60	65	65
		0.4	50	50	50	55	60	65	65	65	65	68+
B2	Dual carriageways where some braking regularly occurs (e.g. on 300 m approach to an off-slip)	0.35	50	50	50	55	55	60	60	65	65	65
		0.40	55	60	60	65	65	68+	68+	68+	68+	68+
C	Single carriageways where traffic is generally free-flowing on a relatively straight line	0.35	50	50	50	55	55	60	60	65	65	65
		0.4	55	60	60	65	65	68+	68+	68+	68+	68+
		0.45	60	60	65	65	68+	68+	68+	68+	68+	68+

(continued)

Table 9.4. (*continued*)

Site category	Site description	IL	Minimum PSV required for given IL, traffic level and type of site									
			Traffic (cv/lane/day) at design life									
			0–250	251–500	501–750	751–1000	1001–2000	2001–3000	3001–4000	4001–5000	5001–6000	Over 6000
G1/G2	Gradients >5% longer than 50 m as per HD 28	0.45	55	60	60	65	65	68+	68+	68+	68+	HFS
		0.5	60	68+	68+	HFS	HFS	HFS	HFS	HFS	HFS	HFS
		0.55	68+	HFS	HFS	HFS	HFS	HFS	HFS	HFS	HFS	HFS
K	Approaches to pedestrian crossings and other high risk situations	0.5	65	65	65	68+	68+	68+	HFS	HFS	HFS	HFS
		0.55	68+	68+	HFS	HFS	HFS	HFS	HFS	HFS	HFS	HFS
Q	Approaches to major and minor junctions on dual carriageways and single carriageways where frequent or sudden braking occurs but in a generally straight line.	0.45	60	65	65	68+	68+	68+	68+	68+	68+	HFS
		0.5	65	65	65	68+	68+	68+	HFS	HFS	HFS	HFS
		0.55	68+	68+	HFS	HFS	HFS	HFS	HFS	HFS	HFS	HFS
R	Roundabout circulation areas	0.45	50	55	60	60	65	65	68+	68+	HFS	HFS
		0.5	68+	68+	68+	HFS	HFS	HFS	HFS	HFS	HFS	HFS
S1/S2	Bends (radius <500 m) on all types of road, including motorway link roads; other hazards that require combined braking and cornering	0.45	50	55	60	60	65	65	68+	68+	HFS	HFS
		0.5	68+	68+	68+	HFS	HFS	HFS	HFS	HFS	HFS	HFS
		0.55	HFS	HFS	HFS	HFS	HFS	HFS	HFS	HFS	HFS	HFS

Table 9.5 Maximum AAV of chippings, or coarse aggregates in unchipped surfaces for new surface courses
From DfT, 2006 © Crown copyright 2006

Traffic (cv/lane/day) at design life	<250	251–1000	1001–1750	1751–2500	2501–3250	>3250
Max AAV for chippings for HRA and surface dressing, and for aggregate in slurry and microsurfacing systems	14	12	12	10	10	10
Max AAV for aggregate in thin surface course systems, exposed aggregate concrete surfacing and coated Macadam surface course	16	16	14	14	12	12

Table 9.6 Road deaths in western Europe per million population
Data taken from Eurostat Code tsdr_420

Country	per million persons
Greece	138
Belgium	88
Portugal	83
Italy	79
Denmark	74
Luxembourg	72
Spain	68
France	67
Eire	63
Germany	54
Sweden	52
United Kingdom	43
Netherlands	41

Table 9.7 Effects on friction for different road conditions

Dry bare surface	0.8–1.0
Wet bare surface	0.7–0.8
Packed snow	0.2–0.3
Loose snow/slush	0.2–0.5*
Black ice	0.15–0.3
Loose snow and black ice	0.15–0.25
Wet black ice	0.05–0.10

* The higher value when the tyres are in contact with the pavement.

9.3.8 International friction index

A major problem is the comparison of skid resistance output in various countries because of the manner in which they are made using different equipment and testing regimes. A proposal is under consideration (2011) to develop an international friction index. This is particularly relevant in the EU due to the desires for harmonisation in the participating countries.

9.4. Development of a skid resistance policy

The policy for managing skid resistance on motorways and trunk roads in the UK is set out in Highways Agency, 2004. This document sets out the survey regime, default site categories and investigatory levels and gives advice about risk management, site investigation and use of slippery road signs once the skid resistance falls below the investigatory level. The implementation of the policy in England is believed to have contributed to the significant reduction in accident numbers during the 1990s.

Guidance on skid resistance for LA roads was given in the updated code of practice for maintenance management (CIHT, 2001). LA roads are more diverse in nature than trunk (national) roads both in terms of their geometric design and the levels of traffic carried. The code of practice recommends that LAs draw up a strategy for managing skid resistance levels following a similar approach to the trunk road policy. This should define

- the part of the LA network to which the policy applies (roads carrying high traffic levels, particularly those with large numbers of heavy vehicles, are most prone to polishing and consequent loss of skid resistance)
- the survey strategy (including the equipment to be used, the frequency of surveys and the quality assurance procedures to be followed for data collection)
- the approach for setting threshold levels for investigation (higher skid resistance should be required at sites where road users are likely at sites to need to stop or change direction – these should be defined and the frequency at which requirements are reassessed should be stated)
- the procedure for investigation and determining the need and priority for maintenance treatment (where there is evidence that improving the condition of the surfacing is likely to significantly reduce the risk of accidents, treatment should be prioritised; less urgent cases should be completed in a reasonable period, taking into account other maintenance requirements, but in some cases there may be little or no benefit in undertaking treatment)
- defined responsibility and a timetable for delivering each part of the strategy
- documentation to be retained.

REFERENCES AND BIBLIOGRAPHY

Bird G and Scott WJO (1936) Department of Scientific and Industrial Research and Ministry of Transport Road Research technical paper no. 1, Studies in road friction 1: Road surface resistance to skidding. HMSO, London.

BSI (British Standards Institution) (2006) BS 7941-1:2006: Methods for measuring the skid resistance of pavement surfaces. Sideway-force coefficient routine investigation machine. BSI, London.

CEN (1997) EN 13036-4:2003: Road and airfield surface characteristics – Test methods. Part 4. Method for measurement of slip/skid resistance of a surface – The pendulum test. CEN, Brussels.

CIHT (Chartered Institution of Highways and Transportation) (2001) Delivering Best Value in Highway Maintenance – Code of Practice for Maintenance Management. Part A – Sections 1–4. (2 of 6). Department of the Environment, Transport and the Regions, London.

Croney D (1977) The Design and Performance of Road Pavements, 1st edn. HMSO, London.

Descornet G, Schmidt B, Boulet M *et al.* (2006) Ferhl (Forum of European National Highway Research Laboratories) Report 2006/01. Harmonisation of routine and research measuring equipment for skidding resistance. Ferhl, Brussels.

DfT (2006) HD 36/06: Surfacing materials for new and maintenance construction. DfT, London.

EU Commission, DG Energy and Transport, CARE database (2011) People killed in road accidents, table code tsdtr420.

Giles CG (1957) The skidding resistance of roads and the requirements of modern traffic. *Proceedings of the Institute of Civil Engineers* **6(2)**: 216–249. doi: 10.1680/iicep.1957. 12360.

Giles CG, Sabey BE and Cardew KHF (1964) Road research technical paper, no. 66: Development and performance of the portable skid-resistance tester. HMSO, London.

Hallas K and Shaw R (2006) HSL/2006/65: Evaluation of Kirchberg rolling slider and slipalert slip resistance meters. Health and Safety Laboratory, Buxton.

Highways Agency (1994) DMRB 7.3.1 (HD 28/94): Pavement design and maintenance. Pavement maintenance assessment. Skidding resistance (including amendment 1 dated February 1999). *Design Manual for Roads and Bridges*. Highways Agency, London.

Highways Agency (2004) DMRB 7.3.1 (HD 28/04): Pavement design and maintenance. Pavement maintenance assessment. Skid resistance. *Design Manual for Roads and Bridges*. Highways Agency, London.

Hosking JR (1976) TRRL Laboratory Report LR693: Aggregates for skid-resistant roads. TRRL, Crowthorne.

Hosking JR and Woodford GC (1976a) LR 737: Measurement of skidding resistance. Part I. Guide to the use of SCRIM. TRRL Laboratory.

Hosking JR and Woodford GC (1976b) TRRL Laboratory report LR 739: Measurement of skidding resistance. Part III. Factors affecting SCRIM measurements. TRRL, Crowthorne.

Hosking JR and Woodford GC (1978) TRRL supplementary report SR 346: Measurement of skidding resistance. Part IV. The effect on recorded SFC of design changes in the measuring equipment. TRRL, Crowthorne.

HSE (2006) Evaluation of Kirchberg Rolling Slider and SlipAlert Slip Resistance Meters, report HSL/2006/65, Buxton.

RLG (UK Road Liaison Group) (2005) Well-maintained highways. Code of practice for highway maintenance management. TSO, London. Additions and supplements can be found at http://www.ukroadsliaisongroup.org (accessed 13/07/11).

Roe PG and Hartshorne SA (1998) TRL report 322: The polished stone value of aggregates and in-service skidding resistance. TRL, Crowthorne.

Roe PG and Sinhal R (2005) Recent developments to the Scrim measurement technique in the UK. *International Conference on Surface Friction of Roads and Runways, Christchurch, New Zealand*. TRL, Wokingham.

Roe PG, Dunford A and Crabb GI (2008) TRL report PPR 324: HA/QPA/RBA collaborative programme 2004/07: Surface requirements for asphalt roads. TRL, Crowthorne.

Roe PG, Perry AR and Viner HE (1998) TRL report 367: High and low speed skid resistance – the effect of texture depth. TRL, Crowthorne.

Rogers MP and Gargett T (1991) A skidding resistance standard for the national network. *Highways and Transportation* **38(4)**: 10–16.

Salt GF and Szatkowski WS (1973) TRRL laboratory report LR 510: A guide to levels of skidding resistance for roads. TRRL, Crowthorne.

Szatkowski WS and Hosking JR (1972) TRRL laboratory report LR 504: The effect of traffic and aggregate on the skidding resistance of bituminous surfacings. TRRL, Crowthorne.

Wallman CG and Åström H (2001) Friction measurement methods and correlation between road friction and traffic safety. A literature review. Swedish National Road and Transport Institute (VTI), Linkoping. (http://www.vti.se/EPiBrowser/Publikationer%20-%20English/M911A.pdf, accessed 17/07/2011).

Walsh C (2005) Machine data collection for UKPMS. Chapter 11: Griptester. In *UKPMS User Manual, Vol. 3*, Version 02. UKPMS Support Contract. http://www.pcis.org.uk/iimni/UserFiles/Applications/Documents/Downloads/UKPMS%20Manuals%20and%20Guides/Manual/UKPMS_Manual_03_11v02.pdf (accessed 17/07/2011).

Wambold JC, Antle CE, Henry JJ and Rado Z (1995) International PIARC experiment to compare and harmonise texture and skid resistance measurements. PIARC Technical Committee on Surface Characteristics, France.

Woodbridge ME, Dunford A and Roe PG (2006) TRL Report PPR 144: Wehner-Schulze machine: first UK experiences with a new test for polishing resistance in aggregates. TRL, Crowthorne.

OTHER USEFUL INFORMATION

A major US study under the auspices of the Transportation Research Board – National Cooperative Highway Research Board under the title NCHRP Project 01–43 Guide to Pavement Friction, was delivered in February 2009 and a free-of-charge document in .pdf format can be downloaded from the NCHRP as a web-only document as follows: onlinepubs.trb.org/onlinepubs/nchrp/nchrp_w108.pdf (accessed 17/07/2011).

Deterioration and Maintenance of Pavements
ISBN: 978-0-7277-4114-1

ICE Publishing. All rights reserved
http://dx.doi.org/10.1680/dmp.41141.109

Chapter 10
Roughness

10.1. Background

Ever since roads carrying wheeled traffic were first constructed there has been concern expressed by travellers about the relative degrees of discomfort when traversing sections which had become rough due to lack of repair, resulting from wear or weather.

Even in Roman days there was concern about roughness of the 'pavmentium' experienced by chariots and Figure 10.1 may give an indication of the background to the problem. In the 1800s – when pavements were constructed of stone setts (in towns) and crushed rock and/or gravel out of town (or at least, the better ones were) – with the rudimentary suspension of the relatively high-speed stagecoach, travel could be a painful experience. It should be remembered that early chariots and the later coaches had timber wheels fitted with iron tyres, which were about 50 mm (2 inches) wide when in contact with the road surface.

In the early twentieth century, with the advent of the petrol engine, the use of self-propelled wheeled travel progressively increased. In 1888, John Boyd Dunlop – a Scottish veterinary surgeon working in Belfast, succeeded in making the first

pneumatic tyre, for which he was granted a patent. After the vet's invention proved successful on bicycles it was only a matter of time before it became popular on other road vehicles. Nevertheless, up to about 1930 solid rubber tyres were the norm, particularly for commercial vehicles.

From about 1930, pneumatic tyres progressively became more normal, as they produced a much superior ride (comfort) compared with solid tyres. From the mid to late 1940s they could be found on trucks in the UK.

During this period of development (1930–1945) the speed of vehicles was relatively slow (max 50 kph (30 mph)), compared with the present day where the typical speed limit in the USA is 50–55 mph and in the UK (non-motorway) 60 mph (100 kph)). Consequently as speeds became higher and a greater number of the population were engaged in travel the need for the highway engineer to deliver smoother running surfaces became more important.

In judging the implications of roughness measurements wavelength needs to be considered, the implications of which are shown in Figure 10.2.

A highway can be considered as a surface with filter components corresponding to hills and valleys and speed bumps. In Figure 10.2(A), has a large slow rolling hill, which because it is very smooth may be acceptable for high-speed travel. Figure 10.2(B) shows a road with a constant series of speed bumps and this is obviously unacceptable for high-speed travel. Figure 10.2(C) has a large slow rolling hill with the same speed bumps on the surface, which is also unacceptable for high-speed travel. The example above illustrates the importance of not just the amplitude or height of surface features, but also the amplitude at given intervals of spatial wavelengths. The example shows the importance of considering the spatial wavelength in addition to its height. The height of the road in Figure 10.2(A) is larger than the speed bumps in Figure 10.2(B), yet the road in Figure 10.2(A) would obviously represent a better surface for high speed travel.

Roughness is calculated by subtracting the waviness from the

Figure 10.1 An early Roman pavement
Courtesy of J.J. Farrington

109

Figure 10.2 Implications of waviness and roughness
Courtesy of Chapman Instruments (2009)

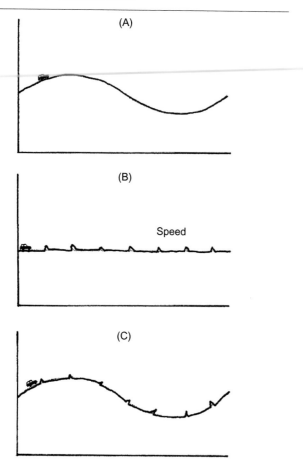

Figure 10.3 Total profile
Courtesy of Chapman Instruments (2009)

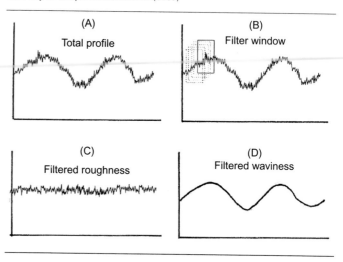

network level, roughness may be used for dividing the network into uniform sections, establishing value limits for acceptable pavement condition, and setting maintenance and rehabilitation priorities. Several agencies combine the roughness condition index with other pavement condition indices, such as distress, to formulate a composite index that is used in various management activities.

At project level, roughness measurements are used to locate areas of critical roughness and to maintain construction quality control. Examining a plot of roughness measurement against distance can identify areas of critical roughness. Specifying acceptable roughness limits leads to the progressive development of increased construction quality.

There are several causes of pavement roughness: traffic loading, environmental effects, construction materials and built-in construction irregularities. All pavements have irregularities built into the surface during construction, so even a new pavement that has not been opened to traffic can exhibit roughness. The roughness of a pavement usually increases with increased traffic loading and environmental exposure.

Short-wave roughness is normally caused by localised pavement distress; that is, depressions and cracking. Roughness may be further aggravated by traffic. For example, corrugations can cause an increase in dynamic wheelforce, which in turn can increase the severity and roughness of the corrugations. Environmental processes in combination with pavement layer properties normally cause long-wavelength roughness. Poor drainage, swelling soils, freeze–thaw cycles and non-uniform consolidation of subgrade may all contribute to surface roughness. Warping and curling of long concrete slabs will also cause roughness.

total profile data. The roughness shows the finer or shorter spatial wavelength features of the surface. Calculated from the total profile, the waviness represents the longer spatial wavelength features of the surface. Waviness over long distances is typically called form, figure, or bow. Figure 10.3 shows how this method of filtering can be applied to surface profile data. First a cut-off filter is selected to separate the roughness from the waviness. The spatial filter is selected such that only the small spatial features are evident in the roughness series (Chapman Instruments, 2009).

Roughness is an important indicator of pavement riding comfort and safety. From a driver's point of view, rough roads mean discomfort, decreased speed, potential vehicle damage and increased operating cost. Therefore roughness is a condition indicator that should be carefully considered when evaluating primary pavements.

The use of roughness measurements in pavement management has been demonstrated at both the network and project level. At

10.2. Measuring equipment and its development

From the 1950s in the US greater attention was being focused on roughness and this became an issue in the AASHO road trails of that period. During the AASHO trials correlations were demonstrated between roughness and panel-derived ride comfort.

At that time in the US there was a concept, which still prevails, of user panel rating, whereby a riding surface was marked on a 1–5 scale by a panel of users to demonstrate their level of acceptance of the ride quality (see Figure 10.4).

By the 1920s highway engineers recognised that the roughness properties in a road of greatest importance were those responsible for causing vibrations in motor vehicles. The 'Via-Log', developed by the State of New York, evidenced this thinking by measuring the suspension travel of a passenger car as an indication of roughness level. The first devices recorded the suspension motion, but were soon modified to sum the motion on a mechanical counter and measure 'inches/mile' statistic.

In the 1930s the difficulties of obtaining consistent measurements by this method, due to the variations in dynamics of motor vehicles, led to the attempt to 'standardise' the vehicle.

The Bureau of Public Roads (BPR) developed the roughometer, which was adapted for use in the UK by TRRL in 1941. The various components, dimensions, mass properties, and tyre and suspension properties were standardised in an effort to achieve comparable performance on all devices. The typical layout is shown in Figure 10.5.

One other important roughness measurement device developed at the time of the AASHO Road Test was the Chloe (an acronym

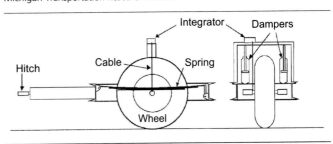

Figure 10.5 The BPR roughometer
Reproduced from Gillespie (1992) courtesy of TD Gillespie and the University of Michigan Transportation Research Institute

formed from the first letters of the inventors' names). The Chloe seen in Figure 10.6 consisted of a trailer towed at low speed on which was mounted two small wheels 9 inches (225 mm) apart with the instrumentation to measure and record local road slope.

The signal recording was the slope deviation (or slope variance), which is generically an 'inches/mile' statistic. The slope variance measured by the Chloe is of particular interest to highway engineers today as it was the historical reference for roughness used in developing the pavement serviceability concept.

By 1960s, the attraction of being able to measure roughness properties from a moving vehicle motivated development of 'roadmeters' (sometimes called 'ridemeters') in the form of the Mays Meter, and other comparable devices. The relatively inexpensive devices could be mounted in any vehicle as shown in Figure 10.7, and would measure axle displacement as the vehicle travelled along a test section.

Most of the roadmeters measured accumulated axle displacement, which is the 'inches/mile' deviation of the road surface coloured by the dynamics of the particular vehicle in which the equipment was fixed. This format of measuring devices became known as response-type road roughness measurement systems (RTRRMSs).

Figure 10.4 Panel rating form
Reproduced from AASHO (1962) with permission

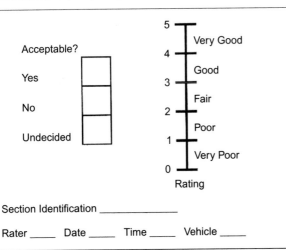

Figure 10.6 Chloe equipment
Reproduced from Gillespie (1992) courtesy of TD Gillespie and the University of Michigan Transportation Research Institute

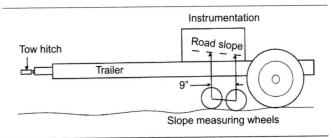

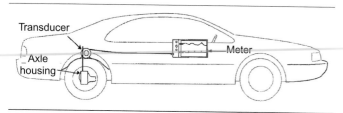

Because of their simplicity and low cost, the highway departments of approximately half of the US states had acquired RTRRMS by the late 1970s. Although they reliably measured high 'inches/mile' on bad roads and lower numbers on smooth roads, they were not accurate enough for most engineering applications. As may be expected, no two roadmeters gave identical measurements because of the differences in the dynamics of the vehicles, and consistent performance from day-to-day with individual roadmeters was also difficult to achieve. Such routine actions as adding fuel or passengers, adjusting tyre pressure, balancing tyres, etc. changed the 'calibration' of the device. As a result it was difficult to develop and maintain a database of road roughness conditions without extensive efforts at controlling or compensating for vehicle changes by frequent calibration exercises.

In 1978, the US National Cooperative Highway Research Program (NCHRP) set off on project 1–78 entitled 'Calibration and correlation of response-type road roughness measuring systems', which began work eventually leading to the development of the International Roughness Index (IRI).

10.3. International Roughness Index (IRI)

The NCHRP project examined the sources of variability in roughness measurement with RTRRMS and identified calibration procedures to compensate for each so that measurements would be consistent and correlate between different systems. Concurrently, the World Bank faced similar although broader problems in obtaining comparable measurements of roughness (for data input to highway cost models) in the many countries in which it was providing loans for development of road systems. Although RTRRMSs were used in many of these countries, to achieve consistent measurement performance rigorous calibration methods were needed that could be based on technology available at these sites. Equally important was the need for a standard scale of roughness that would be stable over time and transportable throughout the world to allow comparison of measurement on a worldwide basis. To address this problem the International Road Roughness Experiment was organised and conducted in Brazil in 1982 by the World Bank.

The outcome of these efforts was the identification of a standard scale now known as the International Roughness Index (IRI). Many factors were considered in its selection.

- The index had to be related to the vibration response of motor vehicles, as most roughness indices were directly or indirectly linked to motor vehicles' performance.
- The scale had to be mathematically related to road profile in order to be stable with time (as all attempts to standardise hardware had been unsuccessful).
- It had to be measurable by the widest possible range of hardware (i.e., rod and level, RTRRMS, profilometers, etc.).
- It had to be transportable (i.e., procedures and hardware requirements had to be defined so that it could be reliably reproduced throughout the world).

10.4. Rationale behind the IRI

The IRI is a scale for roughness based on the response of a generic motor vehicle to roughness of the road surface. Its true value is determined by obtaining a suitably accurate measurement of the profile of the road, processing it through an algorithm that simulates the way a reference vehicle would respond to the roughness inputs and accumulating the suspension travel. Thus it mathematically duplicates a roadmeter.

In the case of roadmeters, the cumulative stroke of the automobile's suspension is measured over a section of road coloured by the particular response characteristics of the automobile. This is done in the computation of the IRI. The relevant response properties of an automobile are captured by a simple dynamic model known as the quarter-car model shown in Figure 10.8. At each wheel position the vehicle behaves as a sprung mass sitting on a suspension with stiffness and damping, which in turn is attached to the unsprung mass of the wheel, brake and suspension components. The wheel contacts the road by a tyre, which acts

Figure 10.8 The quarter-car model
Reproduced from Gillespie (1992) courtesy of TD Gillespie and the University of Michigan Transportation Research Institute

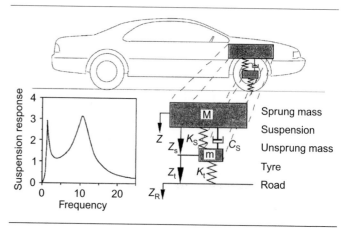

like a spring. The road inputs to the car, flex of the tyre and stroke the suspension, which causes the spring and unsprung masses to vibrate in the vertical direction.

Whether the roughness is viewed as deviations in elevation (displacement inputs), slope (velocity inputs), or change of slope (acceleration inputs), the quarter car responds in a defined manner. The response can be mathematically described with a relatively simple set of dynamic equations known as the quarter car simulation. At very low frequencies (corresponding to long wavelengths in the road) the suspension response is zero because the wheel and the vehicle body move up and down together. Road inputs at frequencies near one Hertz cause the sprung mass to resonate on the suspension-producing stroke that is slightly greater than the road input. The response is maintained up through frequencies near 10 Hertz where axle resonance occurs. Above the axle resonant frequency the response again drops to zero as the road bumps simply deflect the tyre without producing significant suspension stroke.

The frequency response of the quarter car extends from approximately 0.5 to 20 Hz, with some roughness at the body bounce frequency and the axle resonance frequency.

The 'ride' of a motor vehicle is most commonly measured by the acceleration of the body. On a typical road this turns out to be the body acceleration spectrum (a power spectral density or PSD) similar to that shown in Figure 10.9. Also shown in the figure is the PSD from which the IRI accrues. Although slightly different in shape they both cover the same frequency range and both place emphasis on the 1 Hertz body resonance and the 10 Hertz axle resonance.

Roughness is also significant to motor vehicle performance in other ways. The existence of roughness necessitates suspension systems on motor vehicles to reduce the vibration of passengers. A primary consideration in design of suspension systems is the stroke necessary to accommodate the displacement caused by roughness. Ride improves with stroke – the more generous suspension stroke in a luxury car is the primary factor that allows it to ride better than a compact car.

Correlations have been demonstrated between the IRI and pavement serviceability index, as is shown in Figure 10.10.

Of some significance to the pavement engineer is Figure 10.11, which shows the relationship between roughness and dynamic load expressed as the Dynamic Load Index (DLI). The DLI is defined as the standard deviation of the load normalised by the static load. Thus an index of zero implies the load is its static value, whereas an index of 0.25 represents load variation for which the standard deviation is 25% of the static load.

10.5. Speed

On any road the level of roughness to which a vehicle is exposed depends on the travel speed. The perceived roughness generally increases with speed. This arises from the fact that the forces and acceleration imposed on a wheel by a bump increase with the speed at which it must follow the bump. Thus roughness to the road user is not a constant, but may be judged differently on low- and high-speed roads.

Figure 10.9 Comparison of IRI with other vehicle responses
Reproduced from Gillespie (1992) courtesy of TD Gillespie and the University of Michigan Transportation Research Institute

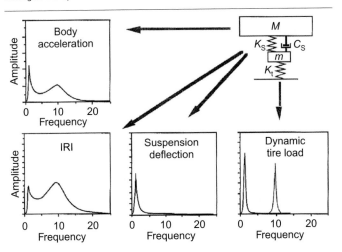

Figure 10.10 Correlation of IRI with serviceability index
Reproduced from Gillespie (1992) courtesy of TD Gillespie and the University of Michigan Transportation Research Institute

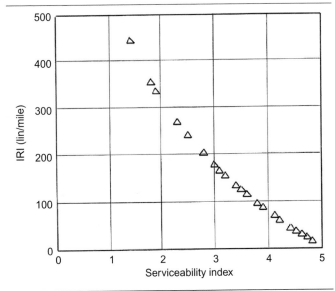

Figure 10.11 Relationship between IRI and truck dynamic load
Reproduced from Gillespie (1992) courtesy of TD Gillespie and the University of Michigan Transportation Research Institute

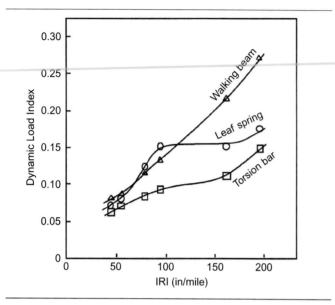

To the highway community, however, roughness is a geometric property of the road. The geometry is constant, therefore a road should have a single roughness value. To accommodate the difference in viewpoints, the IRI is based on quarter-car response at 50 mph (80 kph). A fixed speed for evaluating IRI ignores the fact that the prevailing travel speed varies with the different types of road. Thus, the choice of a fixed speed is a compromise between needs of the highway engineer and the realities of the physics governing the vehicle behaviour.

10.6. Range of values of IRI
See Figure 10.12.

10.7. Recent developments in data collection equipment
As electronics have developed so has the technology for data collection become more sophisticated. The need for increasing data and the need for greater safety during the collection process has progressively led away from walking on pavement data collection.

Figure 10.12 Range of typical IRI values
Sayers et al., 1986

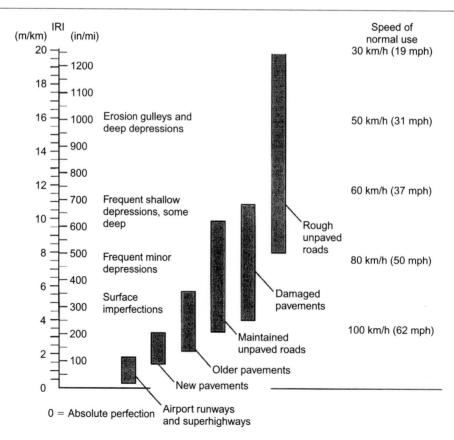

In the case of longitudinal roughness this has resulted from the determination of roughness using accelerometers and lasers and a move away from response type instruments, as illustrated in Figure 10.13.

General Motors (GM), in the USA, initially demonstrated this technology as a consequence of which the modern profiler is normally referred to as a generic GM type of the form shown in Figure 10.13, where one or more accelerometers and lasers are used to determine longitudinal roughness.

The need to measure transverse profile (rutting) along with roughness has led to the development of laser rut bars, the

measurements from which can be interpreted in the form of theoretical string lines, and the arrangement depicted in Figure 10.14 is typical.

Typical of the current range of survey vehicles is that developed at TRL for the Highways Agency as part of a move to collect sufficient data in an economic manner to populate a comprehensive pavement management system.

Diagrams of this vehicle, known as Harris 1, are shown in Figures 10.15 and 10.16.

Figure 10.14 Typical string line for rutting
Courtesy of Dynatest International A/S

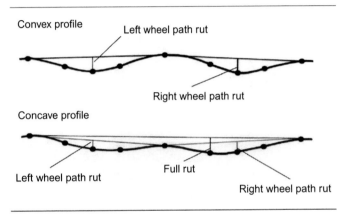

Figure 10.13 Generic GM inertial profiler
From Bundras, 2001. In the public domain

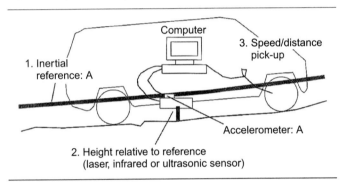

Figure 10.15 Harris data collection vehicle (front)
© HA 2011

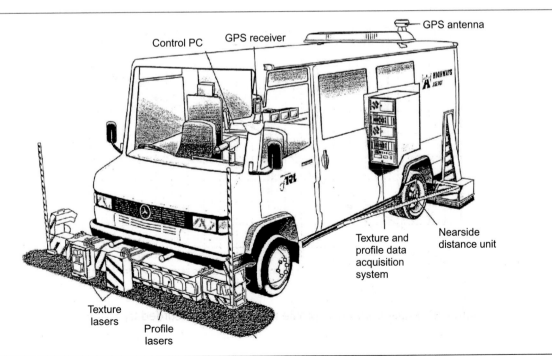

Figure 10.16 Harris data collection vehicle (rear)
© HA 2011

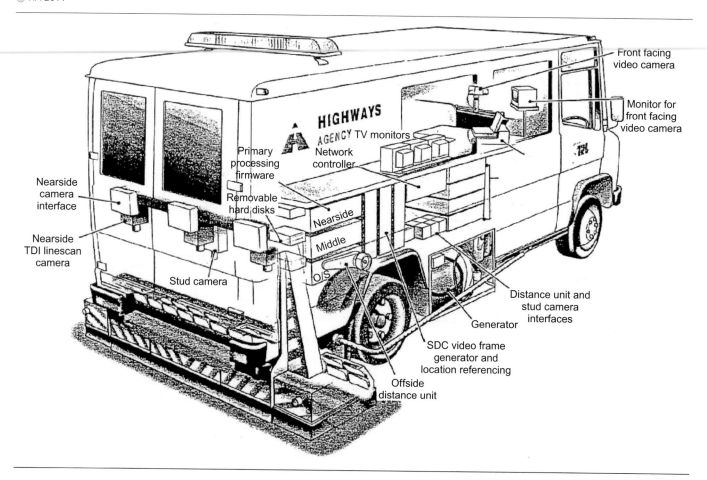

The vehicle can be seen to have a transverse bar at the front, which carries a series of lasers to determine transverse profile. Additional lasers are fitted to measure surface texture.

Locational referencing is controlled using GPS (satellite positioning). In the rear view the presence of downward-facing video cameras can be seen, which are used to take a series of overlapping pictures of the pavement surface. Using this data and recently developed crack recognition software it is possible to detect cracks in excess of 2 mm wide.

Commercial derivatives of this vehicle have several additional video cameras facing to the front, sides and rear, able to locate the position of various features such as traffic signs, barriers and lighting columns. With software developed from military inertial guidance systems it is possible as part of the post-processing of inventory data to produce database files showing the GPS coordinates of the feature, its offset from the pavement, its height

and sign type. An example of the collection format is shown in Figure 10.17.

At least one of the commercially available vehicles is capable of collecting pavement construction information simultaneously using GPR.

In the UK, the current generation of surveys is known as TRACS, which stands for traffic speed condition survey. The application of this technology is developing from the national motorways and trunk roads, where an annual survey is carried out, onto the local road principal road network, where it is intended to replace the slow and expensive walking detailed and coarse visual survey.

While this technology is not welcomed by all, due to its technical sophistication and lengthy phase in period, it has the distinct advantage of being able to produce time series trend data. Experience indicates that there is a good correlation between data

Figure 10.17 Typical inventory data collection system (Aran (Automatic Road Analyser))
Courtesy of Roadware Inc

produced using this technology and conventional walking inspection.

10.8. Present position in the UK

The TRACS system in the UK, which is outlined in Highways Agency interim advice note 42/05 (Hawker, 2005), covers a series of issues in a single vehicle pass and results from the HARRIS project, which is referred to earlier in this chapter, covers the attributes listed below.

10.8.1 Texture depth

The surface texture depth of a pavement is measured by Tracs-type survey (TTS) survey equipment which measures the coarser macrotexture and the finer megatexture elements. This range of texture depth contributes to skidding resistance, primarily at high speeds, in two ways. First, it provides drainage paths to allow water to be removed rapidly from the tyre/road interface. Second, the projections, which contribute to hysteresis losses in the tyre, are an important factor in the braking process. Texture depth, as measured by TTS and when compared with SCRIM results, may therefore be considered primarily as a parameter for assessment of the safety serviceability of a pavement surface.

10.8.2 Rut depth

Rut depth as determined from TTS surveys corresponds to a measurement made with a 2 m straight edge and wedge.

10.8.3 Profile variance

Profile variance, the measurement of longitudinal profile obtained from TTS, is principally a value for assessing ride quality, but may also be used to derive information on pavement distress. The short, medium and long wavelength features found to have the most effect on vehicle ride are represented by variance of profile from 3 m, 10 m and 30 m moving averages respectively.

High levels of 3 m variance typically arise from short wavelength features such as faulting, potholes and poor reinstatements. Extremely high levels of 3 m variance may be linked with the presence of severe wheelpath cracking.

A variance of 10 m is influenced by short undulations, possibly arising from localised subsidence of reinstatements and subsurface utilities, and bay irregularities on concrete roads.

A variance of 30 m covers such a length of pavement that it can be influenced by the road geometry and so caution is required in its interpretation as an indicator of pavement distress. Its application for the purpose is, therefore, typically restricted to reasonably straight sections of pavement, often on high-speed roads, where high levels of 30 m variance will have some influence on the users' perception of ride quality. On such roads high levels of 30 m variance may be due to long undulations in the pavement resulting from the presence of subsidence.

The validity of longitudinal profile data will be compromised by traffic calming measures such as speed humps, cushions and gateway treatments.

10.8.4   Cracking

The resolution of crack detection systems employed on current TTS survey equipment will typically limit the minimum crack width detectable by such systems to around 2 mm. The identification of cracking relies on interpretation of the recording image of the particular TTS system's crack identification software, and experience to date indicates that this may produce a different interpretation than an inspector carrying out a visual inspection of the same pavement.

Consequently, TTS cracking data do not replicate visual survey cracking data, but will generally report a lower intensity of cracking than would be observed visually. Also TTS may misrepresent fretting on a heavily chipped surface as cracking. Good correspondence has been obtained, however, between the two methods in identifying sections where deterioration is present.

At the present time (2011) the development of the interpretation of these parameters is ongoing: this being particularly necessary for urban roads.

10.9.   Highways Agency interim advice note 42/05

Interim advice note (IAN) 42/05 (Hawker, 2005) considers four categories of deterioration as indicated in Table 10.1.

Since the term variance has not been encountered so far in this chapter, Figure 10.18 explains how it is derived. It will be seen to be the square of the difference between the profile and the moving average, as is shown in Figure 10.18.

The threshold values presented in Table 10.2 are set out in IAN 42/05 (Hawker, 2005), relating to the four categories of deterioration described on the previous page.

It should be noted that these levels of deterioration are relevant to the national road network in the UK and are not comparable with IRI values used in other countries.

It should be noted that the above tables taken from IAN 42/05 (Hawker, 2005) relate to the national road network and different values are likely to be used on local networks.

A photograph of a typical TRACS-type vehicle operating in the UK is shown in Figure 10.19.

10.10.   Use of IRI for future problem location – a US case study

The following data result form a research project undertaken by a US State DOT, who use roughness (smoothness) measurements to help deliver longer lasting pavements. The project under consideration was based on the use of standard Aran equipment and sophisticated data processing in an attempt to consider where future pavement distress may be likely to occur.

Problems associated with lack of compaction due to cooling at the end of load during the surfacing operation have been known for many years. An experienced maintenance engineer can in many cases identify visually the problem on site as premature deterioration starts to become apparent.

Figure 10.20 shows one of the outcomes of this project, whereby there is a discernible increase in roughness at about 35 m

Table 10.1 Tracs condition categories
Data taken from Hawker (2005)

Category	Definition
1	*Sound* – no visible deterioration
2	*Some deterioration* – lower level of concern. The deterioration is not serious and more detailed (project level) investigations are needed unless extending over long lengths, or several parameters are at this category at isolated positions
3	*Moderate deterioration* – warning level of concern. The deterioration is becoming serious and needs to be investigated. Priorities for more detailed (project level) investigation depends on the extent and values of the condition parameter
4	*Serious deterioration* – intervention level of concern. This condition should not occur frequently on the motorway and all-purpose trunk road network, as earlier maintenance should have prevented this state from being reached. At this level of deterioration more detailed (project level) investigation should be carried out on the deteriorated lengths at the earliest opportunity and action taken if and as appropriate

Figure 10.18 Derivation of profile variance
© TRL

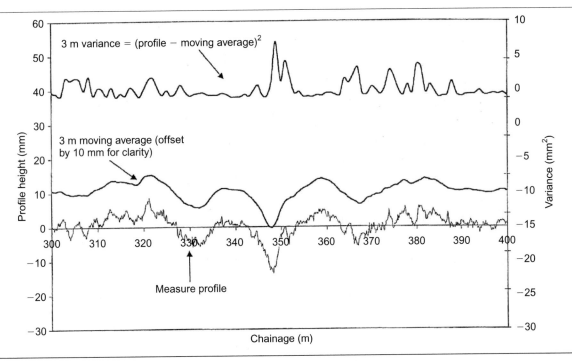

Figure 10.19 Multi-feature data collection vehicle
Reproduced from (HD29/08) © Crown copyright 2008

intervals, which was found to be consistent with the location of a changeover in the delivery truck at the time of laying.

10.11. Use of IRI in the US to monitor construction quality

Virginia Department of Transportation (VDOT, 2007) has developed the use of IRI as the basis of an innovative bonus payment system in the new-build situation.

The ride quality is based on the lowest site average IRI produced by a minimum of two test runs. These test runs will be conducted using a South Dakota-style road profiling device and reported for each travel lane. The device shall measure both wheelpaths with laser height sensing instruments. The test shall be conducted within 14 calendar days of completion of the final surface course over the designated section.

The IRI number in inches/mile (m/km) shall be established for each 0.1 mile (160 m) section and for each travel lane of surfacing. The last section preceding a bridge, the first section subsequent to a bridge, and the beginning and end sections of the surfacing will not be subject to the payment adjustment. When the influence of a bridge approach or pavement joint at the end is determined to extend beyond a partial section (a section of 0.1 mile (160 m) in length that may result from these feature), the partial section may be included in an adjoining section.

Table 10.3 sets out the acceptable quality of pavement based on the finished rideability. Payment adjustments are applied to the theoretical tonnage of the surface mix asphalt material for the lane width and section tested. A section is defined as the lane width and 0.1 mile (160 m) in length.

In addition to the maximum IRI of 1.74 (0.1 mile) on 160 m sections, any (0.05 mile) 80 m that has an IRI which exceeds 1.89 will be subject to correction.

Table 10.2 Threshold values for TRACS on national roads
Data taken from Hawker (2005)

Rut depth

Category	1	Threshold value	2	Threshold value	3	Threshold value	4
Maximum rut (mm)			6		11		20

Texture depth

Category	1	Threshold value	2	Threshold value	3	Threshold value	4
Texture depth (mm) Anti-skid surfacing HFS (high friction surfacing)			0.6		N/A		N/A
All other surfaces			1.1		0.8		0.4

Noise (100 m lengths)

Category A	Threshold B	Threshold C	Threshold D	Threshold E	Threshold F	Threshold G
All surface types (dB(A) (A-weighted decibels))	101.5	102.3	103.8	104.8	105.2	105.6

Ride quality criteria for all types of road construction for Tracs measurements

Category	1	Threshold value	2	Threshold value	3	Threshold value	4
Motorways and rural dual carriageways – enhanced longitudinal profile variance (mm^2)							
3 m			0.7		2.2		4.4
10 m			1.6		6.5		14.7
30 m			22		66		110
Urban dual carriageways – enhanced longitudinal profile variance (mm^2)							
3 m			0.8		2.2		5.5
10 m			2.8		8.6		22.8
30 m			30		75		121
Rural single carriageways – enhanced longitudinal profile variance (mm^2)							
3 m			0.8		2.2		5.5
10 m			2.8		8.6		22.8
30 m			30		75		121
Urban single carriageway roads – enhanced longitudinal profile variance (mm^2)							
3 m			1.4		3.8		9.3
10 m			6.1		18.3		36.6
30 m			48		97		193

(*continued*)

Table 10.2. (*continued*)

Cracking (whole carriageway cracking %)

Category	Low	Threshold value: %	Moderate	Threshold value: %	High
Bituminous surface (HRA)		0.45		1.5	
Bituminous surface (HRA)		0.15		0.5	
Concrete surface		N/A		N/A	

Fretting (100 m lengths)

Category	Low	Threshold value: %	Moderate	Threshold value: %	High	Threshold value: %	Severe
Bituminous surface (HRA)		0.20		1.15		1.8	
Bituminous (other)		N/A		N/A		N/A	

Figure 10.20 Local increase in roughness consistent with end of load during laying
Courtesy G.M. Rowe, Abatech Inc.

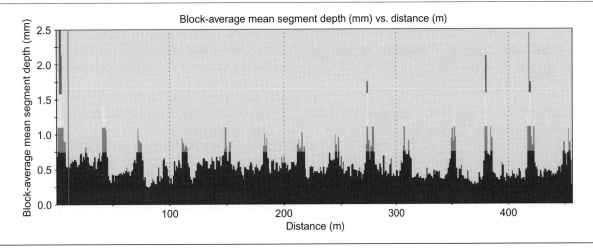

10.12. UK new pavements

In the UK, the standard for compliance for a new pavement surface is set out in the 1994 edition of *Specification for Highway Works* (DfT, 1994) in clause 702, and is as follows:

The longitudinal regularity of the surface of the wearing course is set out in Table 10.4.

The irregularity of the wearing course surface is a variation of not less than 4 mm and no more than 7 mm of the profile of the road as measured by the rolling straight-edge, of the type designed by the Transport and Road Research Laboratory set at 4 mm or 7 mm as appropriate, or equivalent apparatus capable of measuring irregularities within the same magnitudes over a 3 m length. No irregularity exceeding 10 mm shall be permitted.

Compliance with the following table shall be checked by the rolling straight edge along any line or lines parallel to the edge of the pavement on sections of 800 m selected by the engineer, whether or not it is constructed in shorter lengths. Sections

Table 10.3 IRI vs. payment adjustment
VIrginia Department of Transport (DOT). Information in the public domain

IRI after completion: m/km	Payment adjustment (% pavement unit price)
<0.94	103
0.94–1.03	102
1.03–1.10	101
1.10–1.26	100
1.26–1.42	98
1.42–1.58	95
1.58–1.74	90
>1.74	Subject to corrective action

Note: IRI has been converted to m/km

Table 10.4 Roughness compliance for new carriageways (UK)
Data taken from DfT (1994)

| Irregularity | Surfaces of carriageways, hard strips and hard shoulders | | | |
	4 mm		7 mm	
Length (m)	300	75	300	75
Category A road (failures)	20	9	2	1

shorter than 300 m forming part of a longer section shall be tested using the number of irregularities for a 300 m length pro rata to the nearest whole number.

Where the total length of the pavement is less than 300 m the measurements shall be taken on 75 m lengths.

Checking of the wearing course for compliance shall be carried out as soon as possible after completion of the surfacing and the remedial works completed before the road is open to traffic.

There are no criteria laid down in the UK which utilise IRI as a compliance parameter either in new build or as a means of examining rehabilitation needs. There are, however, guidelines for surface irregularity for network management purposes measured with a bump integrator which can be converted to an equivalent IRI as shown in Table 10.5.

Table 10.5 Bump integrator and equivalent IRI measurements

Bump integrator (inches/mile)	IRI (m/km)
220	4.67
240	5.03

REFERENCES AND BIBLIOGRAPHY

AASHO (1962) The AASHO Road Tests, Report 5, Special Report 61E, Publication 954, Highway Research Board, National Research Council, Washington DC, USA.

Boeger R and Crowe RJ (2002) It's the ride that counts. *Public Roads* **65(4)**.

Bundras J (2001) A synopsis of current equipment used for measuring pavement smoothness. US Department of Transportation Federal Highway, Washington, DC.

Chapman Instruments (2009) Chapman technical note-TG-1 spat_fil.doc Rev-01-09: Spatial filtering of surface profile data. http://www.chapinst.com/ApplicationNotes/spatfil2.pdf (accessed 17/07/2011). Chapman Instruments, Rochester, NY.

DfT (1994) *Manual of Contract Documents for Highway Works, Vol. 1: Specification for Highway Works*. DfT, London.

Dynatest (2011) Road Surface Profiler 5051 Mark II. Dynatest, Copenhagen. For more information see www.dynatest.com (accessed 17/07/2011).

Federal Highway Administration (1997) ROSAN, technical notes. US Department of Transportation Federal Highway Administration. www.tfhrc.gov/hnr20/rosan/rosandoc.htm (accessed 17/07/2011).

Gillespie TD (1992) Everything you always wanted to know about IRI, but were afraid to ask! Road Profile Users' Group Meeting, Lincoln, Nebraska, 22–24 September.

Hawker L (2005) IAN 42/05: Traffic-speed condition surveys (tracs): revised assessment criteria (superseded by HD 29/08; supersedes IAN 42/02). Highways Agency, London.

Hegman RR (1993) A close look at road surfaces. US Department of Transportation Federal Highway Administration. www.tfhrc.gov/pubrds/summer93/p93su4.htm (accessed 17/07/2011).

Highways Agency (2008) DMRB HD 29/08: Data for pavement assessment. *Design Manual for Roads and Bridges*. Highways Agency, London.

Highways Research Board (1962) The AASHO Road Test, Report 5: Pavement Research, Special Report 61E, Washington DC. National Academy of Science, National Research Council. Publication No. 754.

International Roughness Index (IRI) (1986) http://www.umtri.umich.edu/divisionPage.php?pageID=62 (accessed 17/07/2011).

Karamihas SM and Gillespie TD (2010) Assessment of profiler performance for construction quality control, Phase 1. University of Michigan Transport Research Institute (Umtri), Ann Arbor. http://www.acpa.org/Downloads/ProfilerPerformanceAssessment.pdf (accessed 17/07/2011).

Robinson R, Danielson U and Snaith M (1998) *Road Maintenance and Management, Concepts and Systems*. Macmillan, Basingstoke.

Sayers MW *et al.* (1986) World Bank Technical Paper Number 45 – The International Road Roughness Experiment, Establishing Correlation and a Calibration Standard for

Measurement, World Bank.

Sayers MW and Karamihas SM (1998) *The Little Book of Profiling, Basic Information About Measuring and Interpreting Road Profiles*. University of Michigan, MI.

Schmidt B (1999) Report 94: Evolution and harmonisation of evenness techniques. Danish Road Institute. www.statensnet.dk/pligtarkiv/fremvis.pl?vaerkid= 12587&reprid=0&filid=578&iarkiv=1 (accessed 17/07/2011).

Shahin MY (1994) *Pavement Management for Airports, Roads, and Parking Lots*. Chapman & Hall, New York, NY.

TRB (Transportation Research Board) (1992) Transportation research record no. 1348: Pavement surface properties: Roughness, rutting, skid resistance and surface dressing. National Academy Press, Washington, DC.

TRB (1988) National Cooperative Highway Research Program Report 308: Pavement roughness and rideability field evaluation. TRB, Washington, DC.

TRB (1990) National cooperative highway research program synthesis of highway practice 167: Measurements, specifications, and achievement of smoothness for pavement construction. TRB, Washington, DC.

Ullidtz P (1987) *Pavement Analysis*. Elsevier, Amsterdam.

VDOT (2007) 2007 Ride Specification Paving Results, Virginia Department of Transportation, 1401E Broad Street, Richmond, VA 23219.

Other useful information may be found on the internet via a google search for 'smoothness of pavement construction'.

Deterioration and Maintenance of Pavements
ISBN: 978-0-7277-4114-1

ICE Publishing. All rights reserved
http://dx.doi.org/10.1680/dmp.41141.125

Chapter 11
Drainage of Pavements

11.1. Introduction

In any book dealing with pavements, drainage is recognised as being important for both the functional and structural condition of the pavement. Nevertheless, comprehensive guidance on its design and especially its maintenance is not easy to find.

Figure 11.1, originated in the early 1950s (TRRL, 1952), and illustrates that there are several issues relating to the drainage of a pavement. They are considerably broader than just the rain which falls on the surface – which, if not removed efficiently, may lead rapidly to a serious reduction in safety due to standing water. Surface water is managed by a range of features, from permitting over-run onto a hardened shoulder, as shown on the left-hand side of the figure, to the provision of channels and gullies leading the water to some form of piped system adjacent to or underneath the pavement, or to adjacent ditches.

Permeability of the pavement surface contributes to a series of surface distresses, generally associated with stripping of the binder from the aggregate, which causes initially fretting and subsequently ravelling of the surface. Other environmental effects such as ultra-violet radiation may contribute to these distresses.

Ensuring the pavement surface is sealed normally controls surface permeability. MN DOT (2007) suggests that the overall permeability of a pavement may be as high as 40%.

The presence of water within the fabric of the pavement can be damaging as it may contribute to the binder stripping from the aggregate, with associated loss of asphalt homogeneity. Additionally, loss of bond between the several layers of the pavement may occur, leading to delamination which will have serious consequences for the structural wellbeing of the pavement. Minimising the amount of water able to percolate to the fabric of the pavement is a challenging task, requiring protection at the sides as well as underneath the pavement – in addition to ensuring that the surface is maintained in a sealed and impermeable condition.

The overall problem becomes more complex when we consider the formation on which the pavement is founded. There is a natural water table in any ground, which fluctuates with the season and with other factors outside the scope of our consideration here. It has long been understood that the equilibrium moisture content of the foundation has a significant effect on its capacity to provide support to the pavement. In simple terms, an attempt is made to control this by ensuring the water table is maintained at least 1 m below the level of the foundation by some system of drainage, the various elements of which are examined in some detail in the following sections. A range of features from drainage blankets to cut-off drains, possibly used together, may accomplish this control, which may be at the sides or under the pavement.

When evaluating the various aspects of a pavement drainage system, consideration must also be given to the surrounding land, as there may well be complex groundwater movements which were not considered at the time of design. This is especially so when the pavement is built on sloping ground where the land on one side is considerably higher than the pavement. Ground surface water control from higher land may necessitate the provision of control ditches, both at the top and the bottom of the slope. The control of complex groundwater movements is a specialist subject and is only dealt with very briefly in this chapter.

Figure 11.1 Water as it may enter a pavement
Reproduced from TRRL 1952 © Crown copyright 1952

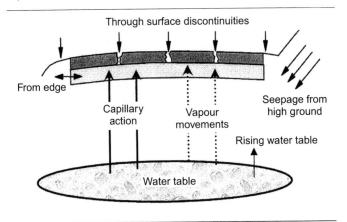

Figure 11.2 Typical UK drainage configurations

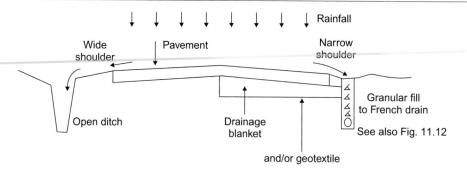

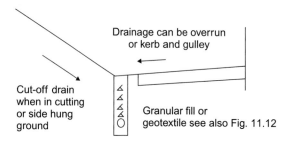

Figure 11.3 Typical minor rural road

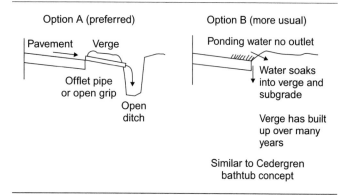

The situation is further complicated by the possible impact of water-based utilities – water mains carrying drinking water, drainage systems carrying waste water and surface water, all of which have the potential to leak and contribute moisture to the pavement foundations. To some extent all water mains and drains leak and this must be borne in mind, especially when undertaking pavement investigations in urban and suburban areas. Direct control of these utilities lies usually within the responsibilities of the individual owning agencies, which are normally anxious to ensure that both infiltration and leakage are minimised.

Whatever the method of drainage provision, the most fundamen-

tal need is for a clear unrestricted outfall to discharge freely into a river or other waterway. In some circumstances where this is not possible it may be necessary to make use of soakaways, which are dealt with briefly later in the chapter.

11.2. Cost of drainage and its maintenance

The cost of drainage provision is within the range 16–25% of the asset worth (construction cost).

The cost of drainage maintenance, as near as it is possible to determine, is of the order of 7% of the overall cost of maintenance. In the UK, this is split fairly equally between the cost of emptying gullies (4%) and the cost of cleaning drains (3%).

If examined in the context of risk assessment – bearing in mind that incorrectly functioning or incompetently designed drainage can lead to a failure of the pavement as well as danger from flooding and other damage – then the amount of money spent on maintenance seems fairly modest.

From personal experience over the period 1980–2010, during which financial resources for highway maintenance were progressively reduced, drainage maintenance was cut back as there did not seem to be any apparent immediate effect. This adds to the major problem of securing appropriate funding.

This very superficial investigation has quickly revealed two major problems.

■ Existing funding levels for maintenance are probably inadequate.
■ There is no established way of rationally demonstrating need.

The remainder of this chapter attempts to deal systematically with the various elements of drainage and considers their provision and maintenance options and possibilities.

11.3. Surface drainage

One problem on many rural UK roads is that the verge is higher than the adjacent carriageway and there is no formal drainage provision. Reliance is made on surface water soaking away into the verge, which may or may not be effective. Where there is an adjacent ditch, which may drain adjacent land as well as the highway surface, water is led to it by either an offlet or a grip in the verge.

11.3.1 Offlet

An offlet is, as the name suggests, a location where the surface water is led from the carriageway to an adjacent ditch in a pipe, generally without any headwall provision. The major problem with offlets is that of restriction or blockage at the entrance by vegetation as can be seen in Figure 11.4. An offlet also requires regular rodding to clear detritus buildup.

In more sophisticated circumstances where there is a kerb rather than just a verge, some form of casting is normally used such as is shown in Figure 11.5.

Figure 11.4 Offlet through verge with vegetation restricted inlet

Small diameter pipe

11.3.2 Grip

A grip is conceptually similar to an offlet except there is not a pipe joining the carriageway to the ditch, rather a shallow transverse ditch across the verge. In addition to causing a discontinuity in the surface of the verge, grips need regular cleaning by digging out any deposit of detritus. Because of their location this usually has to be done manually.

11.3.3 Gully

In the urban area and on most of the rest of the UK highway network, surface water is removed from the pavement into the piped drainage system by gullies, or some other form of offlet. On motorways a specially formed longitudinal dished concrete channel has latterly been used to guide water to a gully. A gully (Figure 11.6) is placed against the kerb. The kerb acts as both an edge support to the pavement and a channel to guide the surface water to the gully.

In current UK practice, a gully is usually provided for every 200 m² of pavement, based on the criterion that the maximum

Figure 11.5 Typical kerb entrance to an offlet

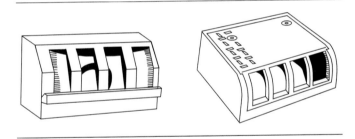

Figure 11.6 Typical cross-section of a road gully

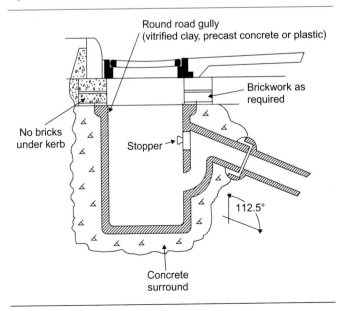

Round road gully
(vitrified clay, precast concrete or plastic)

Brickwork as required

No bricks under kerb

Stopper

112.5°

Concrete surround

acceptable waterway is 0.8–1 m wide from the kerb. While road gullies come in different forms – they may be of vitrified clay, concrete or plastic – their purpose is common, namely to provide a location into which surface water can be channelled by the use of falls in the surface of the road.

All water falling on the road surface collects detritus, which is always present, either from air-blown debris or from the degradation of rubber from tyres. This detritus can have a surprisingly large range of particle size and, as its presence within a drainage system is undesirable, the road gully acts as a convenient opportunity for it to settle out. Since the carrying capacity of water is related to the fourth power of its velocity, any reduction in velocity has a significant effect on carrying power.

While there is a range of capacities for gully detritus retention, a convenient rule of thumb is $0.07 \, m^3$, such that 100 gullies may be expected to yield $7 \, m^3$ of detritus. Typically, the cleaning of gullies is undertaken with a specialist vacuum tanker, which evacuates the combined load of detritus and water before filling the hopper of the gully with water to provide a seal to prevent any drainage system odours escaping. The typical daily output is between 100 and 150 gullies per day per machine.

Emptying rounds are scheduled to minimise unproductive running and a gully would typically be emptied twice annually, with the resulting detritus being recycled for verge or other work. Depending on location and the risk of flooding due to malfunction, some gullies may be emptied more frequently.

Figure 11.7 shows a typical gully emptier. In this case it is provided with jetting capability.

A normal part of the work description is to ensure that the connection between the gully and the drain is clear and it is in this connection that a jetting attachment is of benefit. The jetter attachment is essentially a high-pressure water pump in which the spray nozzle is designed to spray backwards so that the nozzle moves forward into the blockage and the water flushes the loosened material into the pipeline. It is normal practice, where possible, to work upstream, so that loosened material is removed by gravity.

In any investigation, having checked that the various gullies appear to be functioning – i.e. they are not blocked with detritus – it is relevant to consider the number provided. A starting point is the rule of thumb of $200 \, m^2$ of pavement per gully, as suggested previously.

Experience in the urban area, gained in undertaking many visual surveys of pavement surface condition, shows that there is a very high correlation between blocked gullies and high levels of distress.

Figure 11.7 Gully emptier including jetting attachment
Courtesy of Whale Tankers Ltd

Another popular manner of removing water from a pavement is with the use of proprietary linear drainage systems such as the Beany block, which is shown in Figure 11.8.

11.3.4 Beany blocks

Beany blocks (Figure 11.8) were originally patented by Bob Beanland, an employee of the then West Riding County Council, who due to his employed status was not able to gain any royalties, despite inventing a drainage system which has been well used and developed in various forms.

The principle behind the Beany block (for more information, see www.marshalls.co.uk) is that of a rectangular channel which will function so long as there is a positive hydraulic gradient. The concrete block is constructed in two sections, the upper one being cast to have the profile of a normal kerb, with access holes for water. Provided the longitudinal gradient is relatively small the system is efficient, but at higher gradients the water velocity is too high to permit sideways access to the channel. This system provides a very robust edge restraint for the pavement. Detritus is progressively deposited in the channel and requires periodic

Figure 11.8 Beany block drainage system

Figure 11.8 Beany block drainage system

removal. The amount the system can accommodate is considerable as it always develops a hydraulic gradient to permit the outflow of water.

To ensure surface water flows effectively to a drainage system, the gradients listed in Tables 11.1 and 11.2 are recommended.

11.3.5 UK motorway channel

In current use on UK motorways is a longitudinal asymmetric concrete dished channel, generally 0.9 m wide, which is cast in situ and is designed in accordance with MCHW1 HA37/97.

The channel usually discharges into a catchpit and maintenance takes the form of removing detritus from the channel and catchpit.

Table 11.1 Recommend gradients for carriageways

Carriageway	Gradient 1 in	Gradient %
Crossfall	40	2.5
Minimum longitudinal	250	0.4
Preferred longitudinal	100	1
Channel blocks	150–250	0.67–0.4
Beany blocks	< 100	<1

Table 11.2 Recommend gradients for footways

Footway	Gradient 1 in	Gradient %
Minimum longitudinal	100	1
Minimum crossfall	80	1.25
Maximum crossfall	40	2.5

11.3.6 Catchpits

It is considered good practice with surface water drainage to incorporate as many catchpits as possible, especially where pipes join. The philosophy is the same as with a gully, whereby when the water velocity is slowed the ability to carry detritus reduces. Provided the connecting pipes are designed to have self-cleansing velocities, theoretically all detritus should be deposited in the catchpit and can be removed as part of normal maintenance. Figure 11.9 shows a typical catchpit detail. The bottom of the chamber should be at least 150 mm lower than the lowest pipe invert.

11.4. Piped drainage systems

The design of any pipe highway drainage system (TRRL, 1976; National Water Council, 1981) is based on the area to be drained, its assumed impermeability and the intensity of rainfall. Up to and including 600 mm pipe diameter it is not usual to consider the effects of storage capacity within the piped system. Above 600 mm diameter the system is assumed to act as a stilling pond, which assists the attenuation of the flood wave. The design principle is that of self-cleaning velocity of flow. In any drainage system there will be some detritus, which enters and is deposited somewhere in the system, leading to progressive flow restriction.

The serviceability of the drainage system relates primarily to its free running. How blockages occur and how they might be prevented are fundamental questions worthy of consideration.

Most commonly blockages occur due to deposition over a period of time, caused by low velocities of flow or discontinuities in the conduit, which may result from structural movement or the

Figure 11.9 Typical catchpit detail

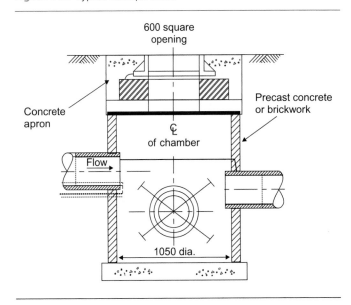

actions of others. For example, when connecting to a pipeline, the use of a saddle connection is normal. In many cases, poor construction practices lead to a restriction of flow in the pipe.

Who damaged the pipe, and did a poorly undertaken repair make things worse? It is surprising how many large culverts have smaller pipes passing through them, which obstruct free flow. If a gas pipe or electricity cable or telecom cable is damaged, the relevant utility must be called to repair it – but with a drain, that's a different story.

Drainage maintenance should ideally be planned on a cyclic basis. Unfortunately it normally happens as the result of a breakdown in serviceability for a range of reasons, some of which are

- location of drains not known
- silting up of the outfall due to a restricted outlet
- gradual silting due to low velocities of flow resulting from faulty design and/or construction
- tree roots are drawn to free water in the pipe and cause regular problems
- mining or other subsidence can alter gradients and/or cause structural damage
- foreign bodies introduced to the system. How a child's pedal car got into a highway drain is something difficult to understand
- collapse due to the effects of increasing traffic and decreasing highway conditions, causing unacceptable impact loading
- washdown due to accidents, for example acid discharge or water main burst
- litter, including drinks cans lodging on lipped pipes which, on initial investigation with rods, do not show as a problem
- illicit discharge – a gully is a very handy place for a concrete truck mixer to wash off or for a motorist to get rid of old engine oil.

Symptoms of possible blockage or faults that should normally prompt further investigation include

- backing up and flooding at entry points to the piped drainage system
- dry outfalls
- wet areas on verges
- presence of lush vegetation.

Ensuring continued functioning of a piped system needs a periodic cyclic inspection. This can comprise a series of techniques, either in combination or isolation; some of these are

- visual inspection
- closed circuit television
- jetter

- jet vac
- probe/rods
- electrolocation.

In a well-designed installation, culverts, particularly those under inaccessible features, should be sized not for minimum hydraulic conditions but for physical accessibility for inspection. Without exception they should be provided with a sloping trash rack at the inlet to prevent access by potential blocking media and, as a security measure, an anti-access barrier is placed on the downstream end. The author remembers a 600 mm diameter culvert under a 10 m deep embankment becoming blocked with a mattress, late one Friday afternoon, and water starting to pond. In cases like this, very great care and elaborate safety precautions are required to remedy the problem.

Physical access to a surface water drain must be made carefully. A formal risk assessment and safety plan must be drawn up and a vital element of this is good communications, which should be capable of dealing with toxic spillages or sudden heavy rainfall and man entry downstream of any possible accident. Communications and procedures should be adequate to ensure workers in the drain can be evacuated rapidly and in safety before any toxic discharge resulting from an accident reaches them.

When access to the drainage system is possible, elaborate safety precautions are required including a comprehensive training of all personnel involved to be capable of working in confined spaces. Gas detection and resuscitation equipment should be present and all personnel aware of the emergency procedure in the event of a problem. While it may be considered safe to enter a storm or highway drain, there is a real possibility of toxic gases formed in organic detritus deposits in the invert being disturbed by an inspection team. Hydrogen sulphide gas may be present in these deposits and can be disturbed by inspectors – with fatal consequences.

In most cases of repair it is necessary to break down the pipe, remove an obstruction and replace a section of the pipe. Consistent problems of emergency excavations is the shoring of these excavations, confined working conditions and particularly the problems of backfilling. Care should be taken and all backfilling undertaken with crushed graded stone consolidated thoroughly in 150 mm layers; alternatively, lightweight foamed concrete may be used. Inadequate attention invariably leads to unforeseen impact loading as well as causing potential danger to passing traffic.

11.5. Subsurface and subsoil drainage
This section examines all other aspects of drainage not associated with the removal of water from the pavement; it deals with the protection provided underneath the pavement, at the sides and

even remote from the pavement to mitigate the effects of ground-water movement.

The possibility for maintaining this element is at best remote and most likely non-existent. For this reason it is necessary that serious consideration is given to its provision in the first instance. Road builders from ancient times have known that water is the greatest enemy of a stable long-lasting pavement. The Romans, who started building the 50 000-mile Imperial Roman Road network in 312 BC, knew the damaging effects of water and tried to keep roads above the level of the surrounding terrain. In many of these roads, they provided a drainage blanket on top of the subgrade.

Little progress was made in the next 2000 years until McAdam (1820) made his often quoted statement to the London Board of Agriculture:

> The road can never be rendered thus perfectly secure until the
> following principles have been fully understood, admitted and
> acted upon: namely that it is the native soil which really supports
> the weight of traffic; that whilst it is preserved in a dry state, it
> will carry any weight without sinking ... that if water passes
> through a road and fills the native soil, the road, whatever may be
> its thickness, loses its support and goes to pieces.

The merits of effective subsoil drainage were commented on by Frost (1910), who observed:

> There are just three things that are necessary to get a good
> roadbed and they are drainage, drainage and more drainage.

11.5.1 Effects of moisture

During the period 1980–2010, the primary emphasis in pavement design has been on density and stability rather than durability. Since pavement designs are based on the strength of subgrades and supporting layers in a saturated position (but without evaluating the dynamic effect of wheel impacts on free water trapped in actual structural sections), it has been widely assumed that drainability is not important (Cedergren, 1974).

The major problem from a maintenance aspect is that the majority of our current main roads have been built since the 1950s and, as Cedergren uses the concept of drainability, one must wonder about their maintainability. Perhaps here is a major problem – most of our roads have no formal subsoil drainage provision. Until very recently, a survey of relevant highway design literature does not instil confidence, as drainage is something dealt with, more often than not, cursorily and any space devoted to it usually features a fairly esoteric culvert design with varying hydraulic inlet conditions without consideration being

given to maintenance. It is this neglect of the principles of whole life costing that causes much of the present funding dilemma.

As the moisture content of bases and sub-bases increases, there is a reduction in their bearing capacity, leading to a consequential increase in the rate of deterioration and reduction in service life of the pavement. Figure 11.1 has been taken from *Soil Mechanics for Road Engineers* (TRRL, 1952), but similar diagrams may be found in most soil mechanics textbooks and graphically illustrate the problem of loss of support.

Considering the effect of free water within the body of the pavement, when free water completely fills the voids and spaces or openings at the boundaries between layers, heavy wheel loads applied to the surface of the pavement induce impacts on the water comparable to a water-hammer type of action. The pulsating water pressures that can build up at such times under wheel impacts not only cause erosion and ejection of material out of the pavement, but can also strip asphalt coatings from bituminous macadams.

To assist understanding, Cedergren (1974) also suggests the concept of severity factor, which may be defined as damage per load application during wet conditions relative to that during dry conditions (Figure 11.12). If a severity factor of 20 (which is relatively low compared with values measured during experimental road tests) is used, the useful life of the road pavement is only 10% of a perfectly drained section if it is wet for 40% of its useful life.

The only significant detailed reference that the author has been able to find is Appendix SS, Hydraulic Design, Maintenance and Construction Details of Subsurface Drainage Systems, which is part of the US project NCHRP 1-37A Design Guide – Mechanistic-Empirical Design of New and Rehabilitated Pavement Structures (1) available at www.trb.org/mepdg/2appendices_SS.pdf.

The document reviews the sources of moisture in a pavement and is the source of Figure 11.1, earlier in this chapter, which has been modified slightly by the author. It is worth re-stating these factors relating to sub-surface drainage as follows.

- Water may seep upward from a high groundwater table due to capillary suction or vapour movements.
- It may flow laterally from the pavement edge and side ditches (from the surface).
- Another important source of water in pavements is surface infiltration of rainwater through cracks, shoulder edges and various other defects, especially in older deteriorated pavements.

The comment is also made that a Minnesota Department of

Figure 11.10 Subsoil drainage – alternative systems

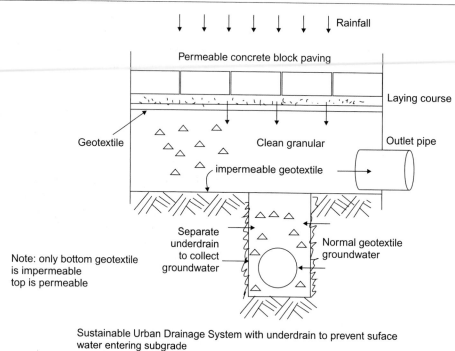

Sustainable Urban Drainage System with underdrain to prevent suface water entering subgrade

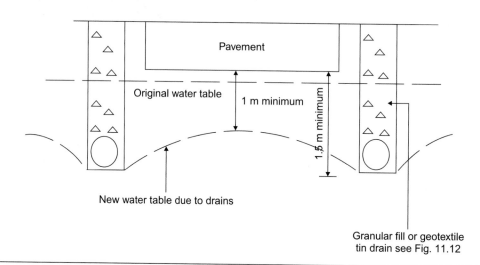

Transportation study, MN DOT (2007), indicated that up to 40% of the rainfall enters the pavement structure.

Table 11.3 sets out a list of the moisture-related distresses in conventional asphalt pavements.

Four approaches commonly employed to control or reduce moisture problems are listed below.

■ Prevent moisture from entering the pavement system.

■ Use materials that are insensitive to the effects of moisture.
■ Incorporate design features to minimise moisture damage.
■ Quickly remove moisture that enters the pavement system.

It is important to recognise that no single approach can completely negate the effects of moisture on the pavement system under heavy traffic loading over many years. Thus it is often necessary to employ all approaches in combination, particularly for heavy traffic loading conditions.

Figure 11.11 Herringbone underdrain layout

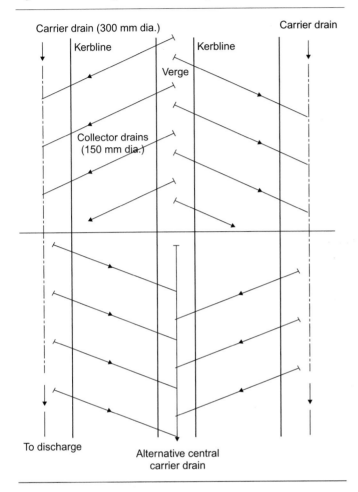

Carrier drain (300 mm dia.)   Carrier drain

Kerbline   Kerbline

Verge

Collector drains
(150 mm dia.)

To discharge   Alternative central
carrier drain

11.5.2 Subsoil drainage provision – piped systems

Consideration may be given to a permeable base, which would have a minimum laboratory permeability of 1000 ft/day (305 m/day). This layer may be asphalt treated, depending on the structural requirements, and its primary function is to lead the water to the edge drain rapidly.

This layout is conceptually similar to the old drainage blanket concept, where a layer of crushed rock with minimal fines was placed on the formation to ensure free unhindered movement of water under the pavement.

A separator layer of aggregate material (treated or untreated) or geotextile or a combination thereof may be placed between the permeable layer and the subgrade. The separator has three main functions

■   to maintain separation between permeable base and subgrade and prevent intermixing

■   to form an impenetrable barrier that deflects water from the permeable base horizontally toward the pavement edge

■   to support construction traffic.

Alternative subsoil drainage systems are shown in Figures 11.14–11.16.

The upper part of the diagram in Figure 11.11 is more feasible if the carrier pipe can be located under the central reservation of a dual carriageway where maintenance access would be possible.

An alternative layout for a piped underdrain system is shown in Figure 11.11, which was regularly used in the UK for many years to draw down the water table as indicated in the lower diagram of Figure 11.10.

Edge drains may be constructed of crushed stone, geotextile or some combination; they should have sufficient carrying capacity for the heaviest anticipated water flows. Typical details are shown in Figure 11.13. At the design stage consideration should be given to the need for access to maintain them in working order.

In the conventional crushed stone French drain option, such as is widely used in the UK, it is normal for the crushed stone filter media to become contaminated with soil fines and they are periodically replaced. Figure 11.17 shows one of the problems that might be faced in maintaining a conventional edge drain. It will be seen that the concrete foundations for the barrier are situated within the filter media of the edge drain and any attempt at maintenance requires the removal of the barrier – at considerable cost.

11.5.3 Subsoil drainage provision – soakaways

Where it is not possible to gain a competent outfall to a river it may be necessary to use a soakaway. Figure 11.14 shows a simple stone-filled installation. The simple type is shown as the concept may be used in reverse (Figure 11.15) to drain a local spring under the pavement as shown in Figure 11.16.

11.5.4 Drainage of local springs

During the earthworks phase of a project it is normal to encounter springs, which must be dealt with. This can be done by conceptually using a simple soakaway in reverse, as shown in Figure 11.15, ideally with the use of a suitably designed geotextile wrapping to prevent migration of soil fines into the drainage system.

11.5.5 Piezometer

On any major pavement project there is great merit in the use of piezometers to monitor the level of the water table. They are particularly important in any drainage investigation as they enable one to assess the effectiveness of an underdrainage system. A typical layout is shown in Figure 11.18.

Table 11.3 Common moisture-related distress in a conventional asphalt pavement

Type	Distress manifestation	Moisture problem	Climatic problem	Material problem	Load associated	Structural defect begins in		
						AC	Unbound	Subgrade
Surface deformation	Bump or distortion	Excess moisture	Frost heave	Volume increase	No	No	No	Yes
	Corrugation or rippling	Slight	Moisture/ temperature	Unstable mix	Yes	Yes	Yes	No
	Stripping	Yes	Moisture	Loss of bond	No	Yes	No	No
	Rutting	Excess in lower layers	Moisture	Plastic deformation/ stripping	Yes	Yes	Yes	Yes
	Depression	Excess moisture	Suction and materials	Settlement, Fill materials	No	No	No	No
	Potholes	Excess moisture	Moisture Temperature	Strength Moisture	Yes	Yes	Yes	Yes
Cracking	Longitudinal	Accelerates crack severity	No	Construction	No	Faulty constrn	No	No
	Alligator (fatigue)	Accelerates crack severity	Spring thaw strength loss	Thickness	Yes	Yes, mix	Yes	Yes
	Transverse	Accelerates crack severity	Low temp fatigue cycles	Thermal properties	No	Yes temp. susceptible	No	No
	Slippage	Yes	No	Loss of bond	Yes	Yes, bond	No	No

11.5.6 Water-based utility apparatus

In an urban or suburban area where there is an unexplained amount of what is apparently groundwater, consideration should be given to the possibility of a leaking water main or sewer, both of which are likely to be in the ownership of the local water company.

It is fairly straightforward to tell which by taking a water sample and submitting it to chemical analysis.

In the event of there being any chlorine present it may be assumed to be potable (drinking) water – indicating a leaking water main.

If there is any trace of ammonia it may be assumed that it is leakage from a waste water sewer, and further investigations will need to be done, having strict regard to the safety aspects of dealing with toxic chemicals.

In either case the water company should be consulted and requested to abate the nuisance caused by their leakage.

11.5.7 Bathtub syndrome

Cedergren (1974) identifies a phenomenon he refers to as the 'bathtub concept'. This is where there is no effective sub-surface or surface drainage. During a wet period the fabric of the pavement fills with water and the asphalt is subjected to the pulsating hydrostatic pressures which are generated by passing traffic.

As the water can only be removed from the pavement as the result of natural evaporation or lateral pressure some 'bleeding' from the pavement edge will be seen. In these circumstances it is necessary to install edge drains as a starting point and monitor the situation. If this is not successful, more radical measures will be required (Figure 11.3).

This is unfortunately common in many rural areas in the UK due to verges being higher than the adjacent carriageway.

11.6. Channel sweeping and fallen leaves

Reference has been made previously to the problems of vegetation blocking gullies and other drainage features. This can be a

Figure 11.12 Typical edge drain details (MCHW3 - Highway Construction Details)

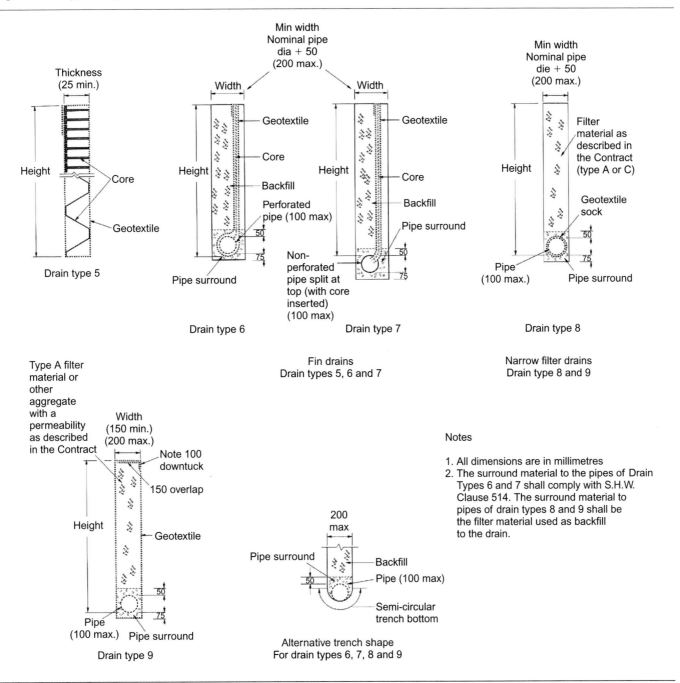

particular problem in autumn when most deciduous trees shed their leaves.

In the case of beech trees, however, which, although deciduous, retain their dried dead leaves until spring when they are pushed off the tree by the emerging new leaf, consideration must be given to the scale of this problem wherever it occurs.

The major problem here is that many of the trees involved are in privately owned land adjacent to the highway and it is not a practical proposition for the highway authority to pursue the owner to 'remove his rubbish' from the highway. Consequently an increased channel sweeping frequency should be implemented throughout this autumn to prevent blockage of gullies and other drainage features.

Figure 11.13 Effect of excess water on pavement life

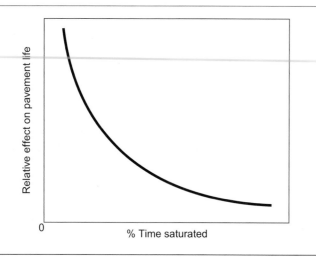

Figure 11.16 Dealing with multiple springs and soft spots

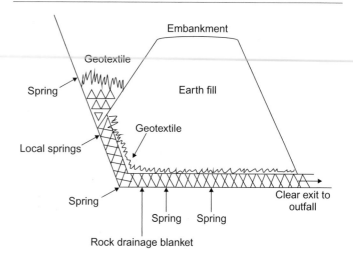

Use of rock blanket ensures no pore water pressure build up.

If springs are few and isolated it may be possible to use arrangements shown in Figure 11.14 and 11.15

Figure 11.14 Simple soakaway

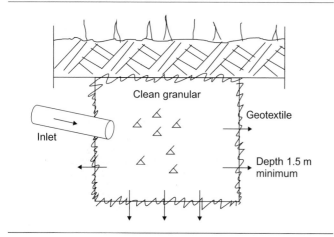

Figure 11.17 Barrier foundations in edge drain

11.7. Maintenance of subsurface drainage systems

Of equal importance to providing sub-surface drainage systems is the maintenance of these systems. Although very little can be done by way of maintenance to separate layers and permeable bases once they have been constructed, post-construction maintenance is of paramount importance for proper functioning of pipe drains, outlets, headwalls and roadside ditches.

An improperly maintained system can clog and cause the pavement structure to become flooded with excess water – a condition which is usually worse than if no system were provided at all. Some of the common problems that occur as the result of improper maintenance of sub-surface drainage systems are discussed below.

Figure 11.15 Reverse soakaway or spring basket

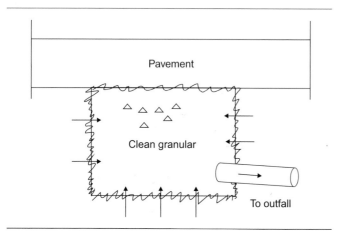

Figure 11.18 Piezometer for measuring the level of the water table

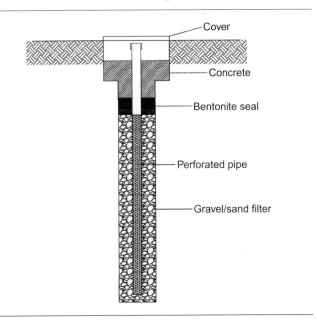

Cover

Concrete

Bentonite seal

Perforated pipe

Gravel/sand filter

For permeable bases with longitudinal edge drains

- crushed or punctured outlets that are left unattended for long periods of time
- outlet drains that are clogged with debris, mice nests, mowing clippings, vegetation and detritus
- edge drains (both pipe and fin drains) that are filled with detritus, especially at sags and slopes of less than 1%
- missing rodent screens at the outlets
- missing outlet markers
- erosion around headwalls and damaged headwalls
- shallow ditches that have inadequate slopes and are clogged with vegetation.

During inspections a variety of animal life may be found (Figures 11.19 and 11.20).

As is succinctly stated in Road note 42 (Nicholls *et al.*, 2008), there are three things to remember about drainage.

- It is essential.
- It needs to be continuous.
- It needs to be maintained.

11.8. Effects of pavement drainage repairs

The following example is based on a real project, albeit idealised somewhat, and for reasons of confidentiality the location must remain undeclared. A new major road, some 3.5 km long, was built and some parts of the drainage design in a particular area had been especially difficult, as the site was on a severe

Figure 11.19 Mouse

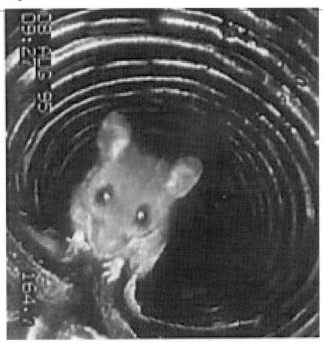

Figure 11.20 Snakes

transverse cross-slope with significant transverse groundwater movement.

As part of the ongoing monitoring of the overall design and related pavement performance, a deflectograph survey was carried out three years after opening which indicated that one particular section, some 800 m long, had a very low residual life which could not be explained following an examination of the design and construction records. Subsequent to a detailed pavement and drainage investigation, which included the measurement of water inflows and outflows in the section under consideration, it was found that the outflow from the drainage system along the length under investigation was lower than on adjacent sections. Modifications were subsequently made to the drainage system, which was essentially an over-run to the shoulders into edge drains with catch drains on the upper slopes. This work rapidly led to an increase in the discharge at the various outfalls within the section – to the extent that they soon equalled those in 'good' areas where the residual life was considered acceptable.

Two years after these works were completed a further deflectograph survey was undertaken, and it became apparent that there had been a significant improvement in the residual life along the length of the section, as is shown in the Figure 11.21.

The conclusion that may be drawn from this project is that the original drainage installation had not fully dealt with the existing volume of groundwater, and this had led to a saturated formation. Once the modifications were completed and a period elapsed such that equilibrium moisture content was allowed to develop, the bearing capacity of the previously poorly performing section increased to an acceptable level, compatible with that of the remainder of the road.

11.9. Rational budget

There are three levels of argument to consider

- the overall highway maintenance budget
- the relative priority of drainage within it
- the economic consequences of damage due to flooding.

The starting point is a comprehensive inventory of what is to be maintained together with any information available to quantify the consequences of danger or flooding due to inadequate

Figure 11.21 Effect of drainage repair on pavement residual life

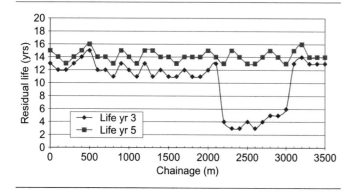

functioning. The following information may be appropriate once decisions have been taken regarding locational referencing.

11.10. Drainage – a relevant inventory

The list given in Table 11.4 is in alphabetic rather than priority or relevance order.

There should ideally be a list of high-risk locations and a maintenance profile for each feature, together with a statement of its necessary serviceability.

Regrettably, in many highway authorities, both national and local, there is a substantial absence of comprehensive drainage records. The collection of this information is time consuming and costly. For this reason a number of authorities take the view that until flooding occurs they will not attempt to create a comprehensive inventory of drainage systems. Realistically, this may be argued to be a derogation of their fiduciary duty.

11.11. Inspection frequencies

The idealised frequency for inspection of drainage systems is set out in Table 11.5, taken from the Highways Agency (1999) *Trunk Road Maintenance Manual*.

Table 11.4 Typical drainage inventory
From Highways Agency 1999 © Crown copyright 1999

1	Area drained	Location, dimensions, topography, impermeability
2	Balancing ponds	Location, size, construction, capacity, retention period
3	Catchpits	Location, dimensions, construction
4	Channel blocks	Location, length
5	Culverts	Location, depth, dimensions, construction, gradient
6	Ditches	Location, chainage, dimensions, ownership
7	French drains	Location, chainage, length, width, depth, materials
8	Grips	Location, chainage, length, width, depth
9	Gullies	Location, chainage, number, type, position
10	Kerbs	Location, chainage
11	Manholes	Location, construction, dimensions, features
12	Outfalls	Location, size, gradient, construction, external factors
13	Pipes	Location, depth, construction, size, gradient
14	Shared facilities	Details

Table 11.5 Typical inspection return periods
From Highways Agency 1999 © Crown copyright 1999

Feature	Inspection	
	Frequency	Method
Piped systems	10 years	CCTV
Gullies, catchpits, interceptors	Annual	Remove detritus
Grips	Annual	Remove detritus
Ditches	5 years	Remove detritus
Filter drains	5 years	CCTV
Culverts	Annual	CCTV or walkthrough
Balancing ponds	6 monthly	Spring and autumn
Headwalls, aprons	Annual	Visual
Flooding	Safety inspection	Visual

11.12. Records

It is necessary to have some form of record system to log any malfunctioning of the system. If this information is available over a period of time and can be correlated to maintenance expenditure and inventory, it will help in developing a probabilistic funding argument that can be incorporated into a zero-base funding bid.

REFERENCES AND BIBLIOGRAPHY

Aziza P (2002) Evaluation of water flow through pavement systems. University of Florida, for MN DOT Office of Materials and Road Research, Maplewood, MN.

Bernsten G and Saaranketo T (2005) Drainage on low volume roads. Roadex II Northern Periphery, Inverness. http://www.roadex.org/uploads/publications/docs-RII-EN/2_6%20Drainage_l.pdf (accessed 23/07/2011).

Caltrans (2006) Highway Design Manual, Chapter 650: Pavement drainage. California Depart of Transportation, Sacramento, CA. http://www.dot.ca.gov/hq/oppd/hdm/pdf/chp0650.pdf (accessed 21/07/2011).

Cedergren HR (1974) Drainage of Highway and Airfield Pavements. Wiley, New York.

Cedergren HR (1987) Seepage, Drainage and Flow Nets. Wiley, New York.

Croney D and Croney P (1997) Design and Performance of Road Pavements, second edition. McGraw-Hill, New York.

DMRB (2006) Design Manual for Roads and Bridges, Volume 4, Section 2, Drainage, Part 3 – HD33/06 – Surface and Subsurface Drainage Systems for Highways. TSO, London.

DMRB (2011) Design Manual for Roads and Bridges, Volume 4, Section 2, Part 4 - HA37/97 - Hydraulic Design of Road-edge Surface Water Channels, The Stationary Office London.

FHWA (Federal Highway Administration) (2002) Construction of pavement subsurface drainage systems: participants' notebook. FHA, Washington, DC.

Frost H (1910) The Art of Roadbuilding. Scientific Press, Brooklyn, NY.

Hagen MG and Cochran GR (1996) Comparison of pavement drainage systems, report no. NM/RD-95/28. Minnesota Department of Transportation, St Paul, MN.

Highways Agency (1999) Trunk Road Maintenance Manual: Volume 2 – Routine and Winter Maintenance Code, Chapter 1.7, Highway Drainage. TSO, London.

Kdot (Kansas Department of Transportation) (2008) Design Manual vol. 1 (part C), Road section – Elements of drainage and culvert design. Kdot, Topeka, KS.

McAdam JL (1820) Report to the London Board of Agriculture. London.

MN DOT (Minnesota Department of Transportation) (2007) Pavement Manual. Chapter 5: Drainage. St Paul, MN.

National Water Council (1981) Standing Technical Committee report no. 31: Wallingford procedure for design and analysis of urban storm drainage. DoE, London.

NCHRP (National Cooperative Highway Research Program) (1997) Pavement subsurface drainage systems, NCHRP synthesis report no. 239. Transportation Research Board, Washington, DC.

NCHRP (National Cooperative Highway Research Program) (2001) 1-37A Design Guide – Mechanistic-Empirical Design of New and Rehabilitated Pavement Structures. Appendix SS: Hydraulic Design, Maintenance and Construction Details of Subsurface Drainage Systems. NCHRP, Washington, DC.

Nevada Department of Transportation (2006) Drainage Manual, 2nd edn. Carson City, NV.

Nicholls JC, McHale MJ and Griffiths RD (2008) Road note 42: Best practice guide for durability of asphalt pavements. TRL, Wokingham.

Queensland Department of Transport and Main Roads (2010) Road Drainage Manual. Queensland, Australia.

Slater RJ (1988) Highway Design and Construction, 2nd edn. Macmillan, London.

Texas DOT (2009) Hydraulic Design Manual. Austin, TX. http://onlinemanuals.txdot.gov/txdotmanuals/hyd/index.htm (accessed 22/07/2011).

Thagsen B (ed.) (1996) Highway and Traffic Engineering in Developing Countries. Spon, London.

TRL (2006) TRL report PPR 082: A study of water movement in road pavements. TRL, Wokingham.

TRRL (1952) Soil Mechanics for Road Engineers. HMSO, London.

TRRL (1976) Road note 35: A guide for engineers to the design of storm sewer systems. HMSO, London.

Watson J (1989) Highway Construction and Maintenance. Longman, London.

Deterioration and Maintenance of Pavements
ISBN: 978-0-7277-4114-1

ICE Publishing. All rights reserved
http://dx.doi.org/10.1680/dmp.41141.141

Chapter 12
Structural Condition Data Collection

12.1.   Introduction

A simple and convenient method to assess the structural integrity of pavements is to apply a load to the surface and measure the resulting deflection. In this chapter a variety of methods for measuring pavement deflections to obtain information about the structural condition and load-carrying capacity of pavement systems are examined.

Pavement deflection measurement techniques are numerous and can be categorised according to the characteristics of the load applied to the pavement surface.

Static measurements with a loaded plate were, from the 1930s, used in the application of basic soil mechanics principles to develop bearing capacity evaluations for the design of building foundations. This process was used in the early stages of pavement engineering, as attempts were made to develop a rationale for the carrying (bearing) capacity of the pavements structure. (First generation.)

Very slow-moving load deflection measurement, which originated with the development in the late 1940s of the Benkelman Beam used at the WASHO (Western Association of State Highway Organizations) Road Test in the early 1950s in the USA, represented a progression from the plate bearing test. (Second generation.)

A development of this, from about 1956, was the Lacroix Deflectograph by Laboratoire Central des Ponts et Chaussées (LCPC) in France and subsequently the British Deflectograph by the TRRL in England, from 1970. This equipment has the shortcoming that it is only possible to measure the amplitude of the central deflection at a relatively low speed. (Third generation.)

The use of a dynamic vibratory load, exemplified by the Dynaflect and Road Rater in the early 1970s in the USA, followed in an attempt to measure the profile of the deflection bowl. (Fourth generation.)

These later pieces of equipment were more mobile than the static plate loading test and led to deflection measurements becoming a routine pavement condition survey task.

A falling weight deflectometer (FWD), first demonstrated at the LCPC in the mid-1960s and developed commercially from 1975, applies an impulse loading which is a close replication of the load of a moving lorry tyre. Using a series of geophones spaced at various distances from the load, it is possible to accurately measure the shape of the deflection bowl. (Fifth generation.)

The FWD test is carried out with the apparatus in a stationary position, which impedes output and can also cause problems in heavy traffic. From 2000, work has been underway in Denmark, Sweden and the USA to develop a rolling wheel deflectometer (otherwise known as the traffic speed deflectograph). Ideally this will allow for the measurement concept of the FWD in deriving deflection bowls rather than just amplitude of deflection, but at traffic speed, once some of the formidable technical problems have been overcome. (Sixth generation.)

A halfway house is the Curviameter, which is used extensively in Europe, which measures a deflection bowl. While a moving test, it must be operated at a constant 8 kph.

12.2.   Deflection uses

Early use of deflection data typically, involved consideration of maximum deflection directly under the load related to empirical standards. Usually some statistical measure of deflections on a pavement section is compared with a 'tolerable' deflection from the section under the anticipated traffic loading. If the measure exceeded the tolerable deflection then an empirical procedure determines the corrective measures required, usually an overlay to reduce the measured deflection to the tolerable level.

Examples of this approach are the UK Highways Agency Deflection Design Method which was described in detail in TRRL LR 833 (Kennedy and Lister, 1978). In the USA the Asphalt Institute's MS-17 (AI, 2000) and Caltrans's test method 356 (Caltrans, 2004) are relevant. Empirical use of the deflection basin data, particularly in the USA, usually involves one of the 'basin parameters' which combine some or all of the measured basin deflections into a single number.

With a trend towards mechanistic pavement analysis and design, which is based on fundamental engineering principles, the use of deflection data has become more sophisticated. Complete deflection basins are used, in a procedure known as back-calculation, to estimate in situ elastic moduli for each of the significant pavement layers. Knowledge of existing construction layer thickness is necessary for this procedure.

Deflection measurement techniques are widely used for the structural evaluation of pavements. In general, these techniques are selected over destructive methods due to lower cost, less interruption to traffic, less damage to the pavement and the ability to make a sufficient number of measurements to quantify variability.

12.3. Plate bearing tests

Plate bearing tests can be used to assess the strength of completed pavements or at intermediate stages, at subgrade, sub-base and roadbase level. At sub-grade level a large plate will stress the soil to a much greater depth than would be the case with an in situ CBR test. However, the test equipment is very cumbersome and the method is not suited to the routine evaluation of the subgrades. The load/deflection curve using a 760 mm plate was described by Westergaard to define what he termed the modulus of subgrade reaction (k). It is largely for that purpose that plate bearing tests are now carried out.

The standard 760 mm diameter plate is normally about 16 mm thick. To increase the stiffness, plates of 660 and 560 mm diameter are often used on top of the standard plate. A moveable trailer, loaded up to 30 tonnes, provides a suitable reaction against which the plate is loaded hydraulically. Care is needed to seat the plate accurately and hand-levelling using a straight edge is necessary on clay soils.

On granular soils, which are difficult to level, a thin layer of well graded sand is used as a bedding. Alternatively, a quick setting plaster bed a few millimetres thick can be used. Gantries, located as far as possible outside the zone of influence of the plate and the trailer wheels support dial gauges set to record the plate settlement at four equally spaced locations around the perimeter of the plate. A proving ring, or alternatively the pressure in the hydraulic system, is used to measure the load.

The value of the modulus of subgrade reaction depends critically on the size of the plate used. Clearly plates smaller than the standard diameter of 760 mm are easier to use and they require a smaller loading rig. Established relationships are available to relate the various different plate diameters.

A typical arrangement for a plate bearing test is shown in Figure 12.1.

There has been considerable progress in the UK recently towards performance specifications for the sub-base and testing can be

Figure 12.1 Plate bearing test

Reproduced from Highways Agency, 2009 © Crown copyright 2009

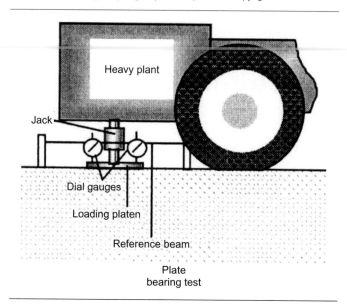

undertaken using a lightweight falling deflectometer (LWD) as shown in Figure 12.2.

Two additional geophones can be added, should that be needed, as shown in Figure 12.3.

The use of this equipment in the UK for proving the foundation surface modulus is set out in DMRB (IAN73/06 – Revision 01 2009) (Highways Agency, 2009).

That document sets out the following equation for calculating the foundation surface modulus:

$$E = \frac{2(1 - v^2) \times R \times P}{D} \qquad (12.1)$$

Where
v^2 = Poisson's ratio (default 0.35)
R = Plate diameter (default 152 mm)
P = Contact pressure (kPa)
D = Deflection under centre of plate (microns)

12.4. Benkelman beam

The Benkelman beam is a simple and inexpensive device for deflection measurements. It was developed in the early 1950s prior to the WASHO Road Test by Dr A.C. Benkelman and has been used extensively by highway agencies for pavement research, evaluation and overlay design around the world.

It consists of a simple lever arm attached to a lightweight aluminium frame. Measurements are made by placing the tip of

Figure 12.2 LWD
Courtesy of Dynatest International A/s

the beam between the dual tyres of a loaded lorry at the point where the deflection is to be measured. As the loaded vehicle moves away from the test point, rebound or upward movement is measured by the dial gauge. A long beam is essential to ensure that the pivot supports are remote from the influence of the loaded wheel at the time of measurement. The equipment is versatile and simple to operate but it is slow and labour intensive.

The geometry of the beam is shown in Figure 12.4.

Before or after the deflection measurement is made the structural condition of the pavement at the point of measurement is assessed by visual inspection and by the use of a 2 m straight edge. The latter is placed transversely across the wheeltrack and a calibrated wedge or a scale measures the rut depth.

The extent of any cracking is noted and the condition classified in accordance with Table 12.1.

In a deflection survey the spacing of the points of measurement depends mainly on the purpose of the survey. To check the uniformity and the potential life of an apparently sound length of road a spacing of between 20 and 50 m is recommended. When the survey is made in connection with the maintenance

Figure 12.3 LWD and geophones
Courtesy of Dynatest International A/s

Figure 12.4 Benkelman beam
© TRL

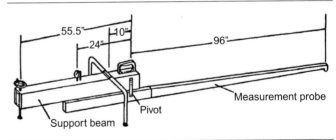

Table 12.1 Classification of pavement condition
Data taken from Kennedy and Lister (1978)

Classification	Visible evidence
Sound	No cracking. Rutting beneath 2 m straight edge <10 mm
Critical	a) No cracking. Rutting between 10 mm and 20 mm b) Cracking confined to a single crack in the wheeltrack, with rutting <20 mm
Failed	Cracking extending over the area of the wheeltrack and/or rutting >20 mm

programme of a road already showing signs of distress a similar spacing of test points is recommended with more frequent measurements around critical or failed areas. The following information should be noted relating to the construction.

While this equipment may be argued by some to be crude it is still used extensively in developing countries due to its robustness and lack of technical sophistication, and, particularly, its lack of electronic equipment.

One of the principal problems with this test is that is carried out with the cumbersome equipment seen standing on the carriageway in Figure 12.5.

12.5. Deflectograph

Automated deflection beam devices, which operate on the same principle as the Benkelman beam, were created to increase the speed of deflection measurements. Deflection beams are mounted on the load vehicle. The beams are positioned and maximum deflection is recorded automatically from test point to test point, while the operator drives the truck along the pavement.

The Deflectograph, originally developed by LCPC in France, was the prototype machine, built in 1956. By the late 1960s, it was in general use in France, monitoring the structural condition of the road network on a comparative basis. Variants of this equipment are widely used in various countries throughout the world with about 18 pieces in operation in the UK.

In 1970, the TRL purchased a second machine from LCPC to a modified format based on the early evaluation studies. The modified format for a short period became the standard for use in the UK and the TRL's first machine was modified to conform with this specification (Figure 12.6).

Figure 12.5 Benkelman beam test

Figure 12.6 Deflectograph measuring arms

In the mid-1970s, a UK version of the Deflectograph was developed and manufactured by WDM Ltd. This machine is based on a Mercedes 16/17 chassis and, in developing the equipment, the need for compatibility of measurements with previous machines was a primary design requirement. This style of vehicle, which included a large crew cab to provide a working area for the operators, is now the UK standard and has also been adopted in a number of countries internationally. The overall arrangement of the beam and the general dimensions and a section through the measuring arrangement is shown in Figure 12.7.

Figure 12.7 Deflectograph layout
Reproduced from Kennedy and Lister (1978) © TRL

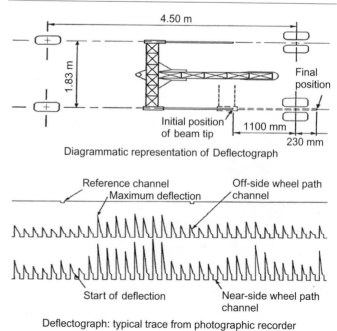

Diagrammatic representation of Deflectograph

Deflectograph: typical trace from photographic recorder

Deflection measurements are taken in both wheeltracks simultaneously at about 4 m spacings.

While it is possible to process deflections manually, as described in LR 833 (Kennedy and Lister, 1978) no details of mechanised processing are given in this text, as the Pandef (processing and analysis of deflections) system of processing which it uses is part of a Highways Agency closed software suite.

Details of the various protocols for the use of the Deflectograph and subsequent data processing are set out in DMRD 29/08 (Highways Agency, 2008b).

Correlation are available to relate Benkelman beam measurements to Deflectograph but care must be taken to ensure that the axle loads are compatible in each case.

Martin (2005) give the following for an axle weight of 40 kN:

$$\text{Deflection BB} = 1.2 \times \text{deflection DEF} \tag{12.2}$$

12.6. Dynaflect

The Dynaflect consists of a small 2-wheeled trailer carrying a dynamic force generator in the form of two counter-eccentric masses rotating at 8 Hz. The peak to peak dynamic load is 1000 lb distributed between the two load wheels which are rigid and located 0.5 m apart. The maximum deflection midway between the wheels is measured by five geophones mounted on a trailer tow bar at 12-inch intervals, which also measure the shape of the deflection basin (Figure 12.8).

The equipment has the drawback of applying unrealistically small loads in relation to those applied by lorry traffic, but there should be no need for the repeat readings that can be necessary when single pulse equipment is used. It is capable of making 50–100 measurements daily and is used in several states in the USA and until recently was used in Southern Ireland, and there are individual machines in several other countries. A further problem that has been noted is that a resonance can be set up within the pavement, which leads to false results.

Nevertheless there is a considerable knowledge base, which has been built up using this equipment and correlated with empirical performance data.

12.7. Falling weight deflectometer

Based on early work in France during the 1960s, the Technical University of Denmark, the National Danish Road Laboratory, two Danish companies, Phønix and Dynatest, developed and employed the falling weight deflectometer (FWD) for use in non-destructive testing of highways and airfield pavements and latterly heavy industrial pavements (Figures 12.9 and 12.10).

Figure 12.8 Dynaflect, layout and dimensions

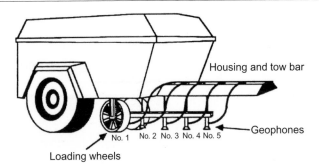

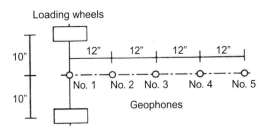

(A) The Dynaflect with load wheels in the test position

(B) Configuration of Dynaflect load wheels and geophones
Illustration of the Dynaflect (Note: 1 in = 25.4 mm)

Figure 12.9 Falling weight deflectometer
Courtesy of Dynatest International A/s

Figure 12.10 FWD deflection bowl
Courtesy of Dynatest International A/s

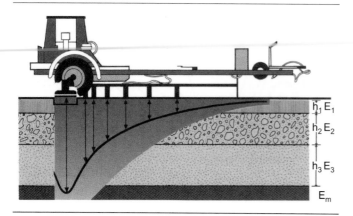

Bohn (1990) and Grontmij (2010) present interesting background information relating to the history and development of the FWD in Denmark.

There are essentially three categories of FWD relating to their capability to transmit forces to the pavement

- standard range   7–150 kN (normal highway)
- heavyweight range   7–250 kN (B747)
- super-heavyweight range   7 kN–300 kN (A380)

FWDs usually are built onto a trailer but they can also be built into a van/four-wheel drive vehicle for additional security in developing countries where a parked FWD trailer is a very attractive piece of equipment for thieves. To assist in minimising the cost of transportation by air it is possible to have a folding chassis frame. Functionality in remote areas is enhanced by the use of an independent generator and the addition of distance measuring capability and GPS tracking means that it is only necessary to hire a towing vehicle locally to be fully operational. As the acceptance of the FWD increases worldwide, the freighting of equipment about the world is becoming fairly common, particularly for the evaluation of airfield pavements. Current specification includes the provision for GPS location recording.

A major advantage of analytically based structural design methods over more empirical methods is that the former may be used with any type of material and structure and under all climatic conditions – so long as the foundation is not frozen, whereas the latter may only be used under those conditions for which the empirical relationships were developed. Most pavement research effort over the last 15 years has therefore concentrated on developing analytically based methods.

Analytically based methods can only be used if the moduli of the pavement layers can be determined. This can only be done if the test method allows for:

(*a*)   A force, amplitude and duration approximating the effect of a heavy moving wheel-load in order to allow for non-linear visco-elastic stress–strain response.

(*b*)   Very accurate deflection measurements ($\pm$ 2 microns), especially at large distances (i.e. larger than the thickness of the pavement, from the centre of the load). This is absolutely essential in order to get an accurate determination of the non-linear subgrade modulus which generally contributes some 60–80% of the total centre deflection.

Grontmij (CarlBro) based in Denmark has an up-rated HWD capable of loads up to 300 kN specifically to replicate the landing and take-off loads from an A380 airbus, which is understood to have an estimated gross weight of 560 000 kg (560 metric tons).

Tests are undertaken with the equipment stationary and a typical output of 350–400 tests per day can be achieved. Typically tests are at 20 m centres; consequently a length of about 8 km can be surveyed in a working day, subject to traffic management availability.

Further information about the FWD may be found on the US FWD Users' website, which among other things examines different manufacturers' equipment in detail.

12.8. Curviameter

The curviameter (Figure 12.11) was developed in the 1970s in France and allows the measurement of the deflection bowl generated by a passing lorry. During measurement the lorry drives at a constant speed of 18 kph (5 m/sec) and can be

Figure 12.11 Curviameter
Courtesy of Euroconsult

ballasted to produce a rear axle loading between 80 kN and 130 kN to cover the range of loading permitted in the various European countries.

The modern curviameter is equipped with three geophones on a chain (Figure 12.12). Only one of the geophones at a time actively registers the deflection bowl observed at a particular position while the lorry moves forward over 4 m at a constant speed of 18 kph. The geophone stays in place since the chain is moving in the opposite direction at the same continuous speed. The distance between two consecutive points where the deflection bowl is measured is 5 m. The geophone starts registering as soon as the rear axle is about 1 m away from the geophone's location. The geophone stops registering when the rear axle has passed the geophone's location by approximately 3 m. The signals from the active geophone are stored as a discrete graph of 100 points (Van Geem, 2010).

The curviameter is the standard pavement structural measuring equipment on the Spanish road network and correlation has been established with both the FWD and the deflectograph.

Domínguez and García (2008) reported on 30 000 km of structural surveys being completed in one year and comment on the output from the machine, which can be normalised for axle load, pavement surface temperature and a minimum deformation modulus for the formation can be set.

The Spanish standard is based on the curviameter, and a correlation with Benkelman beam measurements is given as (Domínguez and García, 2008):

$$BB \text{ deflection} = 1.4 \times CV \text{ deflection} \qquad (12.3)$$

Figure 12.12 Curviameter cross-section showing chain carrying geophones
Courtesy of Euroconsult

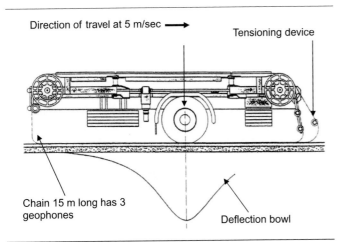

Direction of travel at 5 m/sec ➡
Tensioning device
Chain 15 m long has 3 geophones
Deflection bowl

based on the curviameter ballasted to a 128 kN axle and at a pavement surface temperature of 20°C.

In Belgium, calculations are made of layer stiffness estimates based on a three-layer model, using the deflections at D(0), D(300), D(600) and D(900) using DimMet software.

It is interesting to note that the overall concept is very similar to the traffic speed deflectograph operated in the UK by TRL.

12.9. Rolling wheel deflectometer

The RWD (rolling wheel deflectometer – USA) has been successfully demonstrated in various parts of the USA including Texas; however, the measured deflections are dependent on the speed and estimate significantly higher deflections than other devices. In addition, the device provides only one deflection measurement, which is not sufficient to identify the structural condition of pavements. Similar issues have been identified with the RDT (rolling deflection tester – Sweden). The only device that provides more than one deflection measurement is the HSD (high speed deflectograph – Denmark) manufactured by Greenwood Engineering. The device has been successfully evaluated by LCPC and TRL. The device is currently being evaluated by highways agencies in the UK and Denmark, and results from the evaluations provide an indication of whether the device meets TxDOT (Texas Department of Transportation) requirements (Table 12.2).

The device uses a deflection velocity transducer, and its limitations need to be identified as well. The device has recently been renamed as traffic speed deflectometer (TSD) (Figure 12.13).

The principle of operation is effectively a cross between a deflectograph and an FWD. One of the principal benefits being that it surveys at traffic speed, the target being 80 kph and detailed location is established using GPS.

The loading wheel produces a deflection bowl as shown in Figure 12.14 and the slope of various points on the bowl is established by velocity measurements, compared against a reference sensor which is mounted outside the area of influence of the loaded axle.

While it is unlikely that the TSD will ever measure with the accuracy of an FWD it will be considerably more accurate than the deflectograph. It will also be some 40 times faster as it will measure at 80 kph, which will remove the need for lane possession, thus considerably increasing the safety of the operation (Figure 12.15).

12.10. Road machines/heavy vehicle simulator

The heavy vehicle simulator is a system of accelerated loading of a live pavement. Available equipment is capable of applying a 20-year design load in a period of a few weeks or months.

Table 12.2 Summary of RWD characteristics
Data taken from Arora *et al.*, 2006

Device	Texas rolling dynamic deflectometer	Airfield rolling weight deflectometer	Rolling wheel deflectometer	Rolling deflection rester	High-speed deflectograph
Mfg	UT Austin	Dynatest/ Quest integrated	Applied Research Associates	Swedish National Road Admin.	Greenwood Engineering
Cost	N/A	N/A	N/A	N/A	$2.4M
Speed	1 mph	20 mph	45–65 mph	60 mph	50 mph
Readings	2–3 ft	9 ft	0.5 ins	0.001 s	0.8 ins
Load	10 kips	9 kips	18 kips	8–14 kips (40–70 kN)	11 kips (49 kN)
Sensor accuracy	0.05 mils	N/A	2.75 mils (0.070mm)	10 mils (0.256 mm)	4 mils (0.1 mm)
System accuracy	N/A	1 mil at 6 mph	N/A	N/A	0.2 mils (5 microns)
Other features	GPS	N/A	GPS	N/A	GPS
Operators	2	N/A	2	2	2
Calibration	Yes	N/A	Yes	Yes	Yes
Comment	Too slow for network level	No release date available	No release date available	No release date available	Sold 2 so far

Figure 12.13 TRL traffic speed deflectometer (TSD)
© TRL

Figure 12.14 Principle of operation of TSD
Adapted from DRI, 2002

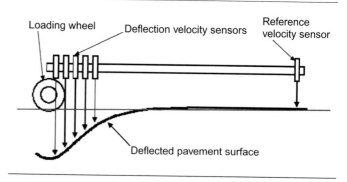

The equipment has been available in fixed form since the 1840s when an early example was developed in the UK for testing the life of various different stones for use in sett paving. By the 1930s further examples were available in both the USA and UK and consisted of a loaded wheel on a radial axle, which was anchored at the centre such that it travelled in a circular arc. Pavements for testing were constructed in a concrete trough.

In Australia and South Africa work was subsequently undertaken developing portable equipment, which could be moved by road to the test site. This clearly has the advantage that 'production' pavements rather than 'experimental' ones can be tested. A considerable difference has been found in the performance of what is supposed to be experimental, and production pavements built to the same design and specification.

The South African version (Figure 12.16) is self-propelled and known as a heavy vehicle simulator (HVS); it is extremely large and essentially consists of a truck bogie, which can be weighted,

Figure 12.15 Principle of deflection measurement by TSD
Adapted from DRI, 2002

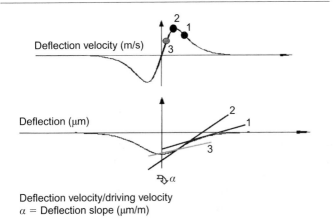

Deflection velocity/driving velocity
α = Deflection slope (μm/m)

Figure 12.16 Dynatest/CSIR heavy vehicle simulator arriving on site
Courtesy of Dynatest International A/s

Figure 12.17 Texas DOT heavy vehicle simulator assembled ready for trials

as required, running along a guide beam. The Australian version is of trailer format and known as Alf (accelerated loading facility).

A further version has been developed in Texas and, while similar in concept to the South African machine, has a greater loading capability. The machine is a trailer with a detachable upper section. When assembled it comprises a vertical flat elliptical track with a total of six full dual axle bogies and has impressive loading capabilities. It is known as a mobile load simulator (MLS) and as befits its Texan origin it is certainly bigger than its competitors (Figure 12.17).

There are very few pieces of this accelerated loading type of equipment available worldwide, although it is a rapidly expanding market, and the machines typically cost in the range $1.5 million to $2 million, depending on the specification, and are purpose-built to order.

Several countries including the UK (TRL) and Denmark (Danish Technical University) have static longitudinal track machines. In both cases the machines are housed inside a building and have a concrete trough some 3 m in depth for the construction of test pavements.

The development of design, build and operate contracts along with toll road systems requires a greater degree of confidence in pavement design, especially when built at commercial risk. For this reason the interest in accelerated loading capability is increasing.

12.11. Deflection testing by FWD
12.11.1 General considerations
The FWD is one of the tools a pavement engineer has available to describe the structural condition of the pavement. The meas-

urement of pavement deflection with an FWD is not a goal in itself, but simply one of the test methods available to assess pavement conditions.

Since the FWD has become accepted as the standard across the world against which other systems are compared the following section seeks to explain some of the more important principles and issues surrounding its use.

Before undertaking FWD measurements it is advisable to first examine the surface condition of the road and look for possible causes of the observed distress. After collecting additional information and evaluating it, a decision can then be made whether to carry out FWD measurements or not.

At network level the FWD is often the primary tool in developing a bearing capacity databank. The primary goal of FWD measurements at the network level is to be able to compare one road with other roads in the network and examine their rate of deterioration. This comparison can be based on measured deflections or on the calculated bearing capacity.

At the project level, measurements are taken on a road section with the aim of obtaining knowledge about the behaviour of that section alone; these measurements may then be used to aid the design of strengthening treatments as can be seen in Chapter 20.

Pavement evaluation (at project level) may consist of one or several of the following items

- making FWD measurements
- direct use of FWD results
- determination of stiffness moduli
- stress and strain calculations
- determination of the estimated (residual) structural pavement (service) life
- determination of overlay thickness (if needed) to achieve a defined bearing capacity.

The FWD generates a load pulse by dropping a weight through a known height onto a damped spring system mounted on a loading plate, as shown in Figure 12.18.

The mass, M, the spring system, k, and the drop height, h, can be adjusted to achieve the desired impact loading on the pavement. Peak vertical deflections are measured at the centre of the loading plate and at several radial positions by a series of deflection sensors, s. These deflections and the peak of the impact load are recorded on a computer, which is also used to control the operation of the FWD.

Using the FWD it is possible to measure the half-shape of the deflection bowl over a radius of up to 2.5 m from the centre of the loading plate. The geophones are typically numbered d1 to dn, starting in the centre of the loading plate. In some systems the label relates to the radial distance, for example d7 may be referred to as, say, d1800, which some argue is more logical and less likely to cause a misunderstanding of where they are placed. When the several layer thickness, h1, h2, h3, are defined it is possible using commercially available back-calculation software to estimate the stiffness of each layer (Figure 12.19).

At this stage a word of caution. Some commercially available software claims to be able to differentiate the stiffness of five or more bound layers. In the author's experience it is not possible to differentiate between the relative stiffness of adjacent bound layers if the modular ratio is less than 2 or even 3.

The stiffness of a bituminous layer depends on the loading speed, and hence the response of a pavement depends on the pulse shape of the applied load. If the load pulse is to simulate a moving vehicle it should have a rise time (zero to maximum) which is approximately equal to the rise time of a moving wheel load.

Most FWDs have a load rise time from start pulse to peak of between 5 and 30 milliseconds and have a load pulse base width of between 20 and 60 milliseconds. The great benefit of the FWD is that the rise time is a reasonable replication of an HGV travelling at 30 mph.

If the applied rise time of the load time of the load differs significantly from the load rise time of the wheel load of the moving traffic to be simulated, a correction can be applied to the calculated stiffness of the bituminous layer.

Figure 12.18 Schematic diagram of an FWD
Courtesy of TRL

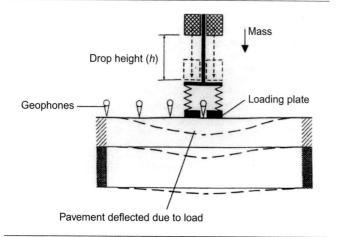

Figure 12.19 Concept of FWD deflection bowl shape

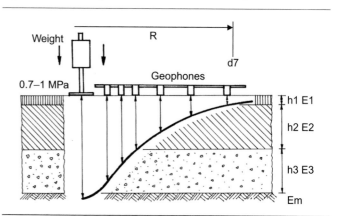

This is the case with the Nottingham Asphalt Tester (NAT) and it is possible to derive a correction factor to relate one to the other. With the NAT the loading time is longer, which means that the calculated modulus is lower than that from an FWD. The actual multiplier depends, among other things, on the individual mix characteristics. As general guidance in the UK, with typical mixes used on the national roads, the Highways Agency recommends the use of 1.5 multiplier such that:

$$NAT \times 1.5 = FWD \qquad (12.4)$$

The number and position of the deflection sensors (geophones) is a matter of some debate. An absolute minimum of six is recommended but there is merit in having more: later FWDs normally have nine. Dynatest edition 25 data capture software is capable of handling 15, as does the Elmod 6 (evaluation of layer moduli and overlay design) analysis software. The latest Grontmij (CarlBro) equipment claims to be capable of working with up to 18 geophones.

The layout (radial spacing) for the deflection sensors is in multiples of the loading plate diameter (300 mm). Ideally, there should be additional sensors nearer the loading plate to facilitate better modelling of the stiff (bound) layers, and the outer spacing should reach 2100 mm to better model the effects of the sub-grade. The idealised location for a range of flexible pavements is set out below using nine sensors and it will be seen that this can also be used with a 450 mm diameter loading plate for airfield work:

0 300 450 600 900 1200 1500 1800 2100 mm

Some commentators advocate the use of different arrangements depending on the strength of the pavement but if the analysis program will cope with nine or more then the above spacings can be standardised. The arrangement is quite different for rigid pavements, especially for joint testing, and this is dealt with separately in Figure 12.3.

If nine or fewer geophones are available a pavement may be categorised as follows:

a strong pavement $d0 \leqslant 500\ \mu m$
a moderate pavement $d0 > 500\ \mu m \leqslant 1000\ \mu m$
a weak pavement $d0 > 1000\ \mu m$

A seismic transducer (geophone) can assess the dynamic deflections measured by a FWD and various options are available

- 'seismometers' (seismic displacement transducers)
- 'geophones' (seismic velocity transducers)
- accelerometers.

Seismometers typically used are a linear variable differential transformer (LVDT) as the displacement sensing element, monitoring the movement of the seismometer housing in respect to a spring suspended (seismic) mass.

A geophone is mechanically similar to a seismometer, but monitors the velocity of its case/housing in respect of the seismic mass, by means of an electrical coil (normally integral with the seismic mass) moving in the field of a permanent magnet (normally integral with the case/housing). It should be noted that velocity (dV) integrated by time (dT) equals distance: consequently it is possible to calculate the deflection of the pavement at each geophone location. From which the shape of the deflection bowl is defined.

When a survey is taking place it is usual to fix the location of the test point by lane position and elapsed chainage. The distance measuring accuracy should be:

$\pm\ 0.5\%$ of length measured or $\pm\ 1m$
(whichever is the greater)

While this may appear simple, in practice it is regularly found to be a major problem of locational referencing, which with the advent of production capable GPS is much less difficult than has been the case in the past. On some projects where different contactors have collected different datasets it is not unknown for the reconciliation of locational referencing to occupy one person for one or more weeks.

The normal survey location is in the nearside wheeltrack and in some cases if comparative data are required then measurements are taken between the wheelpaths. In this latter case it is usual to assume that there has not been any loading between the wheelpaths. This is not strictly true but the assumption is sufficiently credible to be acceptable.

Test spacing is normally 20 m for project level investigation with the caution that there should be a minimum of 12 points in any one section to ensure statistical validity of the measured data; for example, if the section is only 120 m in length then the test spacing should be set at 10 m.

In rural areas and for general network classification larger spacings are acceptable. If the conditions are fairly uniform a maximum of 100 m could be used.

In rural locations in developing countries, where the project may require the evaluation of long lengths of road, up to 1200 km is not unknown; then the challenge is to investigate the overall longitudinal variation. In these circumstances spacings of up to 0.5 km have been used successfully.

The main problem is to have sufficient data to be able to split the section into reasonably homogeneous sub-sections for the purpose of modelling. This depends on the variability of the pavement and an indication of this can be gained from consideration of the coefficient of variation (COV) as follows:

Coefficient of variation = Standard deviation/mean

IF (COV)   < 20%   good homogeneity
             20–30%   moderate
             30–40%   poor
             > 40%   no homogeneity

In some countries the test is (COV) must be <30%.

If the COV is >30% then a greater number of test points should be used. This involves taking more readings until, by iteration, it is possible to achieve a COV of 30%.

While this can be time-consuming it is the only possible way to ensure sufficient test points are taken to obtain sufficient data to get statistically sensible answers.

The load level used is usually 50 kN (represents half of a 10 t (100 kN) axle) in highway applications. If, however, the outer sensors achieve a deflection of <20 μm then the significance of any inaccuracy will increase in the back-calculation process. In these circumstances it is necessary to increase the applied load in increments of 10 kN until the outer deflection exceeds 20 μm.

An alternative is to consider the heaviest axle load that may use the pavement. If, for example, the maximum axle load is say 130 kN (as is the case in France and Spain) then there may be merit in using this value.

The foregoing discussion relates primarily to the European situation. In some Gulf States and African countries there is so little control over the weight loaded onto trucks that care should be taken to examine the range of loading and select the most appropriate value prior to site testing.

It is also important to replicate as near as possible the tyre pressure of the design vehicle. In highway applications this is typically 700 kPa (100 psi), which will be seen to be equivalent to a 50 kN load when a 300 mm diameter loading plate is used. In airfield work, however, the tyre pressure can be as high as 1500 kPa and the overall tyre load as high as 240 kN. In these circumstances it is necessary to use a 450 mm diameter plate and a load of up to 240 kN – which is the maximum range of the Dynatest HWD. This equates to the load applied by a B747, which was the heaviest of all aircraft prior to the A380 Airbus. The CarlBro Prima 2100 S model FWD is understood to be capable of loading to 300 kN, to replicate the effect of a landing wheel for the A380 Airbus.

Measurement at any given test point should ensure:

(a)   There shall be no standing water.
(b)   Care shall be taken to ensure that the whole of the loading plate is in contact with the road surface. This can best be achieved by the use of a 'split plate'.
(c)   At least three loading cycles, excluding a small drop for setting the loading plate, should be made at each test point, and checks made for consistency (before analysis).
(d)   The measurements from the first drop are omitted from the analysis.
(e)   The following data must be stored for each test point :
     (i)   chainage
     (ii)   lane and transverse position in lane (locational reference)
     (iii)   drop number
     (iv)   local time (in hrs and minutes)
     (v)   surface temperature and pavement temperature
     (vi)   the peak load and deflection
     (vii)   it is recommended that the whole life-history of the load and deflection should be stored for one of the test points within each road section.

If the coefficient of variation of the previous measurements is higher than 0.3/0.5 (0.6/1.0 on gravel roads), the measurements will have to be made at 15/20 points per road section to ensure statistical validity.

12.11.2   Testing joints in concrete slab pavement

One reason for using an FWD on a concrete slab pavement is to establish the load transfer efficiency at joints, which is critical for the smooth riding of the pavement. Using this testing procedure it is possible to establish the degree of underslab voiding and consider appropriate underslab grouting remedial measures (Pearson, 1999).

Ideally a test should be carried out on both sides of a joint and, to prevent the need to run the FWD in the direction opposing the traffic flow, it is possible to fit an extension bar with two geophones behind the drop plate and to configure two on the opposite side of the plate (Figure 12.20).

This technique is also used to evaluate concrete slab pavements when considering the possibility of crack and seat as a remedial treatment. This is dealt with in detail in Chapter 17.

12.11.3   FWD – recommended geophone spacing (Table 12.3)

Figure 12.21 is helpful in that it shows what part of the deflection bowl is affected by which layer of the pavement, which allows an

Figure 12.20 Geophone setup for slab joint testing
Reproduced from Highways Agency (2008a) © Crown copyright 2008

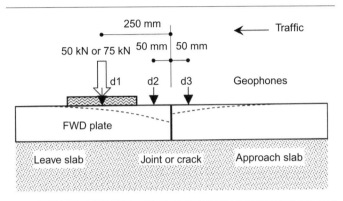

initial analysis to be made from the raw data without the need for sophisticated back-calculation software.

12.11.4 Errors in the FWD back-calculation process

■ **FWD measurements**

Errors in deflection readings are one source of error in the calculation of pavement moduli.

Errors of up to 10% in the measured deflection values translate to a comparable percentage error in the calculated modulus, with the bound and foundation layers equally affected. For example, a 5% error in all geophone readings results in a 5% error in the modulus calculated.

■ **Layer thickness**

Relatively small errors in the bound layer thickness have a very significant effect on the calculated bound layer modulus, although not on the foundation. A 15% underestimate in the bound layer thickness results in a 50% overestimate of the bound layer modulus.

■ **Temperature correction**

Errors associated with the temperature correction of asphalt bound layer modulus values to 20^0C (the standard reporting temperature in the UK) increase progressively as the measurement temperature deviates from 20°C.

For example, the error in temperature corrected modulus values was less than 10% provided the measurement temperature was between 14 and 25°C.

In HD 29/08 (Highways Agency, 2008a) the following equation was given:

$$E_{20} = E_T \times 10^{(0.003 \times (20-T)^2 - 0.022 \times (20-T))} \qquad (12.5)$$

Where

T is the pavement temperature at 100 mm depth from the surface

E_{20} is the stiffness at 20°C

E_T is the stiffness at temperature T

Figure 12.21 Typical deflection bowl shape
Reproduced from Highways Agency (2008a) © Crown copyright 2008

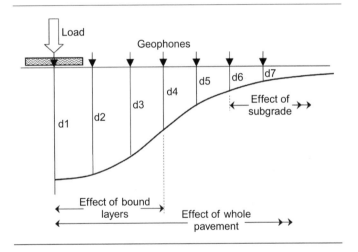

Table 12.3 Typical spacing of FWD geophones
Reproduced from Highways Agency (2008a) © Crown copyright 2008

Type of pavement	Distance (mm) from centre of loading plate						
	Inner		>>>>			Outer	
	Geophone number						
	d1	d2	d3	d4	d5	d6	d7
Flexible and flexible composite	0	300	600	900	1200	1500	2100
Rigid and rigid composite	0	300	600	900	1350	1800	2250

■ **Modelling**

A pavement should be modelled in the minimum number of layers possible – never more than three.

■ The minimum thickness of any single layer should be 75 mm.

■ Asphalt layers should be combined into a single layer.

■ Concrete layers should be combined into a single layer.

Where asphalt overlies concrete it should be modelled as a separate layer, provided neither is less than one-third of the thickness of the other.

■ **Goodness of fit**

Goodness of fit is a criterion relating to the error between the measured and calculated deflection bowls and two tests are specified in HD 29/08 (Highways Agency, 2008a) as follows:

Absolute mean deviation (AMD)

$$\frac{\sum (d_{ci} - d_{mi})}{n} \qquad (12.6)$$

Root mean squared deviation (RMS)

$$\sqrt{\left(\frac{\sum (d_{ci} - d_{mi})}{n}\right)^2} \qquad (12.7)$$

Where

d_{mi} are the measured deflections in microns at position $i = 1$ to n

d_{ci} are the calculated deflections in microns at position

n is the total number of positions (geophones) used in the analysis

Different back-analysis programs vary in their ability to match calculated and measured deflections. Poor fits can also be obtained where cracks or other discontinuities are present in the pavement, where incorrect assumptions about layer thicknesses or material types are made, or where layer is de-bonding is present.

Table 12.4 sets out guide values for goodness of fit.

Most commercial software will output this information and it may well be possible to specify closer tolerances.

Table 12.4 Guide values for goodness of fit
From Highways Agency, 2008a © Crown copyright 2008

Number of layers	Maximum value (microns)	
	AMD	RMS
2	4	11
3	2	5

12.12. Analysis of FWD deflection measurements

When an FWD survey is completed it is possible to undertake a detailed analysis of the raw deflection data before any attempt is made to calculate the various layer moduli, which require additional information such as layer thickness and pavement temperature at the time of test.

12.12.1 Raw deflection data

Table 12.5 shows the raw deflection data for a 0.32 km section of major road.

Plotting the raw deflections from all the geophones simultaneously can make an initial examination (Figure 12.22).

The first section up to chainage 0.25 km suggests a competent pavement with the peak from 0.26 km to 0.30 km which suggests there to be a problem in the second layer. This is followed by an isolated problem at chainage 0.34 km. The increase and spread of deflection from chainage 0.42 km indicates that this second layer degradation continues over the rest of the section becoming more marked towards the end of the section.

12.12.2 Consideration of the individual deflection profiles

There are alternative ways of examining this in greater detail by considering deflection profiles.

d1 represents the response of the whole pavement and is similar to the amplitude of deflection measurement which would be made by the deflectograph, Benkelman beam and curviameter.

d7 represents the response of the sub-grade (foundation) and is particularly relevant when looking for soft spots, which may well

Figure 12.22 Plot of raw deflection data from all geophones

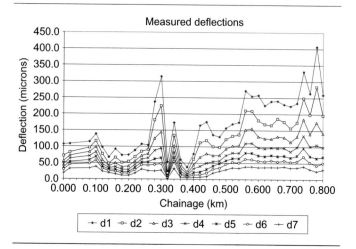

Table 12.5 Typical deflection measurement output at 20 m centres from an FWD

km	d_1	d_2	d_3	d_4	d_5	d_6	d_7
0.000	106.5	71.3	55.5	45.3	36.7	29.5	18.9
0.020	108.0	82.5	72.3	63.2	53.0	44.8	32.1
0.080	114.7	96.7	83.8	71.0	58.6	48.3	33.9
0.100	138.0	117.0	99.0	83.1	69.3	57.5	39.0
0.120	97.4	77.4	59.0	47.2	39.5	32.8	24.1
0.140	67.6	48.2	40.0	34.8	29.7	25.6	19.5
0.160	92.2	66.6	49.7	37.9	29.7	24.1	15.9

be caused by a relatively high local moisture content in the soil, reducing its bearing capacity.

d1–d4 is usually considered to be representative of the response of the asphalt layer.

d3–d6 is usually considered to be representative of the response of the base layer.

These are shown in Figure 12.23.

The response of the bound layer (d1–d4) can be seen to follow the overall pavement response (d1) reasonably well. The response of the subgrade (d7) can be seen to be reasonably consistent except for an indication of a robust section between 0.20 km and 0.45 km. The major problem can be seen to be the base layer (d3–d6), which from chainage 0.28 km shows a significantly

Figure 12.23 Deflection profiles

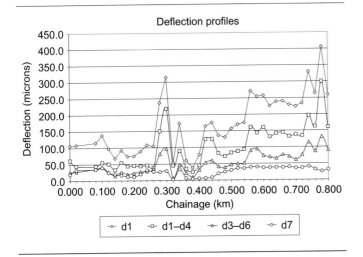

different response to the subgrade – this is a clear indication of a degradation problem in that layer.

12.13. Procurement of pavement evaluation data

12.13.1 Overall considerations

The diagram in Figure 5.1 acts as a useful checklist in assembling the various data needed for a comprehensive pavement evaluation. It should be remembered that the heavy structural maintenance of a pavement is a very expensive process, consequently it is necessary to be systematic and thorough in collecting the needed data to ensure economy and best value are achieved.

There has been a tendency since 1995 to cut down on the detail of the evaluation based on the premise that the less spent on that activity the more there will be for the actual construction works. While this is understandable, in the environment many highway maintenance practitioners currently find themselves, in whole-life cost terms it is false economy, since a properly planned comprehensive evaluation can save many times what it costs.

In those management systems not employing fundamental quality systems the literature and experience indicates that the cost of rework (getting it right) can be up to 30% of the overall. Pavement rehabilitation is no stranger to this situation, partly due to the 'this is how we do it here syndrome' – or, rephrased, 'have for as long as I can remember'. Unless the civil engineering profession asks some basic and fundamental questions then it will not move forward. For example – would you build a bridge without making serious and detailed ground investigations? If not – why is a pavement different?

Having been involved with DBFO projects where the possibility of a 10 mm reduction in overlay (15 km long × 6 lanes wide) was going to be the difference between winning and losing a multi-million pound project it is possible to understand the economic consequences of properly structured pavement evaluation. The cost of this data assembly and interpretation should be not greater than 5–7.5% of the total project cost to ensure best value is achieved on the overall rehabilitation process.

12.13.2 Detailed considerations

The following notes relate specifically to project level investigation.

The most important message in the procurement of pavement evaluation is to be systematic and progressive and not to rush the data collection.

Always try to find out what the current investigation will reveal first before moving to the next. Using Figure 5.1 as a route map the following notes may assist in being systematic.

(a) Start with a decent scale plan, for example, a 1:1250 Ordnance Survey sheet is ideal.

(b) Fix the locational referencing – do not leave this to the survey contractor(s). Ideally, have a standard 1 km length set out using a 'distamat' or similar electronic surveying equipment. A location which is straight and level is to be preferred. Do not trust a measuring wheel as no two read the same length.

(c) Any survey contractor who comes to work for you should be obliged to calibrate his digital measuring equipment against your standard 1 km length so that you know they all mean that the feature in question is at the same place.

(d) Establish and mark out the start and finish points of the section to be surveyed. Every survey contractor should be obliged to carry your observer; if nothing else the observer will learn about the process, and you will know the survey was done at the correct location.

(e) It may be convenient to do the visual survey yourself as part of the systematic process of data assembly and evaluation. The survey should be marked on the 1:1250 plan. Experience, in the urban area, indicates that the surface defects can be related to adjacent buildings.

(f) What does your visual survey tell you? Start by plotting the utility apparatus – for example, if there are lengthy longitudinal cracks do they relate to, say, a telecom track. Similarly, is local settlement likely to be utility related?

(g) Can you explain the defects from the visual survey? One of the most useful tools you have access to is a coring rig. If there are cracks, place a core on them and see how deep they go down. At this initial stage do not try to determine the construction other than in general terms with cores. For example, take one core and then a second and see if they agree and so on. In the urban area agreement will not be the norm.

(h) The next option is to commission a ground radar survey. In the invitation give the contractor as much information as you have. Additionally, specify he must advise on the number and location of correlating cores he needs after his survey. If the contractor tells you his system is so good that he does not need

correlating cores – cross him off your list! The GPR survey is usually carried out at traffic speed and does not normally require traffic management. Based on your preliminary cores try to be clear what you are looking for – even at this early stage.

(i) Prior to the drilling of the cores consideration should be given to possible laboratory tests from samples from the cores. This can make interesting comparisons with the FWD-derived data and also provide guidance on the transfer function, which may be used as it provides details of the state of the bound layers.

(j) As part of the process of taking the cores, the use of the DCP should be specified to get an indication of the thickness of the granular layer and the bearing capacity of the subgrade. These can be compared with the FWD results at a later stage. A note of caution – beware utilities in urban areas!

(k) The ground radar contractor should be required to submit coloured 'slice' diagrams, clearly showing his findings and illustrating the location of the correlating cores.

(l) The ground radar contractor should be required to submit in spreadsheet format the layer thicknesses at 20 m intervals to accord with the FWD survey pitch and location.

(m) You now have a clear idea of what the surface defects are and what the construction is.

(n) Next is the deflection survey undertaken using an FWD. The FWD will need traffic management of some sort, although in the urban area it is usually found to be safer to work during the night – which needs less formal traffic management (TM). The author's preference is to have the TM provided directly by the highway manager, or at least to specify what is needed so that the contractors are not encouraged to 'nip in and out quickly'.

(o) The FWD contractor will need to have the construction data from the cores, and the GPR contractors' output, as this is fundamental in the back-calculation process if this is to be part of the contract. Some organisations are moving towards own data-processing using supplied deflection measurements.

(p) Ensure the FWD contractor provides a site log comprising the following information:
  (i) FWD data file references and direction tested.
  (ii) Distances surveyed in each direction. It is not unusual to get a different distance in each direction due to road curvature.
  (iii) Details of weather.
  (iv) Any problems encountered.
  (v) Location and time of all temperature measurements taken – make sure you specify that both air temperature and pavement temperature at 100 mm into the pavement should be taken every hour.

(q) Specify that you are to be supplied with a copy of the raw deflection data files in electronic format. Why you need them is your business, but it will catch the contractor's attention.

(r) The contractor should be asked to specify which back-calculation program he will use and why.

(s) The contractor should be required to declare what transfer function he has used to relate strains to number of loads and the E1 moduli assumption made in deriving the needed overlay.

(*t*) The contractor should be asked to specify what temperature correction function he has used to declare all asphalt stiffness estimates at 20°C.

(*u*) The contractor should be required to provide a spreadsheet copy of his back-calculation results with graph plots for both sides of the road of the moduli, namely:
   (i) asphalt
   (ii) sub-base
   (iii) subgrade.
   The plots should be shown referenced from the same origin.

(*v*) The contractor should define how he has chosen the 'reasonably homogeneous sections' and provide a table showing the following:
   (i) Asphalt   mean and 15th percentile moduli
   (ii) Sub-base   mean and 15th percentile moduli
   (iii) Subgrade   mean and 15th percentile moduli
   (iv) Residual life mean and 15th percentile moduli
   (v) Overlay   mean and 85th percentile moduli

A correlation check should be made between the visual survey and the needed overlay recommended by the FWD contractor. In the event of there not being a good correlation this should be investigated.

12.13.3 Final thoughts

There are two options for procuring pavement evaluation.

Either a controlled stepwise process such as has been described above – which is the author's preference as there is the opportunity to use this as training and development for your staff.

Alternatively, it is possible to let the whole process to a single contractor who will procure his own visual survey, coring, GPR and traffic management.

In the author's view this second alternative leads to unquestioning reliance on specialists, some of whom are more interested in the commercial aspects of the process rather than attempting to derive best value in pavement maintenance – despite their claim to do so.

REFERENCES AND BIBLIOGRAPHY

Abatech (2011) DAPS (Deflection analysis of pavement structures). http://www.abatech.com/DAPS.htm (accessed 18/07/2011).

AI (Asphalt Institute) (2000) MS-17: Asphalt overlays for highway and street rehabilitation. AI, Lexington, KY.

Arora J, Tandon V and Nazarian S (2006) Project summary report 0–4380-S: Feasibility study for continuous deflection testing for Texas pavements at near highway speeds. Center for Transportation Infrastructure Systems, Austin, TX. http://ctis.utep.edu/publications/Reports/4380%20Project%20Summary%20reportlatest.pdf (accessed 17/07/2011).

Bohn AO (1990) A history of the falling weight deflectometer (FWD). http://sites.grontmij.dk/Pavement-consultants-com/About-us/Fwd-history/Documents/HistoryOfFWD_AxelOBohn.pdf (accessed 18/07/2011).

Caltrans (2004) Test no. 356: Method of test to obtain flexible pavement deflection measurements for determining pavement rehabilitation requirements. California DOT, Sacramento, CA.

Crow E (1998) Deflection profile – not a pitfall anymore. Record 17. Fehrl, Brussels.

Domínguez FS and García JAR (2008) 30,000 km of structural surveys in one year. Challenges of a large road network, auscultation and management. 7th International Conference on Managing Pavement Assets, Calgary, AB.

DRI (Danish Road Institute) (2002) Report 117: Development of a high speed deflectograph. Dri, Roskilde, Denmark.

Dynatest (2011) Elmod 6: Evaluation of layer moduli and overlay design. http://www.dynatest.com/elmod.php (accessed 18/07/2011).

FWD (Falling Weight Deflectometer) Users' Group (2011) Introduction to the FWD Users' Group. http://pms.nevadadot.com (accessed 18/07/2011).

Grontmij (1990) The story of the falling weight deflectometer – in brief. http://sites.grontmij.dk/Pavement-consultants-com/About-us/Fwd-history/Pages/default.aspx (accessed 18/07/2011).

Grontmij (2010) http://grontmij.dk (accessed 17/07/2011).

Highways Agency (2008a) DMRB HD 29/08: Data for pavement assessment, in *Design Manual for Roads and Bridges*. Highways Agency, London.

Highways Agency (2008b) DMRB HD 30/08: Pavement maintenance design, in *Design Manual for Roads and Bridges*. Highways Agency, London.

Highways Agency (2009) DMRB IAN 73/06 Revision 1 (2009): Design guidance for road pavement foundations (Draft HD 25). Highways Agency, London.

Kennedy CK and Lister NW (1978) TRRL report LR 833: Prediction of pavement performance and the design of overlays. TRRL, Crowthorne.

Martin T (2005) IR–88/05: Guidelines for road network condition monitoring: Part 3 – pavement strengthening (sealed granular pavements). Austroads, Sydney.

Pavement Tools Consortium (2005) Pavement guide. http://training.ce.Washington.edu (accessed 17/07/2011).

Pearson DI (1999) Industrial floor slabs: towards a performance specification. *Proceedings of the 3rd European Symposium on Performance and Durability of Bituminous Materials and Hydraulic Stabilised Composites, University of Leeds*. Aedification, Zurich.

Ullidtz P (1987) *Pavement Analysis*. Elsevier, Oxford.

Ullidtz P (1998) *Modelling Flexible Pavement Response and Performance*. Polyteknisk Forlag, Lyngby, Denmark.

Van Geem C (2010) Overview of three interpretation techniques based on measurement of deflections and curvature radius with the Curviameter. 6th FWD Users' Group Meeting, Sterrebeck.

WASHO (Western Association of State Highways Organizations) (1954) WASHO road test – part 1: design, construction, and testing procedures. Transportation Research Board, Washington, DC.

Deterioration and Maintenance of Pavements
ISBN: 978-0-7277-4114-1

ICE Publishing. All rights reserved
http://dx.doi.org/10.1680/dmp.41141.159

Chapter 13
Repair and Maintenance – Asphalt Pavements

13.1. Introduction

The repair of any pavement may be generated by one of several forms of inspection, either independently or as part of larger programmed works. The issue dealt with here, primarily, is items of work which, although they have a relatively modest value, nevertheless add up to a programme to maximise efficiency. While the character of work may vary the process of inspection and programming will be found to be universal. The strengthening of pavements is dealt with in Chapter 20.

13.2. Inspections
13.2.1 Typical inspection frequencies (see Table 13.1)

In order that the need for maintenance is properly assessed and that safe passage for road users is maintained, it is necessary to carry out regular surveys and inspections. These surveys and inspections fall into three categories.

13.2.1.1 Safety inspections

These are designed to identify those defects that are likely to create a danger or serious inconvenience to the public and therefore require immediate or urgent attention. They are normally carried out from a slow-moving vehicle with the occasional need to proceed on foot.

13.2.1.2 Detailed inspections

These inspections are designed primarily to establish the programme of routine maintenance tasks not requiring urgent execution. Condition surveys may provide contributory information to and reduce the scope of detailed inspections. They are normally carried out on foot although in some circumstances it may be possible to undertake the inspection from a slow-moving vehicle.

Table 13.1 Inspection frequencies
Data taken from RLG, 2005

Inspection/survey interval			
Category	Condition	Detailed	Safety
Roads			
2 Strategic routes	1 year	6 months	1 month
3(a) Main distributor	1 year	6 months	1 month
3(b) Secondary distributor	1 year	1 year	1 month
4(a) Local inter-connecting roads	Depends on findings of detailed	1 year	3 months
4(b) Local access roads	and safety inspections	5 years	1 year
Footways			
I Main shopping areas	N/A	12 months	1 month
II Busy urban areas	N/A	12 months	3 months
III Other urban and busy rural	N/A	3 years	6 months
IV Little-u rural	N/A	5 years	1 year

13.2.1.3   Condition inspections

Condition inspections are primarily intended to identify deficiencies in the fabric of the highway which, if untreated, are likely to adversely affect its long term performance and serviceability.

13.2.2   Warning/intervention (investigatory) levels

Table 13.2 sets out a typical recommendation for the standards of maintenance for whole carriageway minor deterioration (RLG, 2005).

Surface treatment covers all forms of surface sealing techniques, including patching, surface dressing using normal or special aggregates and binders, thin coatings with dense material and, in extreme cases of traffic loading, re-laying or overlaying the road surface layers.

Surface treatment should be considered when the warning levels set out in Table 13.2 are reached (or close to being reached).

Note 1   Whole carriageway minor deterioration covers: fine crazing, permeable surfaces, fretting, loss of chippings and fatting up of existing surface dressings.

Note 2   With the commercial introduction of a range of improved binders and chipping application techniques, surface treatment should be seriously considered as an alternative to resurfacing on all categories of road when minor carriageway defects emerge.

Note 3   Patching, either in isolation or prior to surface treatment, should always be carried out where required to ensure a uniform surface with the remainder of the road and to remove isolated weak areas.

Note 4   Patching repairs should be considered when the repairs are those resulting primarily from ageing or thermal stresses and as such lead either to a poor ride or a permeable pavement. The objectives, therefore, are to maintain the impermeability of the surface course and at the same time provide a smooth ride.

Once a certain level of roughness has been reached the rate of structural deterioration caused by commercial vehicle axles in-

Table 13.2 Typical investigatory level
Data taken from RLG (2005)

Category to which applicable	Limitation or severity	Percentage of area	Treatment
2–4	Note 1	20%	Surface treatment

creases at an exponential rate due to dynamic effects rather than those related simply to the flow of traffic.

Bituminous pavements and concrete pavements are considered separately, as the character of work is fundamentally different.

The character of work envisaged in this chapter covers a range including

■   patching
■   surface dressing
■   retread
■   resurfacing.

This area is one of considerable innovation at the present time. Many of the products are proprietary ones and as such it is difficult to obtain much information about them.

13.3.   Damage and distress in asphalt surfaces

The following sets out the more common forms of damage and distress found on asphalt surfaces. It examines the causes, and comments on appropriate maintenance responses. Brief consideration is also given to the materials considered most suitable in each case.

13.3.1   Potholes

Potholes are the result of local materials deterioration, which has allowed pieces of aggregate to become detached from the parent body, allowing the ingress of water, which may lead to stripping of the binder and enhanced deterioration – not to mention damage to passing traffic.

A permanent repair should preferably utilise the parent material. The excavation should be cut square to the level of the course below that deteriorated. In addition to a bond coat placed on the horizontal surfaces to help adhesion, the vertical sides of the excavation should be painted with 50 or 100 pen bitumen to ensure a waterproof seal is achieved. The material used should be at worst a 6 mm dense surface course material laid to a minimum of 25 mm thickness. It is also normal to use 50 or 100 pen bitumen to paint around the edges of the joint. Care must be taken to minimise the width of this at the surface to prevent future skidding danger.

13.3.2   Ageing and weathering

As the name suggests, ageing and weathering is primarily the result of accumulated ultraviolet radiation attack and subsequent rainfall erosion. Additionally bitumen oxidation and binder hardening assists the process.

Bitumen ages from the moment that it is incorporated into a mix. This is caused by oxidation, which hardens the bitumen. In road mixes, as a rule of thumb, bitumen below a penetration of 20 is at the end of its useful life. Loss of binder efficiency and brittleness prevent the material from containing the stresses imposed by traffic, leading to the development of cracks. This process is most obvious in the surface course, where it is most exposed to air and sunlight (ultraviolet radiation). The condition can be assessed during inspection by noting changes in the colour of the bituminous binder, from the initial black to a light grey. Chippings will be more prominently exposed and many will have been plucked out (fretting or ravelling). If handled, pieces of the surface will probably disintegrate, and individual stones can be dislodged due to loss of the adhesive properties in the binder.

The surface will probably look tired and dry and can most effectively be treated using surface dressing. The chipping size and binder spread rate will depend on the traffic using the road and the hardness of the road. With harder roads smaller chippings should be used. Unless the surface is very soft, a 6 mm to 10 mm chipping is to be preferred. If the surface is cracked to a width greater than 2 mm consideration should be given to the use of a polymer modified binder, which is more elastic than normal ones.

In the USA rejuvenators are extensively used on pavements damaged in this way and this is dealt with separately later in this chapter.

If the deterioration is serious the use of retread may be necessary. This is dealt with in detail later in this chapter.

13.3.3 Rutting

Rutting describes the formation of depressions or tracks in the pavement surface caused by wheel loads and high temperatures, combined with the character and design of the carriageway surfacing. Rutting is especially apparent in areas of high stress such as

- the approach to traffic signals
- channelised locations such as bus lanes
- the slow lane of major roads, especially uphill sections which carry a large number of commercial vehicles
- bus stations and industrial yards.

The greater the loads imposed on the pavement, the slower the loading rate and the higher the traffic-induced temperature, the greater will be the rutting tendency. Ruts of over 100 mm depth have been seen in the Middle East at the stop line of traffic signals, caused by grossly over-loaded commercial vehicles combined with pavement temperatures above 75°C, which far exceeds the softening point of the binder.

Rutting associated with longitudinal wheeltrack cracking is usually considered to be a structural defect whereas heat-induced (plastic flow) rutting is not.

If the rutting is confined to the surface it will be necessary to remove and replace the surface course. In the case of a major road, the use of hot rolled asphalt surface course or a 10 mm dense asphalt concrete mix could be used.

In exceptional circumstances it may be necessary to use a mix with rut-resistant properties. This may be achieved by the use of special mix grading and/or the addition of polymer modified binders. A grouted Macadam may also be used.

If the rutting affects the several layers of construction this indicates a failure of the subgrade and reconstruction will be required. The actual construction required depends on the traffic loading and level of foundation support, and is dealt with in Chapter 18.

13.3.4 Deformation

The term 'deformation' is often wrongly used as an alternative to rutting, but it is a term which should apply to a more general distortion, which can be due to a variety of causes. It can be caused by the same processes as rutting, but also, for example, be due to frost heave. In frost-susceptible sub-bases, frost heave deformation can be spectacular and has been observed on a newly constructed carriageway which left the road in a sine wave condition, longitudinally varying from peak to trough by 300 mm. In this instance, the road returned to its 'as constructed' level after thawing.

If a pavement is stressed beyond its load-bearing capacity locally, or if the load-bearing characteristics of the subgrade vary, parts of the whole pavement can deform differentially. If laying machinery is allowed to work on the foundation, which is unable to support the loads imposed by the laying process, damaging deformation will occur. If delivery vehicles are seen to cause rutting and deformation of the subgrade prior to the asphalt layers being placed, action must be taken either to improve the compaction, or replace the subgrade material before proceeding with black-top.

Deformation is usually the sign of underlying failure, possibly settlement of an old excavation or of a subgrade failure, possibly due to overloading. Partial or total reconstruction is usually needed.

13.3.5 Pushing or shoving

Pushing or shoving can be related to rutting and deformation, again occurring in areas of high stress. It can cause the material to flow and fold up on itself. This condition may indicate that the binder is too soft, leading to plastic flow under traffic, or, more rarely, can be due to regular fuel/oil spillage, which has softened the material locally. Pushing is often confined to the wearing course, but the nature of the deformation needs to be investigated using coring techniques.

Bituminous material, which has pushed has usually not been able to transfer the horizontal shear forces of the tyre to a lower layer in the construction. It is the sign of lack of bond between two layers.

Repair can be undertaken by planing (milling) off the area affected, ensuring that a rough surface is left at the binder course interface. A bond coat rather than an emulsion tack coat should be used to ensure adhesion. A 50 or 100 pen binder should be painted on all vertical surfaces. The hot mix surface course, either 10 mm dense AC surface course or hot rolled asphalt, should be thoroughly compacted and sealed around the edges to prevent water entry.

13.3.6 Fretting or ravelling

Fretting affects all materials, particularly asphalt concrete, and is the loss of aggregate particles from the surface course associated with deterioration or cohesion in a material.

It is caused either by ageing of the binder with consequent lack of adhesion, or, on newly-laid surfaces, insufficient compaction or poorly-formed longitudinal joints. Failure at the joints also occurs in old pavements, and is more common in AC type materials, which rely on aggregate interlock for satisfactory performance, compaction being crucial. In any machine-laid material, compaction at the centre of the laying rip is always greater than at the edges due to the rolling pattern. Great care must therefore be exercised to ensure the matching of one longitudinal point with another and to check that the roller is not riding on the cold material.

The effects of fretting can be mitigated by the use of surface dressing or slurry seal.

13.3.7 Cracking

Cracking can be a sign of various problems. Classically, it is usually associated with an indication of failure within the pavement layer system. If the cracking is longitudinal and in the wheelpaths, this may indeed be the reason. If the cracking is multiple, and in the wheelpath, this is usually a sign of subgrade failure.

Cracking can also be due to debonding of the surface course from the binder course. This may be caused by thermal shock, or result from the lack of sufficient bond coat at the laying stage. In the latter case cracking will be in the form of blocks about 1 m square, and is referred to as block cracking. Other forms of debonding cracking are more random in pattern. This is normally the case when hot rolled asphalt has been laid over an old surface dressing.

In many rural areas of the UK it has been a regular practice for a hot rolled asphalt overlay, typically 40 mm in thickness, to be laid over extensive lengths, generally, of an ageing surface dressing. Experience indicates that after about ten years a de-bonding failure can occur and random cracking becomes evident.

One common form of cracking is reflective cracking, which may occur when cement-bound materials (and in some cases crushed rock sub-bases which have a self-cementing capability) are overlaid with a bituminous layer. This form of cracking is commonly transverse, but in older pavements, it can be coupled with longitudinal cracking.

Surface cracking due to temperature gradients on a properly designed, fully-flexible construction, is rare in the UK. However, where the load-bearing capacity of the pavement has been substantially exceeded, a form of cracking, which appears as inter-connected, irregular and segmental, will occur, but this has no connection with the reflective cracking.

It was once thought that reflective cracking always started in the base layer and worked up through the several pavement layers to the wearing course, but recent evidence of bituminous material laid over lean mix concrete suggests that this may not be the case. It is now believed that cracks may be initiated in the surface course and work downwards, and that a lean mix concrete base cracks as soon as the first layer of asphalt is laid on it.

Such cracking over cement-bound materials generally occurs in a regular pattern, and appears as a clear break in the surfacing, which opens and closes according to temperature changes. This movement can be exacerbated later by detritus filling the crack, thus causing additional stress and the breakdown of the edges of the crack, which are also subjected to damage by traffic. Sometimes two parallel cracks appear indicative of a poor contraction joint in the concrete beneath, and this often leads to bituminous material between the cracks breaking down and being dislodged.

Longitudinal cracks in a composite construction are usually the result of the lean mix being laid with a slip form paver in two widths creating a reflective crack in the surfacing over the joint between the two bays.

In the case of a fully flexible construction there is some evidence from CSIR in South Africa, as the result of experience with full-scale accelerated testing, that cracking initiates at about two-thirds of the depth of the bituminous layer due to fatigue, and then migrates to both the upper and lower surfaces (De Beer, 1998).

In industrial areas, roads which were constructed in Victorian times and contain sett paving in the construction, and which have subsequently been overlaid with bituminous material to improve their ride quality, can frequently exhibit random cracking due to a layer de-bonding failure. This is caused primarily due to a thin bituminous layer which has ceased to bond to the underlying setts and which effectively becomes a stiff plate and consequently cracks. On these forms of construction it is quite normal to find extensive multiple cracking in the wheelpaths, due to de-bonding rather than a structural failure.

On a flexible construction a single longitudinal crack, generally in the nearside wheelpath, is usually considered to be an early indication either of ongoing structural failure or of a poorly made joint. Coring through the crack and seeing how deeply it penetrates into the pavement can validate this.

One peculiarity of flexible pavements is the development of localised randomly distributed small areas of 'spider's web' (or crocodile or alligator) cracking, which is usually associated with a failure of the subgrade. It is fairly common to see this type of failure associated with mud-pumping. Mud-pumping is a phenomenon where the fine particles in the subgrade are 'pumped' upwards by the action of free water which has permeated through the cracked pavement. Mud-pumping is a clear sign of foundation failure and this can be seen by a 'fines' deposit on the surface.

All cracks allow the potentially damaging ingress of surface water and should be sealed as soon as possible, by thoroughly cleaning out the detritus and loose material, using compressed air, drying and then sealing with bitumen.

If they are not treated there is a high probability that foundation failure will occur: the only issue to be resolved is when rather than will it occur.

As a short-term expedient sealing with proprietary overbanding, surface dressing or slurry seal can be useful. The only permanent remedy, however, may be to remove and replace the surface course; if this is done, care should be taken to ensure a fairly rough surface results at the interface with the lower layer and to use a bond coat to ensure it does not re-occur.

13.3.8 Polishing

Polishing of a surface is a potential hazard, especially in wet conditions, since it will cause loss of skidding resistance and increase the risk of accidents. All aggregates polish under traffic, but the rate of polishing varies. The polished stone value (PSV) is an indication of the resistance to polishing as a comparative value against a standard aggregate: the higher the number achieved in a standard test the greater the resistance to polishing.

Polishing is usually caused by soft aggregate being used in the mix and not resisting the abrasive effect of passing tyres. For high-stress sites a high-PSV aggregate is normally specified to resist this problem. One reason for the development of hot rolled asphalt wearing course was to maximise the effect of the

minimum amount of expensive high-PSV chippings when they are rolled into the mat after laying.

Temporary relief from polishing on high-stress sites can be gained from surface dressing with a high-PSV chipping and the use of a polymer modified binder to ensure adhesion to the substrate.

In some very high-stress sites – roundabouts and braking areas and for pedestrian crossings – proprietary systems are used where calcined bauxite is laid with a polymer adhesion/bedding coat or an epoxy resin adhesive.

The availability of retexturing is growing and is dealt with in Section 13.11.

13.3.9 Stripping

Stripping of binder from the aggregate is the result of the action of free water within the layer acting under great pressure from the transient loading of passing traffic.

Most aggregates are hydrophilic (water-loving) which makes them more easily wetted by water than bitumen. A thin film of water on the aggregate surface will reduce the possibility of an adequate bond forming between the aggregate and bitumen during mixing. During the conventional hot mix process the materials are heated to around 150 to 175°C, which ensures any moisture is removed from the mix. At this high temperature the bitumen is liquid and in the absence of water readily coats the surface of the aggregate. After compaction, a hot mix material should therefore, instantaneously, possess good durability. During the mixing of cold mix bituminous material the aggregate is coated while it is both cold and wet, using a bitumen emulsion. An emulsion is a material in the form of droplets, which are held in suspension in water by emulsifying agents. Until the emulsifying agent is removed the droplets of material in suspension are prevented from coalescing with each other. Water, a substance that is undesirable in hot mixes, is used in bitumen emulsion.

To understand the importance of bitumen/aggregate adhesion it is necessary to consider their interactions in more detail. Curtis *et al.* (1993) considered a model of aggregate/bitumen interaction. This model considered three zones of interaction between aggregate and bitumen, an absorbed region, an interface and an interphase.

The absorbed region of bitumen molecules occurs within the pores of the aggregate. Bitumen molecules attached to the surface of the aggregate are in the interface region. Molecules not attached to the aggregate, but structured around the interface, were considered to be in an interphase region. During mixing, provided there isn't a reaction between the surface chemistry of the aggregate and the bitumen (or bitumen emulsion), all three zones considered in the model should be filled with bitumen. However, due to the slow evaporation of the emulsifying agent the bond between the bitumen and aggregate may continue gaining strength for several months. Additionally, some research suggests that cold mixed bituminous mixes never achieve the same strength as hot mixed materials and coupled with the use of water in the emulsion they are more susceptible to moisture deformation (stripping).

When a thin film of water separates the bitumen and aggregates in a compacted bituminous material, a state of detachment is said to have occurred. Provided the water is removed from the detached bond, the bitumen will eventually adhere to the aggregate. Unfortunately, traffic and/or environmental effects can cause detached bonds to be broken before the moisture evaporates and the mix re-adheres. One or more of the following may break a detached bond and cause premature failure of the mix

- film rupture
- interfacial tension
- hydraulic scouring
- pore water pressure.

(a) Film rupture can occur if the aggregate has sharp edges. Weak detached bitumen bonds are more susceptible to rupture.

(b) At a bitumen/air/water interface a weak or detached bitumen film could be drawn up along the air/water interface due to the difference in surface tension (interfacial pulling).

(c) Hydraulic scouring can occur as a wheel passes over the surface of the pavement and forces water into the surface voids. A moving wheel will generate a tension–compression cycle that is sufficient to break a detached bond.

(d) Water can be trapped in the mix as the material is compacted, this is more likely in cold mixed materials, which can then cause high pore water pressures as the moisture expands due to either high temperatures or freezing.

Material exhibiting stripping must be removed and replaced by new hot mix material with appropriate binder–aggregate affinity.

13.3.10 Plucking

Plucking is the loss of aggregate under trafficking, most commonly the loss of coated chippings from a chipped asphalt surface in high stress areas, such as roundabouts, but it can also be extensive if chippings are not properly embedded in the asphalt. There will always be some loss of chippings in a surface with a texture depth requirement averaging 1.5 mm. During laying, adverse weather, particularly wind, causes rapid surface chilling; adequate chip embedment can be difficult to achieve, and any 'proud' chippings will be rapidly plucked out by traffic. This same situation can occur with surface dressing for the same reasons, but is normally referred to as chipping loss.

13.3.11 Embedment

Embedment is the loss of surface texture when chippings in HRA are applied and compacted into a wearing course that is

- too hot
- too rich in binder
- a combination of these factors
- of low stability.

Embedment of chips can occur in surface dressing due to a binder layer being too thick, from opening to traffic too soon, or when over-estimation of the existing surface hardness results in the choice of inappropriate size of chipping. In HRA, compliance with a specified texture depth is normal, and excessive embedment will mean that this value will not be consistently achieved. Similarly, after surface dressing the surface may appear fatty and lack texture. In both instances the skidding resistance will be lowered, perhaps dangerously. In the case of HRA, the matrix may wear away under traffic, as it is softer than the chippings, but this would be a lengthy process and should not be relied on.

With a hot mix asphalt the surface texture can be reinstated using surface dressing but the only long-term solution is resurfacing.

Where the problem affects a surface dressing there are several proprietary methods of high-pressure water or shot blasting the surface to remove the excess binder.

13.3.12 Bleeding

This is primarily related to surface dressing, but can also affect hot mix asphalt surfaces. It can be caused by several reasons, the most common being an excess of binder in the wearing course.

A surface dressing bleeding in hot weather can be minimised by dressing with sand or crushed rock.

It can also result from an over-heavy application of bituminous bond coat onto the binder course before the surface course is laid. The effect is then to cause the newly laid material to have an excessive amount of bitumen, which inevitably breaks through to the surface. This is a problem with some SMAs where there is a flushing of binder within the matrix, which may result from inadequate distribution of the cellulose (generally recycled paper) additive, designed specifically to absorb excess binder.

In all cases bleeding may result in slippery conditions and require treatment by high-pressure water blasting or removal and replacement of the layer.

13.4. Asphalt pavements – repair types and methods

The following repair procedures identify the range of response to a number of problems, ranging from immediate requirements to the large-scale planned expenditure involved in reconstruction of the pavement.

13.4.1 Potholes

■ Remove all mud, dust, leaves and loose material.
■ Cut holes to a regular shape with all sides vertical or undercut.
■ Remove debris and any collected water.
■ Paint the interior surfaces with a thick coat of bitumen emulsion, hot bitumen or cold thixotropic bitumen.
■ Slightly overfill the hole with coated Macadam.
■ Fully compact the material in layers not exceeding 75 mm using a plate rammer or vibrating roller.
■ Seal all surface joints with bitumen approximately 50 mm wide.

A number of proprietary 'instant' pre-mixed materials are also available, usually designed to resist deformation. Whichever material is used the importance of preparation of the hole and compaction of the filling material is stressed, and for these specialised preparations adherence to the manufacturers' instructions is necessary.

Traditionally, filling potholes has been a low-tech manually intensive operation rarely satisfactorily carried out and where the life of the intervention is short. A recent alternative is spray injection pothole patching (Figure 13.1). The name is used generically here as there is a range of machines and techniques which appear to be very similar and it is not clear what patents may be involved.

The various pieces of equipment, an example of which is shown in Figure 13.1, are fairly similar and each comprise a 7–10 t truck with a hopper for aggregate, a tank for bitumen emulsion and an air compressor. A combination of air, emulsion and

Figure 13.1 Velocity jetpatcher for pothole repair
Courtesy of J.J. Farrington

aggregate is supplied by way of a counterbalanced hose. In some systems there is the capability to spray heated air, which enhances the process.

The operation is a moving one and depending on the location may well need traffic control support. This may vary in the urban areas from the use of a crash cushion and stop–go boards, in which case a total of five persons may be needed – alternatively, in rural areas, only the driver and operator may be required.

The process is comprised of the following stages.

■ High velocity compressed air is used to clean the pothole removing all water, dust and debris.
■ A bitumen emulsion coat is forced deep into every crack and crevice to improve the adhesion of the bond coat while at the same time sealing the base from further water damage.
■ Bitumen emulsion and an appropriate aggregate are mixed, then immediately compacted into the void using high velocity compressed air. The new material is keyed into the existing surface with superior compaction without causing further damage to the base.

The result is a level, sealed repair that quickly blends into the existing surface. The repair is completed within minutes and is immediately ready for traffic.

In some systems a small amount of fine dry aggregate is finally distributed to prevent the possibility of adhesion to vehicle tyres.

Some emulsion blends have been found to be more satisfactory than others, this being critical to the success of the operation.

13.4.2 Patching

Patching is a response to dealing with localised cracking, loss of surface integrity and depressions, and may be defined as the replacement of defective flexible material, laid by hand up to 100 mm in thickness to effect a permanent restoration of the stability and/or riding quality of the pavement.

Excluded from the work of patching is

■ the filling of depressions and cracks not involving removal of existing pavement surfacing
■ the sealing of pavement surfacing by the application of dry or pre-coated aggregate and/or binder unless this is an essential component of the patching method
■ the use of concrete
■ the use of mechanical spreaders and spreader boxes.

The replacement or repair of the sub-base or subgrade may be regarded as a local reconstruction. In some cases, however, it is normal to undertake isolated patching involving both the surface course and binder course to deal with areas of severe cracking.

In a well-organised company or authority there should be protocols in place for how patching should be treated and how decisions should be made. For example, there is a maximum amount of patching that it is economical to do in any given location at any one time before it becomes more economical and cost effective to resurface. This may apply particularly where some form of surface treatment is planned. The format and detail of the rules will depend on the unit cost of various activities and the contractual arrangements.

Guidelines for inspectors should be established which take account of the following issues

- regularity of patch shape
- proximity of adjacent patch(s) or kerbline
- when more than single course treatments are appropriate and how they should be used
- at what stage it becomes uneconomic to undertake patching compared with machine-laid resurfacing
- when the inspector should seek technical advice.

13.4.3   Hand excavation
In small areas where urgent work is required it is normal for the deteriorated materials to be excavated by hand using compressed air or hydraulic breakers. While this process has been extensively used there is a view that the inherent vibration from the equipment may well cause damage to the immediate surrounding pavement, as well as the hands of the operative.

13.4.4   Planing or milling
Planing is the mechanical removal of the existing surface so that the new surfacing can be laid to the original surface levels, but it does not mean that the existing profile is necessarily followed exactly, with the same amount removed everywhere. There should be an improvement in surface regularity and profile after planing, achieved by removing more on the high spots and less on the low spots.

As there is a range of machine capability, planing can be used from localised to substantial areas, to remove the degraded bound layers of a pavement.

Cold planers have drums fitted with hardened steel picks that can be adjusted in shape, number and pattern according to the material being planed or the finish required. They vary in drum width from 0.35 m to 2.2 m and achieve high rates of progress, removing depths in one pass of up to 350 mm, dependent on the material encountered. Asphalt or concrete materials can be removed and the majority of machines now produced are self-loading by way of conveyor into lorries, thus enabling material to

be removed as rapidly as it is milled. Computerised sensing devices operating from kerblines, or existing surfacing, allow precise control of the finished profile. Small planing drum attachments can be fitted to tractors or shovels to deal with reinstatement work and specialist drums can also plane to a pre-set profile.

The availability of such machines has had a significant effect on how pavements may be maintained. Figure 13.2 gives an indication of the size and capability of a machine capable of removing 2.2 m in a single pass.

13.5.   Pavement preservation
13.5.1   Introduction
Figure 13.3 sets out the general deterioration profile of a designed pavement over its anticipated life cycle, and the points at which different types of maintenance response are required and are most relevant.

At the first stage in the life cycle there is a need to consider and manage safety issues, which is principally about skidding resistance and roughness as the result of activities by utilities and serious winter conditions.

At the second stage comes the need to try and preserve the surface condition and reduce the onset of cracking resulting from both environmental and fatigue distress.

The third stage involves rehabilitation, whereby the overall bearing capacity can be substantially restored by a replacement of the surface and binder courses. Because of the effects of

Figure 13.2 Wirtgen 2500 surface milling machine
Courtesy of Wirtgen UK Ltd

fatigue in the lower layers of the pavement this may not restore the pavement to its original bearing capacity.

The fourth stage is when the pavement has deteriorated to the extent that the minimum acceptable serviceability level has been reached, and there is a need to consider strengthening/reconstruction to return the pavement to its original bearing capacity and condition.

Figure 13.3 assumes that the pavement has been designed and constructed correctly for the anticipated traffic loading and has been constructed with competent drainage.

As budgets come under increasing pressure and overall pavement conditions worsen it is natural to concentrate on responsive repairs resulting from safety inspections and maximise the amount of money available for structural maintenance. In the context of a formal pavement management system this will not be found to be the optimal use of scarce resources and the most effective spending will be found to be on pavement preservation or preventative maintenance. While this might not improve the overall bearing capacity of the network it will delay the ongoing rate of deterioration. One problem here, however, is public reaction – 'why can't they do it properly?' – this being particularly so in residential and rural areas.

The progressive move in the UK over the last 30 years to the increased outsourcing of maintenance has allowed the development of a range of new technologies. Whereas pavement preservation was once usually considered to be the exclusive role of surface dressing, the increasing use of contractors – particularly large ones – has led to the development of different techniques requiring significant investment in sophisticated plant and equipment. This has led to a greater range of possible responses attempting to arrest the ongoing pace of deterioration. Some of these are explored below.

13.5.2 Available pavement preservation processes

What may be described as pavement preservation will vary depending on the location/country under consideration, but Table 13.3 provides a starting point for an examination of the available responses and technologies.

Table 13.3 Pavement preservation: available techniques

	Process	Effect
1	Crack sealing	No increase in bearing capacity but may well benefit ride
2	Asphalt rejuvenation	
3	Chip seal/surface dressing	
4	Slurry sealing	
5	Micro-asphalt	
6	High friction surfacing	
7	Thin surfacing (<40 mm thick)	
8	Cold in-place recycling (retread)	Some limited increase in bearing capacity of the pavement
9	Hot in-place recycling (repave)	
10	Conventional surfacing (>40 mm thick)	Progressive increase in bearing capacity of the pavement

Figure 13.3 Life cycle of a designed pavement

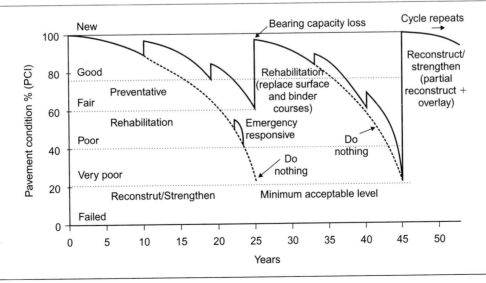

13.5.2.1 Crack sealing

The first indication of distress on a pavement is cracking of one form or another, the layout of which is dealt with in Chapter 6. This can range from single isolated cracks to multiple map cracking. The important issue is to seal the crack to prevent the ingress of detritus and water.

Crack sealing extends the useful life of the pavement by preventing the ingress of water, which would otherwise progressively gain access to the formation and reduce its bearing capacity. The presence of detritus acts as an abrasive on the edges of the crack, leading to spalling and possible compression failures. With an unsealed crack, widening by spalling is made worse by the effect of traffic.

While HD 31/94 (Highways Agency, 1994b) refers to crack sealing and also has a photograph showing its effect, the process is not as widely used in the UK as it is in the USA. In the USA, there is considerably more literature, some of which is included in the bibliography section for this chapter, and in some cases the process is used where crack sealing can prove unsightly – like a lot of black snakes on the carriageway as shown in Figure 13.4.

In many instances in the UK, surface dressing would probably be used as a response: it may be argued that a combination of these two treatments would enhance the degree of waterproofing and preservation.

The treatment preparation depends on the crack width. In the UK, typically a crack is described as narrow if <2 mm and wide if >2 mm. In the USA, however, the information from Table 13.4 is more typical.

In the UK, HD 31/94 (Highways Agency, 1994b) advises the following.

Figure 13.4 Crack sealing in Texas

- Narrow cracks can be sealed by infilling, wider cracks require surface sealing using textured skid resistant materials.
- The sealer on the surface should have a skidding resistance value (SRV) of at least 60.
- If the SRV becomes <50 the site should be investigated to consider if remedial works are necessary.
- The sealing band width should be <40 mm.
- The sealing band thickness on the surface should not exceed 3 mm.
- The sealing band should not be mistaken for road markings, particularly in high-reflective wet and night conditions.

Relevant standards:
UK   BS 2499 (BSI, 1993) or BBA certificate (BBA, 2011)
US   American Society of Testing and Materials (ASTM) D5078

Table 13.4 Treatment of crack depending on width
Data taken from Unified Facilities Criteria (UFC, 2001)

Description	Width	Treatment prior to sealing
Hairline crack	<6 mm	None required
Small crack	6–19 mm	Should be widened to 3 mm greater than its nominal width by routing, which will eliminate the potential for revelling along the edge and will provide a reservoir that has vertical faces. If the crack is >19 mm deep a backer rod should be used.
Medium crack	19–50 mm	Clean out the crack using a hot air lance or sandblasting with a final cleaning with compressed air immediately before filling. The crack must be inspected to ensure that it is clean and dry.
Large crack	>50 mm	Crack widths greater than 50 mm should be prepared in the same manner as potholes. A saw should be used to cut away any damaged pavement to provide vertical faces. The areas should then be cleaned and filled instead of sealed.

(ASTM, 1995), ASTM D6690 – 07 (ASTM, 2007), SS-S-1401C (US General Services Administration (USGSA, 1984))

If used on an airfield there is a need to ensure that the sealer is resistant to both fuel and heat generated by aircraft exhaust:
ASTM D7116 - 05 (ASTM, 2005), Federal Specification SS-S-1401C (USGSA, 1984).

13.5.2.2   Asphalt rejuvenation

When a pavement has become brittle it may be possible to rejuvenate it by applying a mineral-based solution onto the existing surface course. Typically, this may be a dilute solution including Gilsonite, which is a naturally occurring material found only in the Unitah Basin of Utah in the USA.

The resulting solution, which is sprayed onto the pavement surface, is made up of asphaltenes and maltenes to provide the physical characteristics needed for a good asphalt pavement. Weather and ultraviolet rays from the sun damage the maltene fraction of the asphalt causing it to become dry and brittle (Pavement Rejuvenation (UK) Limited (PRL), 2011).

Pavements exhibiting early signs of ageing (minor hairline cracking and moderate fretting) are excellent candidates for a rejuvenation seal treatment, which will seal out moisture and rejuvenate the asphalt to help maintain the pavement in a nearly new condition by restoring the asphaltenes and maltenes balance. The asphalt becomes pliable again as the solution fluxes with the asphalt cement, healing minor cracking, and restores the aggregate/asphalt bond.

The solution will penetrate down from the surface (the major area of damage) with depth depending on the application rate and surface porosity. Normally the treatment will last for two–three years before another application is required. To ensure the skid resistance of the pavement is maintained until penetration and curing of the solution has taken place the application of a small amount of sand may be applied, but other than this no other aggregates are required.

The pavement can be re-treated every three years, no waste is generated, and typically there is a 94% saving in CO_2 omissions when compared with hot mix asphalt.

13.5.2.3   Fog seal or mist spray

The Asphalt Emulsion Manufacturers' Association (AEMA) (http://www.aema.org) defines a fog seal as 'a light spray application of a dilute asphalt emulsion used primarily to seal an existing asphalt surface to reduce ravelling and enrich dry and weathered surfaces'. Others refer to fog seal as enrichment treatments since they add fresh asphalt to an aged surface and lengthen the pavement surface life. These are referred to as flush coats or mist sprays.

This is a technique widely used in the USA, Africa and Australia but rarely used in the UK. As with the previously described pavement preservation technique it may well be more appropriate in warmer climates where the effect of ultraviolet radiation is greater.

Fog seals are also useful in chip seal applications to hold chippings in place in fresh seal coats. They can also prevent vehicle damage arising from flying chippings. The Asphalt Institute also suggest that fog seals can seal small cracks.

On the travelled way, fog seals should only be used where there is adequate surface texture such as aged and ravelled hot mix surfaces, chip seal surfaces and open graded asphalt surfaces. For projects requiring that the pavement be opened to traffic shortly after the application of the seal, fast break emulsions can be considered; however adequate break times or cure times should be allowed. A blotter coat of sand may be used to prevent pick-up. The sand will generally be removed by the traffic leaving a good surface finish.

13.5.2.4   Surface dressing (chip seal)

Surface dressing (in the UK and called chip seal in most of the rest of the world) is a long-established proven pavement maintenance technique. In simple terms, it involves the even spray application of an emulsion binder through a purpose-built spray tanker onto an existing road surface, followed immediately by the application of aggregate chippings to 'dress' the surface. This process provides a seal and enhanced skidding resistance. The technique has many advantages, some of which are listed below.

- It seals the pavement surface against ingress of water, one of the several causes of deterioration.
- It arrests the deterioration of the surface and underlying structure.
- Timely intervention enhances extends the life of the surface prior to the need for structural maintenance.
- It can help reduce spray caused by vehicles travelling on wet surfaces.
- Careful selection of aggregate colour can enhance the visual impact of urban streets.

While, ideally, it should be applied prior to an increase in surface deterioration, which would require patching, in the UK it has been used as one of the mainline maintenance programmes for many years and progressively the surface course of many roads has become a build-up of several layers of surface dressing. These sections can be susceptible to serious problems in periods of hot weather caused by softening and bleeding of the binder accompanied by plunging of the chippings. During these periods of hot weather it may be necessary to apply a blotter coat of sand or finely crushed stone.

At the present time where traffic-generated noise has become a political issue, the use of a surface dressing, which uses a large chipping (>14 mm), can cause problems but the use of multiple dressing techniques can minimise this.

In some literature it is argued that the increased resistance to a rolling wheel caused by a high level of surface texture leads to an increase in vehicle operating costs. While this may be true it is believed that the economic benefits generated by a reduction in the needed maintenance spending outweigh the disadvantages.

Increases in binder technology have led progressively to binders of enhanced capability, some examples being the capability for work over a longer season particularly in cooler parts of the year, the ability to span wider cracks and resistance to embrittlement in cold weather with associated better chipping retention. While there is an argument for the use of pre-patching to ensure a better substrate to dress on, the use of crack sealing as a preparatory treatment, as it is used in some countries, is not normal in the UK.

Surface dressing is an extremely cost-effective treatment and can be used in a variety of ways ranging from single to multiple dressings, examples of which are shown in Figure 13.5.

Figures 13.6 and 13.7 show a conventional system using four vehicles – binder tanker, chipper, chipping delivery lorry and pneumatic tyred roller (PTR). The chipper has only a small

Figure 13.6 Binder spray tanker with extending spray-bar
Courtesy of Eurovia Ltd

Figure 13.5 Examples of surface dressings as used in the UK
British Standards Institution, 2006. Permission to reproduce extracts from BS EN 12271:2006 is granted by BSI

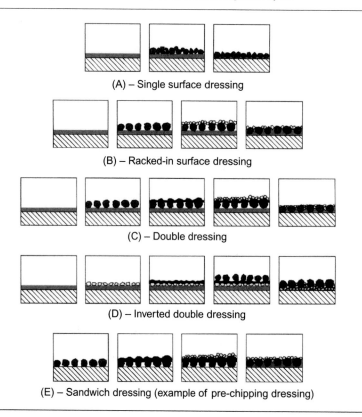

(A) – Single surface dressing

(B) – Racked-in surface dressing

(C) – Double dressing

(D) – Inverted double dressing

(E) – Sandwich dressing (example of pre-chipping dressing)

Figure 13.7 Surface dressing – chipping spreader and roller
Courtesy of Eurovia Ltd

Figure 13.9 Surface dressing: combined binder sprayer and chipper
Courtesy of Eurovia Ltd

The equipment shown above is the latest development of a single machine train with extending spray and chipper bar, which will deliver up to 4.2 m in a single pass. Made by Schaefer in Germany (www.schaefer-technic.de) it carries 13 t of binder and 20 t of chippings and has the advantage that the chippings are laid straight onto the hot binder. The only other vehicle in the train is a PTR.

hopper and requires continuous chipping delivery support. See also Figures 13.8 and 13.9.

Surface dressing (chip seal) is a rapid process which, when carried out by a competent contractor in suitable weather conditions, gives an effective result. It can be carried out more than once but care has to be taken when repeating the operation because a build-up of binder can cause fatting up and bleeding of excess binder in hot weather. Such faults are especially apparent in the wheeltracks and, if developed, removal of the old surface dressing by planing is the only remedy.

Properly employed, however, surface dressing is a cost-effective process which, when carried out at say seven–ten year intervals, extends the life of a surface. Usually, it is carried out on a surface that is still sound but beginning to show signs of ageing. Often there are planned cycles of maintenance; for instance, after an open-textured Macadam or AC surface has been laid for, say five–seven years, surface dressing may be considered. High performance surface dressings are now available with polymer modified binders for use on heavily trafficked major routes, but great care is needed due to their characteristics in changing weather conditions.

Chippings can be uncoated, or lightly coated with bitumen, to improve their adhesion They are spread by hand for small areas, or by machine when unconfined, ensuring that the whole surface has a dense layer of chippings. It is important that excess chippings are finally swept away after rolling and again after several days trafficking.

Figure 13.8 Combined binder sprayer (600 l) and chipper with 6 t hopper and onboard HIAB to load chippings. Remaining vehicle in train is a PTR.
Courtesy of Eurovia Ltd

Rubber-tyred rollers are preferred for compaction immediately after spreading chippings and subsequently by the action of traffic. There is a serious risk of damage both to the surface dressing and to the windscreens of vehicles if traffic is allowed to pass over the newly completed dressing at unrestricted speeds after laying, or if removal of surface chippings is not carried out effectively.

Many recent developments in surface dressing methods have been under active consideration at trial sites including

- a pad coat treatment, which is used on variable road surfaces to counteract changes in embedment. The initial application of a 6 mm surface dressing is followed after an extended interval (one–three years) by a second similar application
- a racked-in technique, in which an initial dressing of 10 or 12 mm chippings is spread to approximately 90% coverage, followed by a further coating of 6 mm chippings without additional binder being spread
- a process similar to racking-in, but with a second application of binder between chipping applications. This is referred to as a double dressing technique.

Following is a contribution from a contractor colleague, which is relevant at this point:

The action to be taken when being offered sites which have an SMA type surface for surface dressing, relates to the type and mode of failure of the SMA.

Where large areas of patching are not an option, or a necessity, we would apply a 6 mm pad coat dressing. This would prepare the surface to receive a normal surface dressing.

Sites where SMAs are likely to have been used are rarely lightly trafficked so it is likely that following the application of a 6 mm pad coat a rate of spread of $1.5 +/- 0.2$ l/m^2 (dependant on the condition of the SMA – likely to be at the higher end of the range) a 10/6 racked in would be applied.

Figure 13.10 indicates the stages in the development of the planning and specification of surface dressings.

Table 13.5 sets out the common types of failure of surface dressing. Judgement is needed when deciding at what stage repair and replacement should take place. The major concern is to ensure there are a minimum number of potential skidding accidents.

During the laying season, which is through the summer months, climatic conditions can lead to bleeding when the free binder causes a traffic and safety hazard. In these circumstances it is necessary to stabilise this with sharp sand or crushed limestone, which is applied by mechanical spreader, possibly on more than one occasion.

Following laying there will be a small excess of chippings which require removal by suction sweeper to maintain safety. This should be allowed for in the contract.

In Table 13.5, mention has only been made of a K1–70 emulsion binder. Also in regular use for specialised applications are developments such as foamspray, and polymer modified thermoplastic bitumens. Epoxy resin binders have also been used extensively for difficult sites, usually associated with premium aggregates, such as calcined bauxite.

Specification primarily relates to end result performance, rather than being prescriptive. In the UK MCHW(1) (DfT, 1992) clause 918 is relevant as is the quality assurance (QA) system (United Kingdom Accreditation Service (UKAS), 2011). There are many international standards and guidelines for surface dressing (chip seal), some of which are very comprehensive and are listed in the bibliography at the end of this chapter.

It is necessary to take a systematic approach to the preparation of a site prior to the application of a surface dressing and the following stages are identified.

(a) Check the condition of the existing surface. Minor cracking and limited variations in level can be corrected or accommodated in the process, but there is no gain in strength, and if the carriageway is in distress from traffic loading, more drastic repair in the form of patching will be needed.

(b) Ensure that the machinery to be used is serviceable and calibrated.

(c) Check that the materials are ordered in accordance with the specification.

(d) Where premium binders are to be used, check that the contractor and especially the supervisory staff are experienced in the laying of such materials.

(e) Programme the works to take advantage of weather conditions suited to the process, and take necessary traffic arrangements into account.

(f) Ensure that effective steps are taken to minimise the effects of opening to traffic in terms of damage to the surfacing (consider the use of 'convoy' systems as a speed restriction) and danger to road users.

(g) Ensure adequate sweeping resource is available.

(h) Carry out subsequent checks on the condition of the surfacing, especially where previously untried materials have been used.

13.5.2.5 Slurry surfacing

'Slurry surfacing' is the generic name for a range of cold applied emulsion asphalt processes. This range has evolved to include 'slurry seal', 'slurry surfacing', and 'microsurfacing', providing thin, intermediate and thick layers respectively. The thickness of a single layer ranges from a minimum 1.5 mm with slurry seal to a maximum 4 mm with slurry surfacing, and 15 mm with microsurfacing. Microsurfacing is frequently laid in two or more coats.

Microsurfacing is dealt with separately in a following section.

Figure 13.10 Flow chart for planning and specification of surface dressing
From Atkinson, 1997

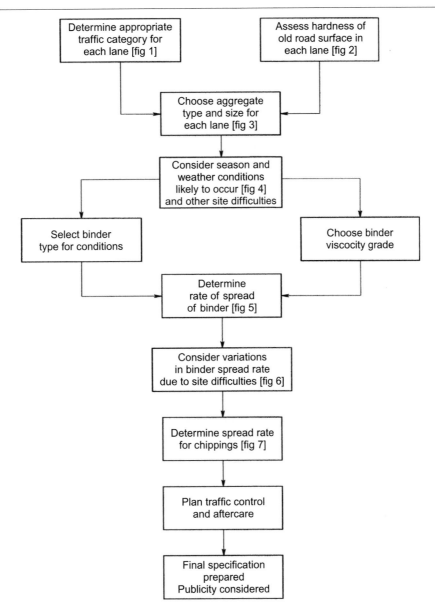

Note: This chart is to illustrate the basic principles of surface dressing design. Due to the large number of options available further detailed guidance can be gained from TRL road note 39 (Roberts and Nichols, 2008) or TRL overseas road note 3 (TRL, 2000) or other international guides, examples of which are listed at the end of this chapter.

The main purpose of slurry surfacings is to stop fretting of the pavement surfaces caused by loss or ageing of the binder, seal imperfections and repairs and provide an even, consistent running surface. Standard slurry seals/surfacings provide an excellent skid resistance for low-speed traffic but because of their relatively greater texture depth, microsurfacings are usually preferred for higher-speed traffic. Slurry surfacing is therefore preferred in towns or airport environments where its freedom from dust and flying chippings is an additional advantage (see Table 13.6).

Slurry surfacings are now designed by the contractor to achieve an end performance rather than the original recipe formulations, in accordance with the move towards European Standards EN 12273 and EN 12274 (BSI, 2008a, 2008b) however the following

Table 13.5 Surface dressing – common types of failure

Fault	Cause	Remedy
Loss of chippings at an early stage	May be slow break in emulsion or poor wetting (cut-back bitumen)	Increase binder content – use pre-coated chippings
Loss of chippings during first winter	Lack of embedment or binder too brittle	Check surface hardness, choice of binder and weather
Bleeding of binder during first hot summer	Wrong binder viscosity for the temperature range	Revise specification
Fatting up	Excessive use of binder, binder/chipping ratio increased due to crushing of aggregate or dust absorption, chipping embedment	Plane off and resurface

Table 13.6 Typical uses of slurry seal
Data taken from Robinson (2010)

Use	Comment
Housing estate roads	Slurry surfacings offer the clean, dense surface desirable in these areas, where loose chippings may create a nuisance.
Fretted surfaces	Slurry surfacings may be used to restore mechanical stability to the carpets which are deteriorating due to fretting.
Sealing basecourses	Slurry surfacings are ideal for filling the voids of, and thus sealing, a basecourse construction. A fast-setting slurry surfacing can provide a big advantage over other sealing methods for what is often an 'out of season', in other words winter, problem.
Trenched or patched surfaces	Slurry surfacings may be used to provide a uniform sealing coat over the whole surface, provided the reinstatements are sound and reasonably level.
Polished surfaces	Slurry surfacings are a means of restoring skid-resistance to general areas.
Surface dressing failures	Slurry surfacings offer a solution to the essentially difficult problem of treating surface dressings which have partially stripped.
Crazed surfaces	Slurry surfacings will go some way to restore the shape of roads where minor foundation faults have resulted in unevenness, but existing surface crazing may reappear. Fibre-reinforced treatments may help with this but a cure cannot be guaranteed.
Airfields	Authorities responsible for maintenance of civil airfields have found slurry surfacings to be a safe useful form of surfacing for runways, taxiways, holding areas and perimeter tracks.
Car parks and playgrounds	Slurry surfacings are an effective seal on car parking areas and playgrounds. To take full advantage of rapid-set slurry surfacings, configuration of these areas must not inhibit the manoeuvrability of mixing/spreading equipment. The surface should be finally lightly dusted to allow tyres to turn.
Pad coats	A slurry surfacing treatment may be used as a 'pad coat' for surface dressing in circumstances where the chippings would not otherwise embed sufficiently to ensure long-term retention, for example on cement concrete.
Footways, cycle tracks and pedestrian areas	Coloured slurry surfacings are used widely.

general principles still apply to the composition of conventional slurry surfacing. In the UK MCHW(1) (DfT, 1992) clause 918 is relevant, as is NHSS 13 (UKAS, 2011b).

Aggregate is blended with 70/100 or 100/150 pen based rapid-setting bituminous emulsion (sometimes with the addition of a polymer modifier for additional performance), adhesion agents, water and cement or hydrated lime. The residual bitumen content depending on grading and requirements can vary from 6.5–16% by weight of dry aggregate. Batches can be up to 2 tonnes/mix and thus at a thickness of 3–10 mm, large areas can be surfaced daily. The water in the mix evaporates, and the emulsion sets on 'breaking', the timing of which can be adjusted by the mineral filler content and the chemical agents.

The resulting mix is fed to a spreader box mounted on the back of a purpose-designed spreader unit (truck). The setting time can vary from 15 minutes to 12 hours depending on weather conditions.

The carbon footprint of slurry surfacing is about 50% that of a hot mix asphalt.

13.5.2.5.1 PREPARATION OF EXISTING SURFACES

The surface to be treated must be freed from all dust and loose material by thorough cleaning with a mechanical broom and/or suction sweeper, supplemented if necessary by hand brooming. Open cracks must be cleared of vegetation and other loose material, for which purpose a jet of compressed air may be useful. All debris and loose material arising must be removed.

Although not usually necessary, circumstances may make the use of a bond coat desirable. In such cases the emulsion should be class C40B3 (K1–40) applied in accordance with Real (Road Emulsion Association Ltd) Technical data sheet no 5, 'Bond Coating' (Real, 2006). The use of a tack coat is recommended if applying slurry seal to a concrete surface.

In the past when embarking on major footway sealing it was found to be beneficial and cost-effective to wash the surfaces with a hand pressure washer to ensure adhesion of the seal to the substrate.

13.5.2.5.2 COMPACTION

This is not normally required. However, with slurry surfacings which are virtually untrafficked, one or two passes of a pneumatic tyred roller may be given as soon as the material has set sufficiently to ensure that rutting will not occur. In these cases the pneumatic tyred roller should be multi-wheeled with smooth treads and with off-set front and rear wheels giving a small overlap when rolling. Individual wheel-loading should be between 0.7 and 1.3 tonnes and pressures should be such that the tyre profile is neither convex nor concave.

13.5.2.5.3 AFTERCARE

It is usual for slurry surfacings to shed a small amount of their larger aggregate particles during a short period after the treatment. This period may vary from a few days to a few weeks depending on the extent of the trafficking. On the public road system a routine highway sweeping arrangement will usually suffice for the removal of these particles since their size is such that windscreen damage does not occur and nuisance to pedestrians is minimal.

On airfields, depending on the nature of aircraft and their movements, sometimes it may be desirable to increase the frequency of sweeping.

13.5.2.5.4 SPECIFICATION – STANDARDS

In the UK MCHW(1) (DfT, 1992) clause 918 is relevant, as is NHSS 13 (UKAS, 2011b).

In the USA, ASTM D6372 – 05 (ASTM, 2010), 'Standard practice for design, testing, and construction of micro-surfacing', is a combined reference with the Issa (International Slurry Surfacing Association) publication 'Recommended performance guideline for emulsified asphalt slurry' (ISSA, 2010a).

13.5.2.6 Microsurfacing

In the USA, ISSA publishes comprehensive guidelines for slurry seal and microsurfacing, which can be found at www.slurry.org.

Microsurfacing is a mixture of polymer modified emulsion asphalt, mineral aggregate, water and additives proportioned, mixed and uniformly spread over a properly prepared surface. It should be capable of performing in variable thickness cross-sections such as ruts, scratch courses and milled surfaces. After curing and initial traffic consolidation, it should resist further compaction. The microsurfacing should be applied as a homogeneous mat, adhere firmly to the prepared surface and have an acceptable skid resistant texture throughout its service life.

Microsurfacing is a quick-traffic system that allows traffic to return shortly after placement. Normally these systems are required to accept straight, rolling traffic on a 13 mm thick surface within one hour of placement in specific conditions. Stopping and starting traffic may require additional curing time.

Three types of seal are identified in the US literature relating to aggregate type and usage location (Table 13.7).

Type 1 is a slurry seal and types 2 and 3 are microsurfacings. The differences can be seen more clearly in Table 13.8.

When required, microsurfacing may be used to fill ruts, utility cuts, depressions in the existing surface, etc. Ruts up to 13 mm, or greater are to be filled independently and ruts over 40 mm in

Table 13.7 Types of slurry and microsurfacing and rates of application
Data taken from www.slurry.org

Aggregate type	Location	Suggested application rate
Type 1	Parking areas Urban and residential streets Airport runways	4.3–6.6 kg/m^2
Type 2	Urban and residential streets Airport runways	5.4–9.8 kg/m^2
Type 3	Primary and interstate routes	8.1–12 kg/m^2

Table 13.8 US grading curves for microsurfacing
Data taken from ISSA (2010a, 2010b)

Sieve size		Type 1 % passing	Type 2 % passing	Type 3 % passing	Tolerance from gradation
US	Metric				
3/8	9.5 mm	100	100	100	
#4	4.75 mm	100	90–100	70–90	± 5%
#8	2.36 mm	90–100	65–90	45–70	± 5%
#16	1.18 mm	65–90	45–70	28–50	± 5%
#30	600 μm	45–65	30–50	19–34	± 5%
#50	330 μm	25–42	18–30	12–25	± 4%
#100	150 μm	15–30	10–21	7–18	± 3%
#200	75 μm	10–20	5–15	5–15	± 2%

depth may require multiple applications. All rut filling and level-up material should cure under traffic for at least 24 hours before additional material is placed.

Immediately prior to applying microsurfacing, the surface should be cleaned of all loose material, silt spots, vegetation and other objectionable matter. Any standard cleaning method is acceptable. If water is used, cracks should be allowed to dry thoroughly before applying the microsurface. Any ironwork, for example inspection chambers, valve boxes and gullies, should be protected from microsurfacing by a suitable method.

The use of tack coat is not normally required unless the surface to be covered is extremely dry and ravelled or is concrete or brick. The tack coat should be allowed to cure sufficiently before the application of microsurfacing.

It is recommended that cracks wider than a quarter of an inch (6 mm) in the pavement surface should be sealed with an approved crack sealer prior to the application of the microsurfacing.

13.5.2.6.1 SPECIFICATION/STANDARDS
Microsurfacing systems, in the UK, are essentially proprietary products and the details of mix are not available; consequently the client must rely on the QA system.

13.5.2.7 Cape seal
Generically similar to chip seal, Cape seal (Figure 13.11) was developed in South Africa in the Cape Province. This procedure, first specified in 1950 (Solaimanian and Kennedy, 1998), was largely an effort to improve the durability of the existing single- and multi-coat chip seal methods; initially it was used on new roads where traffic did not exceed 300 heavy vehicles per day. With time, improvements made to this process led – around 1957 – to the modern Cape seal process: a 19 mm chip seal with

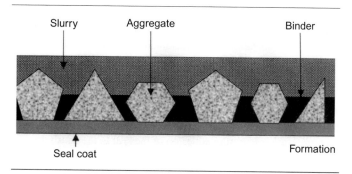

Figure 13.11 Cape seal (idealised)

two layers of slurry seal and a 13 mm chip seal coated with a single layer of slurry.

In Australia, the use of Cape seals dates from the early 1960s and, as in South Africa, they were used primarily for new construction. In Australian practice, anionic slurry was applied over large stone chip seals to improve the ride and increase durability. More recently the slurry has been used as a rehabilitation process over chip seals as a means of replenishing binder (as the seal ages). Slurry in this instance is used as a void filler.

In terms of cost-effective rehabilitation of pavements, Cape seals fill the gap between straight surfacings (such as slurry seals) and hot mix asphalt. Cape seals are viewed as alternatives to more costly overlays. The Cape seal, if constructed properly, provides a smooth dense surface, one having good skid resistance and a relatively long service life; additionally it provides a durable and an impervious surface. The rich slurry mix over the chip seal eliminates the problem of loose aggregate, holds stones and the seal coat firmly in place, and reduces traffic noise (Solaimanian and Kennedy, 1998).

13.5.2.8 Otta seal

Otta seal is a particular type of bituminous surfacing which was originally developed by the Norwegian Road Research Laboratory (NRRL) in the late 1960s. It derives its name from the location in Norway where it was developed – the Otta Valley.

The Otta seal (see Figure 13.12) is essentially a 16–32 mm thick bituminous surfacing comprising a mixture of graded aggregates, ranging from natural gravel to crushed rock, in combination with relatively soft (low viscosity) binders with and without a sand seal cover. It is laid first as a sprayed binder in a thick layer at twice or more of the spread rate associated with conventional chip seal, prior to being chipped.

After rolling and trafficking, the binder works its way upwards through the aggregate voids which results in a dense, durable matrix that relies on both mechanical interlock and bitumen binding for its strength – similar to a bituminous premix. This is in contrast to one or two layers of single-size crushed aggregate that are placed on a relatively thin film of comparatively hard binder to constitute the more traditional single or double chip seals (Pinard and Obika, 1997).

Although initially intended for use as a temporary surfacing on newly constructed roads, its good performance has led to its adoption as a permanent single or double seal with or without a sand seal coat for both new and existing roads in a variety of traffic situations ranging from light to heavy.

The design of the Otta seal is relatively simple. It relies on an empirical approach that is based on experience in the selection of both an appropriate type of binder and an aggregate application rate. Guidelines are now available for practitioners in the design of Otta seal and are referred to below.

The construction of an Otta seal is similar in principle to that of a conventional bituminous surface treatment. However, many of the construction activities can be undertaken using labour-based methods – a major advantage in terms of employment provision in developing countries.

Figure 13.12 Otta seal (idealised)

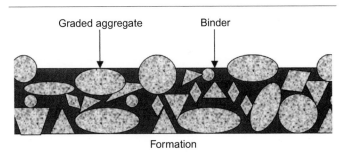

Otta seals have a number of important advantages over traditional surface treatments including

- an ability to tolerate the use of relatively inferior aggregate, such as screened gravel, rather than crushed rock, without impairment of the performance of the surfacing
- an enhanced durability that is better able to combat the high solar radiation that causes rapid ageing and hardening of the binder with consequent degradation of the surfacing
- scope of utilising labour-based methods in many aspects of its construction
- a favourable life cycle cost–benefit ratio of the order of 50% to 60% of the more commonly used seals, such as chip seal.

The use of Otta seal is becoming more widespread as more experience is gained. Otta seal is now used in a number of countries in eastern and southern Africa, in Bangladesh and in Australia.

In situations where traditional approaches to upgrading earth roads or maintaining unsurfaced roads by continuous gravelling/regravelling are no longer tenable, consideration should be given to the use of Otta seal as an alternative to the other traditional types of surface treatments.

The typical range of service lives and binder spread rates of various seals used in Africa are set out in Tables 13.9 and 13.10 respectively (Overby and Pinard, 2007).

13.5.3 Pavement preservation – comparative costs and expected life

Table 13.11 reflects UK practice and has been adapted from www.rsta-uk.org.

Table 13.12 has been adapted from publication FHWA-CFL/TD-05–004a (FHWA, 2005).

Table 13.9 African experience – typical service life of various seals
Data taken from Overby and Pinard, 2007

Type of seal	Typical range of service life (years)
Sand seal	2–4
Slurry seal	2–6
Single chip seal	4–6
Double sand seal	4–9
Double chip seal	7–10
Single Otta seal + sand seal	8–10
Cape seal (13 mm + single slurry)	8–10
Cape seal (19 mm + double slurry)	10–14
Double Otta seal	12–16

Table 13.10 Typical binder spread rates for Otta seal
Data taken from Overby and Pinard, 2007

Traffic (AADT)	Binder spread rate l /m^2
<100	1.8–2.2
100–500	1.8–2.0
>500	1.6–1.8

13.6. Thin surfacing (<40 mm thick) (TSCS – thin surface course systems)

In the UK thin surfacings are proprietary systems in which a hot bituminous mixture is machine laid onto a bond coat. They are generally between 15 and 40 mm thick compared to conventional hot rolled asphalt at 45–50 mm thick. Over the last 15 years they have gained in popularity as they are cheaper and quieter and may be laid more easily than HRA as there are no chippings to be rolled into the surface, consequently less labour is required. TSCS are moderated by BBA HAPAS (British Board of Agrément).

Originally TSCSs were seen as a response to the general move towards quieter surfaces, but their development has not been without problems and it is not generally realised that in addition to adding nothing to the bearing capacity of a pavement they do in fact detract from it, since on average they have only about 0.5 to 0.7 times the stiffness of the original layer. Consequently, if there are any signs of distress in the substrate its removal and replacement with a new binder course should be considered.

Mixtures consist of aggregate, filler and a bituminous binder,

Table 13.11 UK experience with various pavement preservation techniques
Data taken from Robinson (2010)

Type	Application	£/sq m ± 10%	Expected life years
6 mm single surface dressing	Estate roads, rural areas	1.50	7–10
10 and 6 mm racked in dressing	Urban roads, quieter	1.80	7–10
14 and 6 mm double dressing	Busy urban roads, higher stress, gradient, bend	2.20	7–10
Pre-patching additional cost	Rural, urban roads	1.00–1.50	N/a
Micro-asphalt 14 mm	Mainly urban locations	3.00	7–12
Micro-asphalt + regulating + ironworks raised	Mainly urban locations	3.50–4.00	7–12
High friction surfacing	High stress sites	9.00–12.00	5–10
Re-texturing – bush hammer	Anywhere exposed aggregates	2.00–3.00	3–5
Gilsonite preservative	Anywhere	2.00–3.00	3–5
Asphalt reinforcement – Geo-composites/geotextiles	Urban, trunk roads	5.00–8.00	Increases life

Table 13.12 US experience with various pavement preservation techniques
Data taken from FHWA (2005). Information in the public domain

Type	Application £/sq m ± 10%	Expected life years
Cape seal	2.50	7–15
Chip seal	1.25	3–7
Chip seal over geotextile	2.50	3–7
Fog seal	0.50	1–3
Microsurfacing	23.5	5–8
Multiple surface treatments (chip seals)	1.75	4–8
Open graded friction course	12.5	8–12
Otta seal	2.5	4–8
Sand seal	1.00	2–6
Scrub seal	1.40	3–8
Ultrathin friction course	7.5	10–12

which may be modified by the addition of polymers, rubber, resins, fibres and fillers such as hydrated lime and cement.

Suitable for use in both new constructions and maintenance there are three types, classified according to their thickness, as shown in Table 13.13.

The following summarises a study by Walsh (2011).

In the last two cold wet winters the durability of thin surfacings has been less than expected, as among other things TSCS are more porous than either the HRA or AC surfacings previously used.

Before a wholesale surface treatment is required a maintenance engineer will almost certainly have to carry out localised patching works to fill potholes and/or seal cracks. This is normally economic up to about 15% of the surface, as patching costs, at £50 per sq m, are between five and eight times the cost of machine-laid hot mix.

One of the major problems facing the maintenance engineer is the great lack of hard performance data from which to develop a preservation maintenance strategy. TRL 660 (Nicholls *et al.*, 2007) which examines the durability of thin surfacing systems and presents findings after six years of monitoring, presents some interesting conclusions.

This study has noted the significant difference between robustness of the national road network compared with the local road network, since in the latter case the majority of the network was never designed – rather it has evolved over time. This has highlighted the fact that the performance of thin surfacings is much more predictable on the more robust national network than on the local one. The performance of any surfacing is inseparable from the performance of the existing surface upon which it is laid.

It has also been observed that the mode of failure of thin surfacings is different from and much less predictable than previous materials. HRA on heavily trafficked roads tended to fail by a gradual increase in rut depth and loss of skidding resistance as the chippings polished. A similar gradual effect

together with slow accumulation of hair cracks could also be seen on AC surfaced roads.

Thin surfacings deteriorate quite differently and much less predictably. The aggregate does not polish, but as the binder ages there comes a time, quite suddenly one winter, when the aggregate in less well compacted areas and especially at joints frets out, creating potholes. A road surface apparently in good order one summer may need replacement after a hard winter. Many thin surfacing systems are only now reaching the age when this phenomenon is becoming widespread. Life cycle planning is very difficult at scheme level when the performance of the principal surfacing material is unpredictable.

To help overcome the problem, agreement has been reached between a number of relevant organisations within the UK, about a 'target design life' for thin surfacings as part of the overall move towards highway asset management. These are based on collective agreement and not as the result of statistical evaluation and are set out in Table 13.14.

One of the key reasons for poor performance of thin surfacing is that the properties of the constituents can vary, and mix proportions can go out of specification, although these are much better controlled than they were 20 years ago. Workmanship, however, continues to be a serious source of poor performance. National Highway Sector Scheme 16 (UKAS, 2011d) attempts to improve this by introducing training requirements, and some clients are reintroducing site supervision to pick up gross abuses.

A client's asphalt supervisor's guidance document has highlighted 35 obvious things that can go wrong during the laying process.

Table 13.13 Classification of thin surfacing systems by thickness
Data taken from BBA (2011)

Type	Thickness
Type A	<18 mm
Type B	18–25 mm
Type C	>25 < 50 mm

Table 13.14 Target design life for various treatments
Data taken from Walsh (2011)

Treatment	Target design life	
	Designed roads	Evolved roads
High friction surfacing (hot)	4	4
High friction surfacing (cold)	8	8
Surface dressing	10	15
Micro-asphalt	10	10
Thin surface course systems	15	10
Asphalt concrete surfacing	8	6
Hot rolled asphalt design mix	20	20
Hot rolled asphalt recipe mix	–	25
Hot rolled asphalt binder course	40	40
SMA binder course	35	30
Asphalt concrete binder course	30	20

However, if the client's programme demands work at night and/or in cold, wet and windy weather, this can make good workmanship almost impossible. In order to focus attention of both the client's designers and contractors or installers on quality, the Highways Agency and many local authorities now specify a five-year guarantee (MCHW(1) (DfT, 1992) Clause 942.16).

Road note 42 (Nicholls *et al.*, 2008) is another document that may help to facilitate longevity of asphalt pavements.

In an attempt to improve performance of thin surface course systems, in terms of reducing the variability and increasing the target design life, four initiatives have recently come to fruition

- the inclusion in specifications of a maximum texture depth requirement as well as a minimum
- the publication by the Highways Agency of an interim advice note (IAN xx/yy in draft) [late 2011] – Thin surface course systems – installation and maintenance
- the recognition that not all thin surface course systems are the same
- the continued update of BS 594987 (BSI, 2010) and of the BBA guidelines for thin surface course systems (BBA, 2008)

Thin surfacings are not generally designed to treat pavements where structural deterioration or cracking is present in the underlying layer (whether this is asphalt, hydraulically bound material, or pavement quality concrete). Generally, structural deterioration, cracking or open joints already present in the layer directly beneath the TSCS will rapidly propagate to the surface. Such defects in the surfacing mat tend to disrupt the integrity of the TSCS resulting in a local loss of aggregate interlock. Consequently, surface disintegration (fretting) occurs, and reduced life of the surfacing is the likely outcome.

13.7. Cost benefit of surface treatments

At a scheme-specific level, the life of a surface treatment can vary very significantly from the figures shown in Table 13.15: under normal circumstances, by ±30%. However, if there are adverse circumstances – poor design, erroneous materials selection and specification, materials manufacturing faults, or poor installation practices – 80% of the treatment life can be lost.

Risk of the defects listed below can be reduced if detailed attention is paid to certain preventative measures (also noted below):

- Fretting
  - Reduce the texture depth requirements and specify a denser mix.
  - Improve site quality control and supervision.
  - Ensure material is not laid too thin for the stone size.

Table 13.15 Cost benefit of some surface treatments
Data taken from Walsh, 2011

Properties	Surface benefits				Noise		Cost effectiveness				Remarks	
	Skid resistance	Seals surface	Texture depth	Profile	Less dBA	Score out of 5	Unit cost £/m²	Life years	WLC Index £/m²/yr	Score out 20	O/A score	Failure mode
Treatments	Score out of 5											
SMA 10 single layer	4	3	H	5	−4	3	£6 (40 mm)	10	0.6	13	28	Fretting Cracking
SMA 6 + binder	5	4	M	5	−7	5	£12 (65 mm)	12	1.0	11	30	Cracking Fretting Delamination
SD 6	5	4	H	1	−3	2	£1.25	12	0.1	20	32	Fatting
SD 8 + 4	5	5	M	1	−4	3	£2.00	15	0.13	20	34	Fatting
Micro Asph	3	3	M	4	−4	3	£3.50	8	0.43	16	29	Texture/skid resist
Seal + MA	3	5	M	4	−4	3	£4.25	10	0.43	16	31	Texture/skid resist
Local velocity patching	3	3	M	3	N/A	1	£1.00 5% treat	8	0.13	20	30	Fretting Rutting
Local patching	3	2	L	3	N/A	2	£2.50 5% treat	6	0.41	16	26	Potholing
Local Over band	2	5	L	1	N/A	3	£0.6/m	5	0.12	20	31	Cracking Skid resist

- Limit cold weather working to 5°C minimum air/surface temperature and conditions that are not too windy.
- Enforce minimum temperatures for materials delivery and compaction.
- Cracking
  - Increase the thickness by putting a flexible SMA binder course and thin surfacing, for example, 45 mm SMA binder course and 20–6 mm thin surfacing instead of 40–14 mm thin surfacing.
  - Introduce a stress absorbing membrane (SAMI) geotextile or spray system when overlaying concrete/cement-bound material. It is possible to use glass geogrids for small areas.
  - Specify flexible products.
- Rutting
  - Ensure the binder course is rut resistant.
  - Ensure the surface course is rut resistant.
  - Do a design check for structural rutting (is the overall pavement too thin for traffic level?) if this is suspected.
- Delamination
  - Limit cold weather working to 5°C minimum air/surface temperature.
  - Ensure material is not laid too thin for stone size.
  - Always use bond coats sprayed by driven spray tanker.

Every site should have a technician checking technical matters: temperature, thickness, texture, density (bases only), ride quality, etc.

The HAPAS guidelines (BBA, 2011) (Table 13.16) for thin surfacing give three levels of performance for the systems described in sections 13.9, 13.10 and 13.11 in this chapter. This is used in accordance with the traffic figures on demonstration sites given in the certificate to provide information on the performance of the system.

13.8.   Skid resistance – ensuring it is adequate

The skid resistance of a road surface involves a combination of texture depth (macrotexture) and microtexture. The latter can be assessed by the PSV of the aggregate at the surface of the road. In early life a new surface has a PSV masked by the bitumen film surrounding it, which takes time to wear away. The skid resistance is also affected by the contact stress at the tyre–road interface as well as the aggregate size and shape.

The surface roughness, or texture depth, helps the tyre tread disperse the water away from the contact patch, so the tyre can grip a 'dry surface'. The macrotexture is more important at higher speeds than at low speed. It is important to specify the texture depth correctly as if it is too great it can affect pavement life adversely. This is because not only do air and water have increased access but there is an enhanced likelihood of surface aggregate loss in areas of high breaking and turning stresses.

In the UK MCHW(1) (DfT, 1992) clause 921, which sets the standards for skid resistance for national roads, is the normal starting point in the literature available on skid resistance, and while local highway authorities can set their own standards concern over possible litigation usually means they keep to the national standards – although there may be an argument that in the urban area, where traffic is moving more slowly, these requirements could be relaxed somewhat.

For convenience, Table 9/3 from MCHW(1) (DfT, 1992) Clause 921 is reproduced in Table 13.17.

13.9.   High friction surfacing

High friction surfacing is essentially a form of surface dressing that uses a highly specialised aggregate and is performed when there is the need to ensure a very high skid resistance on a pavement surface. Typically this is at the approach to traffic signals and pedestrian crossings: where necessary the binder can be pigmented to differentiate usage.

The system comprises an epoxy resin binder and calcined bauxite aggregate, which are applied either by specialist machine or by a hand screed. A service life of between five and ten years may be expected providing it has been laid on a substrate in good sound condition to prevent the need for expensive repairs.

Bauxite is a sedimentary rock won by open mining and subsequently calcined in a rotary kiln prior to grinding. Chemically it is principally Al_2O_3 (80+%) with a low Fe_2O_3 content (<2%) and has a PSV in excess of 68 (in the case of Guyanan grey as high as 75), as such producing SRV in excess of 60. The usual sources of calcined bauxite are Guyana and China and it has either a grey or buff natural colour.

To reduce the risk of premature failure, high friction surfacing systems are best applied to surface courses that have been trafficked for some weeks prior to the installation of the surface and are in good sound condition.

Table 13.16 BBA HAPAS guidelines for thin surfacing – texture depth requirements
Data taken from BBA (2011)

Level	Minimum macrotexture depth (mm)	
	Untrafficked	After two years' trafficking
3	1.5	1.0
2	1.2	0.8
1	1.0	0.7
0	No requirement	No requirement

Table 13.17 Requirements for initial texture depth for trunk roads including motorways
From DfT (1992) © Crown copyright 1992

Road type	Surface type	Average (mm) per 1000 section	Average (mm) for a set of ten measurements
High speed roads	Thin surface course systems to Clause 942 aggregate ≤ 14 mm	Not less than 1.3	Not less than 1.0
Posted speed limit ≥ 50 mph (80 kph)	Chipped hot rolled asphalt surface dressing and all other surfacings	Not less than 1.5	Not less than 1.2
Lower speed roads	Thin surface course systems to Clause 942 aggregate ≤ 14 mm	Not less than 1.0	Not less than 0.9
Posted speed limit ≤ 40 mph (65 kph)	Chipped hot rolled asphalt surface dressing and all other surfacings	Not less than 1.2	Not less than 1.0
Roundabouts on high speed roads Posted speed limit ≥ 50 mph (80 kph)	All surface course materials	Not less than 1.2	Not less than 1.0
Roundabouts on lower speed roads Posted speed limit ≤ 40 mph (65 kph)	All surface course materials	Not less than 1.0	Not less than 0.9

HFS transmits high horizontal stresses to the underlying surface, which may quickly develop cracks if it is aged or poor. It is not unusual, however, to find cracking in HFS beds extending into the surface course, which in addition to the effects of high horizontal shear forces appear to be exacerbated by the result of thermal ratcheting, as described by Croll (2009). This problem can be treated by using a suitable epoxy or similar resin to repair the HFS.

Where thermosetting high friction surfacings – such as epoxy resin – are applied over thin surface course systems, at approaches to roundabouts and other highly stressed sites, the deep 'negative' texture in the surface can reduce the coverage of resin binder to such an extent that the adherence of the calcined bauxite chipping may be reduced, resulting in premature chipping loss (Figure 13.13).

13.10. Cold in-place recycling

There are two fundamentally different types of cold in-place recycling: shallow-depth and full-depth. The shallow-depth cold in-place recycling, generally known as retread in the UK, is a technique that has been used with great effectiveness for many years.

13.10.1 Shallow-depth cold in-place recycling (retread)

The work involves the reduction of a 50–100 mm thickness of the upper layers of a pavement to a granular mass, usually achieved by a milling machine (planer). It is then 'mixed' with a

Figure 13.13 High friction surfacing

mechanical harrow prior to rolling, partly to break up some of the larger pieces prior to re-harrowing and the introduction of 10 mm aggregate, where required, and the introduction of bitumen at a rate of about 2.5 l/sq m (Figures 13.14–13.17).

The mass is remixed with a harrow prior to the introduction of further binder, at 2.5 l/sq m remixing and rolling. Following a further application of binder the surface is dressed with a 6 mm chipping and this is repeated. In total some 8–10 l/sq m of binder will have been used, leaving the double dressing of 6 mm chippings to over-winter prior to the laying of a third surface dressing the following season.

Figure 13.14 Retread – planing and rolling

Figure 13.15 Retread – mixing dry planings

Figure 13.16 Retread – shaping

Figure 13.17 Retread – adding binder

If funding permits, the most satisfactory surface in the following season is a 25 mm AC carpet, which can then be left for seven–ten years before a preventative programme of surface dressing is instigated at about a seven-year cycle. This process is particularly suitable for both the carriageways and footways of suburban housing estate roads as it is the cheapest way of restoring the shape of the pavement and effectively carrying out a very economical 'reconstruction'. Experience indicates that this treatment, in addition to restoring the shape of a distressed pavement, increases the consistency of the section and results in a modest increase in its bearing capacity. In urban areas this treatment has been found to be successful on bus routes. Retread can also be used effectively on rural roads, but where regular heavy traffic is likely the use of a minimum 40 mm AC overlay is preferred as it adds to the bearing capacity of the pavement.

One problem with retread, for no obvious reason, is the occasional occurrence of small transverse corrugations, which can degrade the riding quality. This can only be cured by an AC overlay.

13.10.2 Full-depth in-place recycling

This involves much heavier, purpose-built machinery, capable of milling to a depth of 350 mm and to a width of up to 2.5 m in a single pass. This pulverises both the bound layers and part of the unbound layers. A picture of the relevant machine is shown in Figure 13.18.

The process is considerably more complex and involves the need for careful mix design by the addition of cement/lime/fly ash (hydraulic binder) and foamed bitumen emulsion binder. One benefit of full-depth in-place recycling is that during the construction phase the subgrade is not exposed, reducing the risk of soft spots.

Once the recycling is complete the material is again compacted and the surface shaped by a grader to the required levels. Finally, the surface is coated with a bituminous emulsion and chippings, after which it can be open to traffic. Depending on the design requirements the final surface is laid, once site conditions are appropriate for this to be done.

In the UK, the process is specified according to TRL 611 (Milton and Earland, 1999) and approved under MCHW(1) (DfT, 1992) clause 947.

13.10.3 Hot in situ recycling (repave and remix)

Hot mix in situ recycling can be carried out by two similar processes: repave and remix. These are techniques for rehabilitat-

Figure 13.18 Wirtgen 2500 used for full-depth recycling
Courtesy of Wirtgen UK Ltd

ing deteriorated bitumen-bound pavement surfaces in situ. They can restore defective surfaces on roadbases free from structural defects. Recycling may also provide an economic short-term solution for pavements with structural defects prior to major strengthening works at a later date.

The repave and remix process can address the following pavement defects

- deteriorating skid resistance
- cracking and crazing caused by hardened binder in the existing surface
- ravelling and fretting or chipping loss
- ruts, potholes and poor ride quality
- reflective cracking above cement-bound bases but not structural cracking or crazing
- provide economic short-term remedial measures prior to major strengthening at a later date.

The process is performed by a machine which heats and scarifies the surface of the existing road pavement in a continuous process with, where required for the remix process, the addition of a rejuvenating agent and new asphalt from a coating plant as it travels along the road. Repave can be undertaken by a similar machine, provided the new material is laid while the scarified surface is at the required temperature.

13.10.3.1 Hot in-place recycling – repave

When the surface has deteriorated without excessive hardening of the binder, new surface material can be overlaid as a veneer on the heated, scarified and re-profiled existing road surface. The characteristic feature of repave is that a thickness of about 20 mm of existing pavement surface is heated, loosened and overlaid usually with 25 mm but not less than about 15 mm of new central plant-mixed material.

13.10.3.2 Hot in-place recycling – remix

This can take place when the surface needs replacement because of deteriorating skid resistance and/or surface regularity. The heated and scarified existing pavement material is gathered into a pugmill on the machine, where it is mixed with new central plant-mixed material, to form a single homogeneous layer. A bitumen-rejuvenating agent may be added during the process. The characteristic feature of remix is that the existing pavement surface has its hardened bitumen rejuvenated, either by a rejuvenator or by the addition of central plant-mixed material containing a soft bitumen.

Repave/remix is suitable where the penetration of the recovered binder is between 20 and 80. If tar dressing or surface dressing is present the process is unsuitable. If tar is present the pavement will need to be reconstructed due to the carcinogens involved. If surface dressing is present it must be removed first as it may catch fire during the heating phase. A surface course containing a polymer modifier may also be unsuitable.

Care must be exercised when selecting candidate sites due to the overall length of the train of machinery involved, which can reach 100 m. For this reason it is very suitable for use on airfields.

The pavement, although sound, can sometimes show signs of deformation or surface fretting. In such a situation repave provides a faster, more cost-effective alternative to traditional forms of resurfacing.

The repave process, which can treat up to 5000 sq m per day, allows flexibility of programming. The heat from repave penetrates deep into the road materials, allowing work to take place virtually any time of the year. The process is suitable for any class of road, especially heavily trafficked roads, as work can take place at night. Material is recycled in situ, cutting lorry movements, considerably reducing the use of new aggregates, and minimising waste material. The process offers savings of up to 45% in new material compared to a 40 mm conventional inlay.

The existing road surface is heated to 150°C using infrared heaters, and scarified to a depth of up to 30 mm using a two-stage scarifier with spring-loaded tines to avoid damage to street furniture. Next an oscillating, floating screed reprofiles and corrects levels for the required crown or crossfall. The process is completed by the immediate application of either a 25 mm bituminous wearing course, HRA with 20 mm pre-coated chippings, high stone content asphalt or a proprietary thin surfacing.

The heat from the repave machine (Figure 13.19) welds the new materials, removing the need for tack coat. Repave can be combined with a proprietary thin surfacing to aid tyre noise reduction, improve grip and reduce spray in cold weather.

Further useful information can be found in DMRB 31/94, amended in 1995 (The Highways Agency, 1994b), MCHW(1) (DfT, 1992) clause 926 and www.colas.co.uk.

13.10.4 Recycling off site

13.10.4.1 Central plant cold recycling

Central plant cold recycling is where existing pavement materials, both cement-bound and bitumen-bound, are broken down to be recycled as capping material. The compacted capping material should comply with MCHW1 (DfT, 1992) Clause 613.

Recycling bitumen-bound pavement materials by processing planings (arisings) in a pugmill with bitumen, fluxed bitumen or rejuvenators is very much a developing science in the move to maximise the use of arisings and minimise the use of energy.

Figure 13.19 Repave machine in action
Courtesy of Colas Ltd

13.10.4.2 Central plant hot recycling

Ongoing research continues to demonstrate the increasing possible usage of arisings mixed with new graded materials. Among other things this has required the modification of normal drum mixers to control the emission of vaporised bitumen which occurs if bitumen in the reclaimed material comes into direct contact with the very high gas temperatures in the drum. Heat is usually transferred to the whole mix by heating the new aggregate to which the recycled material is added. This is very much an ongoing area of research.

13.11. Retexturing

Skid resistance is a measure of road surface friction under controlled conditions. Low skid resistance and wet skid crashes are a problem for most highway maintaining authorities in the UK. The UK's high standards for safety require regular monitoring and maintaining network skid resistance.

RLG (2005) states:

> Authorities should endeavour to ensure to ensure the appropriate skid resistance is provided across the whole network, both for safety reasons in respect of skidding and to provide a defence in cases of litigation.

Retexturing is the mechanical reworking of a sound surface to restore either skidding resistance, texture depth or both. Being a totally non-material processes means that retexturing is effectively 100% recycling; used on a cyclic basis it will reduce whole-life costs significantly.

13.11.1 Use of retexturing processes

- To address sites where low skid resistance has led to wet skid accidents.
- To maintain skid resistance above investigatory levels over the whole network – minimising wet skid accident risk.
- To extend effective surface life – retexturing as opposed to resurfacing when skid resistance is low.
- To reduce whole-life costs – retexturing as opposed to high friction materials is cheaper and can be repeated over a period of time.
- To accelerate the weathering on recently laid (six months +) thin surfacing to provide adequate early life skid resistance.

13.11.2 Considerations before specifying retexturing processes

- Is the road surface sound? If not, retexturing is not the solution.
- What is the problem? Micro? Macro? Or both?

- Will the process follow the surface profile?
- Will the process treat a full lane width? Consistency is very important, especially for motorcycles.
- Is the process weather-dependent?
- Will the process cause much disruption? Consider rates of productivity and traffic management requirements.

13.11.3 Retexturing options

- Carbonising – used to burn off excess bitumen from 'fatted up' surfaces.
- Bush hammering – impact of tool on surface: pressure and speed are controlled to tailor the treatment.
- Shot blasting – impact of steel shot on surface. The longest lasting method; however it gives rise to concerns about errant shot.
- Grooving/grinding – saw cutting, predominantly used on runways to improve surface drainage.

Table 13.18 Comparison of retexturing techniques

Process	Type of texture improvement	Advantages	Limitations
Carbonising	Macro	Improves texture on fatted up surfaces Can be used to remove white lines Repeatable	Noisy Difficult to control Concerns on health and safety
Bush hammering	Micro and macro	Can be used in any weather Suitable for any natural aggregate surface Fast Repeatable Follows surface profile	Limited improvement of macro texture Extremes of temperature limit operational window on surface dressing
Shot blasting	Micro and macro	Improves both micro and macro texture in one operation Repeatable Follows surface profile	Cannot be used in damp or wet conditions Slow Expensive
Grooving/grinding	Macro	Improves surface drainage	Disruption Better suited to concrete Must be transverse Slow Cannot be repeated
Longitudinal scabbling	Micro and macro	Improves both micro and macro texture in one operation Low cost	Cannot be repeated Not suitable for surface dressing Does not follow surface profile Can reduce texture depth
Water jetting	Micro	Improves texture on fatted up surfaces Modern systems are environmentally friendly	Over-use can polish micro texture Does not improve micro texture

- Longitudinal scabbling – impact of groove roller on surface: can reduce texture depth.
- Water jetting – impact of high pressure water jet on surface.

13.11.4 Advantages and limitations of retexturing processes

See Table 13.18.

See also Highways Agency (1999) and National Roads Authority (1997).

REFERENCES AND BIBLIOGRAPHY

ASTM (American Society for Testing and Materials) (1995) ASTM D5078 – 95 (reapproved 2006): Standard specification for crack filler, hot-applied, for asphalt concrete and Portland cement concrete. ASTM, West Conshohocken, PA.

ASTM (American Society for Testing and Materials) (2005) ASTM D7116 – 05: Standard specification for joint sealants, hot applied, jet fuel resistant types, for Portland cement concrete pavements. doi: 10.1520/D7116-05. ASTM, West Conshohocken, PA.

ASTM (American Society for Testing and Materials) (2007) ASTM D6690 – 07: Standard specification for joint and crack sealants, hot applied, for concrete and asphalt pavements. ASTM, West Conshohocken, PA.

ASTM (American Society for Testing and Materials) (2010) ASTM D6372 – 05: Standard practice for design, testing, and construction of micro-surfacing. ASTM, West Conshohocken, PA.

Atkinson K (1997) *Highway Maintenance Handbook*, 2nd edn. Thomas Telford, London.

Austroads (2003) AP-T26/03: Guidelines and specification for bituminous slurry surfacing. Austroads, Sydney.

Austroads (2006) AP-T68/06: Update of the Austroads sprayed seal design method. Austroads, Sydney.

BBA (British Board of Agrément) (2008) Guidelines document for the assessment and certification of thin surfacing systems for highways. BBA, Garston. http://www.bbacerts.co.uk/PDF/SG308256_May08.pdf (accessed 20/07/2011).

BBA (British Board of Agrément) (2011) BBA Hapas guidelines. http://www.bbacerts.co.uk/hapas.aspx for further details (accessed 19/07/2011).

BSI (British Standards Institution) (1993) BS 2499–2: Hot applied joint sealant systems for concrete pavements – Code of Practice for application and use of joint sealants, BSI, London.

BSI (British Standards Institution) (2007) BS EN 12271:2006: Surface dressing. Requirements. BSI, London.

BSI (British Standards Institution) (2008a) BS EN 12273: Slurry surfacing requirements (see also PD 6689:2009 – Surface treatments, guidance on use of EN 12273). BSI, London.

BSI (British Standards Institution) (2008b) BS EN 12274: Slurry surfacing test methods. BSI, London.

BSI (British Standards Institution) (2010) BS 594987:2010: Asphalt for roads and other paved areas. Specification for transport, laying, compaction and type testing protocols. BSI, London.

Caltrans (2003) Fog seal guidelines. Caltrans, Sacramento, CA.

Caltrans (2010) Maintenance technical advisory guide (MTAG), Vol. 1: Flexible pavement preservation. 2nd edn – training module. Caltrans, Sacramento, CA.

Croll JGA (2009) The role of thermal ratcheting in pavement failures. *Proceedings of the Institution of Civil Engineers – Transport* **162(3):** 127–140. doi: 10.1680/tran.2009.162.3.127.

Curtis CW, Ensley K and Epps J (1993) Strategic highway research program report SHRP-A-341: Fundamental properties of asphalt aggregate interaction including adhesion and adsorption. National Research Council, Washington, DC.

Davis L and Milner J (2010) Chip sealing over paving fabric in various climatic conditions. *First International Conference on Pavement Preservation, Newport Beach, CA.* http://www.pavementpreservation.org/icpp/paper/21_2010.pdf (accessed 19/07/2011).

De Beer M (1998) Personal discussion.

DfT (Department for Transport) (1992) MCHW(1): Specification for highway works. Vol. 1. *Manual of Contract Documents for Highways*. DfT, London. http://www.dft.gov.uk/ha/Standards/mchw for further details (accessed 14/07/2011).

DfT (Department for Transport) Standing Committee on Highway Maintenance (1988) Preferred method 1: Patching.. Cornwall County Council. Truro. http://www.adeptnet.org.uk/assets/userfiles/documents/000260.pdf (accessed 19/07/2011).

Done S, Ford WG and Edwards AC (2001) R7470: Appropriate surfacings for low-volume roads: Interim report. http://www.transport-links.org/transport_links/filearea/documentstore/122_Interim%20Report.pdf (accessed 21/07/2011).

FHWA (Federal Highway Administration) (2002) PL-03–001: Pavement preservation technologies – in France, South Africa and Australia. FHWA, Washington, DC.

FHWA (Federal Highway Administration) (2005) FHWA-CFL/TD-05–004a: Context-sensitive roadway surfacing selection guide. FHWA, Washington, DC.

FHWA (Federal Highway Administration) (2010) Performance evaluation of various rehabilitation and preservation treatments: final report. FHWA, Washington, DC.

Hein D and Rao S (2010) Rational procedures for evaluating the effectiveness of pavement preservation treatments. First International Conference on Pavement Preservation, Newport Beach, CA. http://www.pavementpreservation.org/icpp/paper/28_2010.pdf (accessed 21/07/2011).

Highways Agency (1994a) *Design Manual for Roads and Bridges*, vol. 7. TSO, London. http://www.dft.gov.uk/ha/standards/dmrb/vol7 for further details (accessed 21/07/2011).

Highways Agency (1994b) DMRB HD 31/94: Maintenance of bituminous. *Design Manual for Roads and Bridges*, TSO,

London.

Highways Agency (1994c) DMRB HD 32/94: Maintenance of concrete roads. TSO, London. http://www.dft.gov.uk/ha/standards/dmrb/vol7/section4/hd3294.pdf (accessed 21/07/2011).

Highways Agency (2006) DMRB HD 36/06 Surfacing materials for new and maintenance construction. TSO, London. http://www.dft.gov.uk/ha/standards/dmrb/vol7/section5/hd3606.pdf (accessed 21/07/2011).

Highways Agency (1999) DMRB HD 37/99: Bituminous surfacing materials and techniques (amendment 1). TSO, London. http://www.dft.gov.uk/ha/standards/dmrb/vol7/section5/hd3799.pdf (accessed 21/07/2011).

Highways Agency (2001) DMRB HD 40/01: Footway maintenance. TSO, London. http://www.dft.gov.uk/ha/standards/dmrb/vol7/section4/hd4001.pdf (accessed 21/07/2011).

ICCP (International Conference on Pavement Preservation) (2010) First International Conference on Pavement Preservation, Newport Beach, CA. http://www.pavementpreservation.org/icpp/for further details (accessed 21/07/2011).

ISSA (International Slurry Surfacing Association) (2010a) ISSA A105: Recommended performance guideline for emulsified asphalt slurry surfacing, ISSA, Annapolis, MD. http://www.slurry.org/downloads/A105.pdf (accessed 19/07/2011).

ISSA (International Slurry Surfacing Association) (2010b) A143: Recommended performance guideline for micro surfacing (revised Feb. 2010) ISSA, Annapolis, MD. http://www.slurry.org/downloads/A143.pdf (accessed 20/07/2011).

Kucharek (2008) Modern chip sealing technology. *AEMA Emulsion Technologies Workshop, Indianapolis.* Asphalt Emulsion Manufacturers' Association.

LRRB (2006) 2006-34: *Minnesota Seal Coat Handbook 2006.* Minnesota DOT, St Paul, MN. http://www.lrrb.org/pdf/200634.pdf (accessed 21/07/2011).

LRRB (2009) *Preventative Maintenance Best Management Practices of Hot Mix Asphalt Pavements*, Minnesota DOT, St Paul, Minnesota.

Lynch L, Steffes R, Chehovits J, Voigt G, Evans L and Al-Qadi I (2000) Joint- and crack-sealing challenges. TRB, Washington, DC. http://www.trb.org/publications/millennium/00064.pdf (accessed 21/07/2011).

Milton LJ and Earland M (1999) TRL 611: Design guide and specification for structural maintenance by cold in-situ recycling. TRL, Wokingham.

NAPA (National Asphalt Pavement Association) (2009) Thin Asphalt Overlays for Pavement Preservation (IS 135), NAPA, Lanham, MD. http://www.hotmix.org

National Roads Authority (1997) DMRB HD 38/97: Pavement design and maintenance. Surfacing and surfacing materials. Concrete surfacing and materials (including amendment 1 and NRA addendum). National Roads Authority, Dublin.

NCHRP (National Cooperative Highway Research Program) (2005) NCHRP synthesis 342: Chip seal best practices. TRB, Washington, DC. http://onlinepubs.trb.org/onlinepubs/nchrp/nchrp_syn_342.pdf (accessed 21/07/2011).

NCHRP (National Cooperative Highway Research Programme) (2004) NCHRP synthesis 523: Optimal timing of pavement preventative maintenance treatment applications, TRB, Washington, DC.

NCHRP (National Cooperative Highway Research Programme) (2009) NCHRP synthesis 388: Pre-overlay treatment of existing pavements. TRB, Washington, DC. http://onlinepubs.trb.org/onlinepubs/nchrp/nchrp_syn_388.pdf (accessed 21/07/2011).

NCHRP (National Cooperative Highway Research Programme) (2010) NCHRP synthesis 411: Microsurfacing. TRB, Washington, DC. http://onlinepubs.trb.org/onlinepubs/nchrp/nchrp_syn_411.pdf (accessed 21/07/2011).

Nicholls JC, Carswell I, Thomas C and Walter LK (2007) TRL 660: Durability of thin asphalt surfacing systems, Part 3: Findings after 6 years monitoring. TRL, Wokingham.

Nicholls JC, McHale MJ and Griffiths RD (2008) Road note 42: Best practice guide for the durability of asphalt pavements. TRL, Wokingham.

Olsen S (2008) An introduction to slurry seal and microsurfacing systems. University of California, Berkeley, CA. http://techtransfer.berkeley.edu/pavementpres08downloads/PP08Olsen.pdf (accessed 21/07/2011).

Overby C and Pinard MI (2007) The Otta seal surfacing – an economic and practical alternative to traditional bituminous surface treatments. World Bank, Washington, DC. http://www4.worldbank.org/afr/ssatp/Resources/HTML/LVSR/English/Added-2007/2007-Otta-Seal-Guide-by-ChOverby-MPinard.pdf (accessed 19/07/2011).

Patrick J (2009) NZ Transport Agency research report 390: The waterproofness of first-coat chipseals. Opus International Consultants, New Zealand, Wellington.

Pierce LM, Mahoney JP, Muench ST *et al.* (2010) Utilization of bituminous surface treatments for maintaining asphalt concrete pavements due to restricted budgetary constraints in Washington. First International Conference on Pavement Preservation, University of California, Berkeley, CA. http://www.techtransfer.berkeley.edu/icpp/presentations/PIERCE_wed.pdf (accessed 21/07/11).

Pinard MI and Obika B (1997) Optimal use of marginal materials for achieving cost-effective surfacing on low-volume roads in developing countries. 13th IRF World Meeting, Toronto.

PRL (Pavement Rejuvenation (UK) Ltd) (2011) Information on pavement rejuvenation. www.pavetechnology.co.uk (accessed 19/07/2011).

Rajagopal A (2010b) Effectiveness of chip sealing and micro-surfacing on pavement serviceability and life: report for Ohio DOT. FHWA, Washington, DC.

Real (Road Emulsion Association Ltd) (2006) Technical data

sheet 5: Bond coating. Real, Storrington. http://www.rea.org.uk/uploads/ds05-bond_coating.pdf (accessed 19/07/2011).

RLG (2005) Well-maintained highways. Code of practice for highway maintenance management. TSO, London. Additions and supplements can be found at www.ukroadsliaisongroup.org (accessed 13/07/2011).

Roberts C and Nichols JC (2008) Road note 39: Design guide for road surface dressing, 6th edition. TRL, Wokingham.

Robinson H (2010) Surface dressing and microsystems. *SCI presentation*, Road Surface Treatment Association, Colchester. See www.rsta.org.uk for further details (accessed 21/07/2011).

Solaimanian M and Kennedy TW (1998) Project report 1788-S: Evaluation of Cape seal process as a pavement rehabilitation alternative. Centre for Transportation Research, University of Texas, Austin, TX.

South African National Roads Agency (2007) TRH3: Technical recommendations for highways: The design and construction of surfacing seals. South African National Roads Agency, Pretoria.

Stannard D (2010) Airfield slurry surfacing in the United Kingdom. AEMA ISSA Annual Convention, Florida.

TRL (Transport Research Laboratory) (2000) Overseas road note 3: A guide to surface dressing in tropical and sub-tropical countries. TRL, Wokingham.

TRL (Transport Research Laboratory) (2010) Nicholls, J.C., Durability of Thin Asphalt surfacing systems, Part 4: Final report after 9 years monitoring, Transport Research Laboratory, Wokingham, UK.

UFC (Unified Facilities Criteria) (2001) UFC 3–270–02: Asphalt crack repair. US Department of Defence. www.wbdg.org/ccb/DOD/UFC/ufc_3_270_02.pdf (accessed 19/07/2011).

UKAS (United Kingdom Accreditation Service) (2008) Sector scheme document 14 – for the quality management of asphalt mixes (edn 7). http://www.ukas.com/library/Technical-Information/Pubs-Technical-Articles/Pubs-List/NHSS%2014%20Jan%2008.pdf (accessed 21/07/2011).

UKAS, Feltham.

UKAS (United Kingdom Accreditation Service) (2011a) Sector schemes for quality management in highway works. See www.ukas.com for further details (accessed 21/07/2011). UKAS, Feltham.

UKAS (United Kingdom Accreditation Service) (2011b) NHSS 13 – Sector scheme for the supply and application of surface treatments to road surfaces (edn 1). UKAS, Feltham. http://www.ukas.com/library/Technical-Information/Pubs-Technical-Articles/Pubs-List/NHSS13_Issue1_April%202011.pdf (accessed 19/07/2011).

UKAS (United Kingdom Accreditation Service) (2011c) Sector scheme document 15 – for the supply of paving bitumens (edn 7). UKAS, Feltham. http://www.ukas.com/library/Technical-Information/Pubs-Technical-Articles/Pubs-List/NHSS15_Jan2011.pdf (accessed 21/07/2011).

UKAS (2011d) Sector scheme document 16 – for the laying of asphalt mixes (edn 5). UKAS, Feltham. http://www.ukas.com/library/Technical-Information/Pubs-Technical-Articles/Pubs-List/NHSS16_Jan2011.pdf (accessed 21/07/2011).

USGSA (US General Services Asministration) (1984) SS-S-1401C: Federal specification: sealant, joint, non-jet-fuel-resistant, hot-applied, for Portland cement and asphalt concrete pavements. Office of Federal Supply and Services, Washington, DC. http://www.everyspec.com/FED_SPECS/S/download.php?spec=SS-S-1401C.010654.pdf (accessed 17/07/2011).

VicRoads (2001) Technical bulletin no. 38: Guide to Geotextile reinforced Sprayed Seal Surfacing Guide to the selection and design of geotextile reinforced sprayed seal surfacing. VicRoads, Victoria.

VicRoads (2004) Technical bulletin no. 45: Bituminous sprayed seal manual. VicRoads, Victoria.

Walsh ID (2011) The durability of surfacings. 10th International Conference, Sustainable Construction Materials and Pavement Engineering, February, Liverpool John Moores University.

Deterioration and Maintenance of Pavements
ISBN: 978-0-7277-4114-1

ICE Publishing. All rights reserved
http://dx.doi.org/10.1680/dmp.41141.191

Chapter 14
Pavement Maintenance – General Considerations

14.1. Introduction

This chapter sets out to examine the more important issues relating to the use of asphalt materials in pavement construction and maintenance and also provides some background information. It is effectively, a link between Chapter 14 – 'Pavement Maintenance' and Chapter 21 – 'Strengthening of pavements', the former being more conceptual as it examines a range of possible options, which – while enhancing the ride – do not have any significant effect on the bearing capacity of the pavement. Chapter 21, however, specifically considers the options for enhancing the bearing capacity of the pavement. In this chapter there are a number of considerations explored, which are relevant to both maintenance and strengthening of pavements. The reader will, hopefully, find information that is not usually dealt with in a single text elsewhere.

Common to both maintenance and strengthening is the concept of durability. Durability, which according to the *Concise Oxford Dictionary of Current English* (1964), is defined as 'Lasting, not transitory; resisting wear, decay, etc.', – which, frankly, the user (public?) may well reasonably expect a 'highway maintenance professional' to deliver.

14.2. Pavement durability

The following section references Road note 42 – Nicholls *et al.* (2008).

Pavement durability is defined as the retention over the structure's expected service-life of a satisfactory level of performance without major maintenance for all properties that are required for the particular pavement's situation in addition to asphalt durability.

The main aspects that lead to durability are

■ the control of water (getting it away from the structure if not actually stopping it ever entering)
■ limiting the number of sealing joints (both vertical and horizontal)
■ adequate compaction (particularly at the joints)
■ consistent foundation.

14.3. Compaction

Compaction is the process by which the volume of air in an asphalt mixture is reduced using external forces to reorient the constituent aggregate particles into a more closely spaced arrangement.

This reduction of air volume in a mixture produces a corresponding increase in HMA unit weight, or density (Roberts *et al.*, 1996). Numerous researchers have stated that compaction is the greatest determining factor in the performance of dense graded asphalt pavements.

The volume of air in an HMA pavement is important because it has a profound effect on long-term pavement performance. An approximate 'rule-of-thumb' is that for every 1% increase in air voids (above 6–7%), about 10% of the pavement life may be lost (Linden *et al.*, 1989).

According to Roberts *et al.* (1996), there is considerable evidence that in a dense graded mixes the air voids should not exceed 8% nor fall below 3% air voids during their service life. This is because high air void content (above 8%) or low air void content (below 3%) can cause the following pavement distresses

■ deceased stiffness and strength – tensile strength, static and resilient moduli and stability are reduced at high air void content
■ reduced fatigue life – fatigue properties can be reduced by 30–40% for each 1% increase in air void content
■ accelerated ageing/decreased durability – compacting a well-designed paving mix to low air voids retards the rate of hardening of the asphalt binder, and results in longer pavement life
■ ravelling – this becomes a severe problem above approximately 15% air voids
■ rutting – the amount of rutting that occurs in an asphalt pavement is inversely proportional to the air void content
■ moisture damage – if air voids in insufficiently compacted

HMA are high they tend to be interconnected with each other, allowing easy access for water.

There are a number of issues that affect the compaction of a HMA, most of which are related to the rate at which the mix loses heat energy (cools and solidifies). Hunter (2000), suggests the following aspects are relevant in respect of the cooling rate (energy loss).

- Wind speed has a major effect on the cooling rate.
- Layer thickness has a major effect – although thicker layers lose heat at a higher rate, the percentage loss is lower.
- Ambient temperature has little effect on the cooling rate.
- Thermal conductivity has a major effect.
- Density and specific heat of the hot layer have little effect.
- Incidental solar radiation has little effect on the cooling rate.
- The underlying layer temperature, thermal conductivity, density and specific heat have little effect on the cooling rate.

What is interesting here, and is consistent with other findings in the literature, is that the ambient air temperature has only a marginal effect on the loss of heat energy in a newly laid asphalt mat. The basis of current practice in the UK for delivery and temperature control is set out in BS 594987 (BSI, 2010).

14.3.1 Compaction equipment

It is interesting to look back in the history of pavement construction and maintenance following the development by McAdam of his process of effectively creating what would now be called a granular base, and the subsequent development of tar binding. Probably the most significant development was that of compaction. Initially a horse was used to pull a roller, and subsequently the steam roller was developed.

The earliest steam rollers were made in France in 1860. Thomas Aveling produced his first rollers in England in 1865 (Figure 14.1). Experiments continued in England, France and the USA, and by 1880 the familiar three-wheel form of steam-roller had evolved. Many traction engine builders later took up roller manufacture, as the products were so similar.

In these early days compaction was a judgemental art – based on the principle of refusal: essentially rolling continued until deflection ceased – or soft spots were dug out and reconstructed, at which time they were re-rolled to refusal.

The advent of tar-bound and subsequently bitumen-bound macadams led progressively to the need for a greater understanding of materials technology – to the extent that today, in the most modern compaction equipment, the driver simply has to keep an eye on a compaction density gauge mounted below his roller.

Figure 14.1 Early Aveling & Porter steam roller

At the present time there are four basic pieces of equipment available for the compaction of hot mix asphalt

- the paver screed, which generates 75–80% of the theoretical maximum density when the mix passes out from under the screed (TRB, 2000)
- the steel-wheeled roller
- the vibrating roller
- the pneumatic-tyred roller.

Each piece of equipment compacts hot mix asphalt (HMA) by two principal means

(a) by applying a weight to the asphalt surface and compressing the material underneath the ground contact area
(b) by creating a shear stress between the compressed material underneath the ground contact area and the adjacent uncompressed material.

All rollers should be equipped with a means of wetting the rolls or rubber tyres to prevent pickup of asphalt materials.

14.4. Bond between pavement layers

A pavement is made up from a number of layers and in the analytical design process the assumption is made that there is full bond between each layer, such that they act compositely. In practice this is not always the case, due to both poor specification and poor construction practices, leading to a reduced service life of the pavement. It was not until 2008 that Clause 903.4 of MCHW(1) DfT (1994) required all layers to be bonded after a similar requirement in Clause 5.5 of BS 594987 (BSI, 2010), following the findings during the preparation of RN 42 (Nicholls *et al.*, 2008). Figure 14.2 sets out a fairly simple analysis to illustrate the significance of ensuring bond between the several layers develops to minimise deflection of the pavement. Think about plywood without the glue!

In system 1 of Figure 14.2 the material is laid as a single layer of thickness '*d*' and the deflection resulting from the loading system shown is a typical standard case, which will be recognised from the study of strength of materials. In system 2, however, the material consists of two layer of equal thickness '*d*/2' and the equation for deflection is developed using standard data. It will be seen that the effect of two layers acting independently may have a combined deflection of four times that of a single layer of the same overall thickness. This analysis here takes no account of friction, which may well reduce the deflection to two times, rather than the four times that is shown in Figure 14.2.

If the several layers do not act compositely then the load will not be transmitted equally through the structural system and local overloading will occur leading to progressive fatigue failure of the pavement.

14.5. Different asphalt materials

See Figure 14.3 and Table 14.1.

14.5.1 Grouted macadam

Grouted macadams form a semi-flexible class of composites whose behaviour lies somewhere between concrete and conventional asphalt materials, having both excellent rut resistance and a degree of flexibility. In addition they are very resistant to point loads. All products available in the UK are proprietary ones and there is no relevant national standard, although there is BBA HAPAS certification for individual products.

Grouted macadams comprise a skeleton of a carefully designed asphalt matrix with a very high level of air voids, which can be laid by paver. A cementitious or resin grout, or asphaltic grout is then vibrated into the receiving coat, filling the voids and sealing the surface.

The semi-flexible material, shown in Figure 14.4, is used as a surface course and is composed of a combination of an asphalt mixture and a cementitious grout in the same layer. In essence, grouted macadams comprise a substantially single-sized aggregate asphalt mixture, containing 25–35% air voids, which forms a continuous skeleton into which a cementitious grout is poured.

Figure 14.2 Deflection of an un-bonded pavement

1. Standard loading case

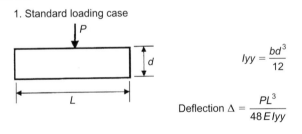

$$Iyy = \frac{bd^3}{12}$$

$$\text{Deflection } \Delta = \frac{PL^3}{48\,E\,Iyy}$$

2. With layer debonding (assumes 2 layers with no bond)

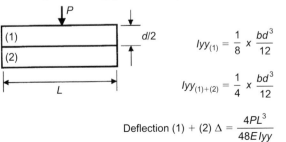

$$Iyy_{(1)} = \frac{1}{8} \times \frac{bd^3}{12}$$

$$Iyy_{(1)+(2)} = \frac{1}{4} \times \frac{bd^3}{12}$$

$$\text{Deflection (1) + (2) } \Delta = \frac{4PL^3}{48\,E\,Iyy}$$

Lack of bond between adjacent layers leads to a reduction in the section properties, which leads to a significant increase in the deflection under the same load.

Figure 14.3 Asphalt core showing different asphalt materials

Table 14.1 Characteristics of different pavement materials

Material	Characteristic features
Stone mastic asphalt (SMA)	Gap graded with high proportion of large aggregate, relies for its strength on aggregate interlock and durability from thick binder film, very rut resistant, medium/high permeability
Hot rolled asphalt (HRA)	Gap graded, relies for its strength on robust matrix, very low permeability, poor rut resistance, but very durable
Asphalt concrete (AC)	Continuously graded, relies on aggregate interlock for its strength, robust but more permeable than HRA

Figure 14.4 Core taken from grouted macadam to show aggregate and cementitious grout penetration

Reproduced from Oliveira *et al.* (2007) with permission of the *International Journal of Pavements – IJP*

The final product combines part of the best qualities of concrete and asphalt pavements, namely the flexibility and freedom from joints that characterise asphalt and the high static bearing capacity and wear resistance of concrete. The impervious grouted macadam layer protects the underlying layers and its high strength, typically in the range 8000–10 000 MPa at 20°C, effectively reduces the stress level in the base layer. This type of surface layer is normally applied with a thickness of 30–60 mm although some work has been done with thicknesses in the region of 80 mm and some grout suppliers claim it is possible to use thicknesses of up to 200 mm.

The construction of grouted macadam is a two-stage process, since it is necessary to allow the asphalt layer to cool down before applying the grout into its voids. The porous asphalt layer is laid using a normal paver and then lightly compacted using a steel roller without vibration to avoid the formation of cracks or tracks in the material. As soon as the porous asphalt mixture has cooled down, its voids can be filled with the selected high-fluidity cementitious grout. The grout is spread on the surface, with the help of rubber scrapers (squeegees).

Depending on the plasticiser used to produce the grout and the producer's specification, a light steel roller may be used in vibration mode to make sure that the voids of the asphalt are completely filled with the grout.

14.6. Materials selection
To use Table 14.2, follow the suggested procedure below

(*a*) Select location and usage.
(*b*) Select needed attributes.
(*c*) Select material based on required characteristics for:
  - surface course
  - binder course
  - base course.

14.6.1 Effects of different maintenance treatments
See Table 14.3.

14.6.2 Properties of typical surfacing materials for footways
See Table 14.4.

14.7. Pavement surfacing materials – various data
14.7.1 Permeability
See Table 14.5.

14.7.2 Coefficient of linear expansion
The following has been taken from Read and Whiteoak (2003, p. 197):

Typically, the linear coefficient of thermal expansion for an asphalt mixture is between 2 and $3 \times 10^{-5}/°C$.

This generally accords with 'Asphalt-concrete water barriers for embankment dams' Creegan and Monismith (1996, p. 76):

Mixing asphalt with aggregate introduces the thermal expansion characteristics of the aggregate. This changes the coefficient of expansion of the mix to about $2 \times 10^{-5}/°C$. This compares to about $1 \times 10^{-5}/°C$ for [. . .] Portland cement concrete.

Table 14.2 Selection of materials

Location/usage	Needed attributes	Materials
Road – traffic	Skid resistance	Marshall asphalt
Road – residential	Toughness	Hot rolled asphalt
Road – shared	Durability	Asphalt concrete
	Low permeability	Stone mastic asphalt
Car parks	High permeability	Thin surface course system
	Rut resistance	Grouted macadam
Lorry parks	Anti-fretting	Microsurfacing
	Compactability	Slurry seal
Airfield – runway	Abrasion resistance	Chip seal (surface dressing)
Airfield – apron	Creep resistance	Concrete block paving
Airfield – taxiway	Fuel resistance	Clay brick paving
	Fatigue resistance	Stone setts
Bus station	High stiffness	Concrete slabs
	Low noise	Natural stone slabs
Industrial yard	High texture	Bonded surface
	Colour	High friction grip surface
Port container stacking area	Anti-spray	
	Rapid application	
Suds (sustainable drainage systems) – porous pavements	Low thermal response	
Footways – pedestrian-only		
Footways – some overrun		
Footways – regular overrun		
Pedestrian precincts		
Feature areas		

Table 14.6 can be seen to be in agreement with the above information.

14.8. Pavement materials containing tar

The following note references Wilkinson and O'Farrell (2008).

UK pavements constructed prior to 1980, or surface dressings prior to the late 1980s, may contain tar. Due to concerns about the possible carcinogenic effects of tar, maintenance works on these roads may involve excavation of materials containing tar. Disposing of tar to landfill is expensive and unsustainable since there is only a very limited number of locations licensed to accept tar and then not without certain precautions.

The European Directives which were implemented in the UK by the Hazardous Waste Regulations 2005 (HWR) and the List of Waste Regulations 2005 (LoWR) classify certain materials containing tar as 'hazardous waste'.

From the mid-1800s, road tar derived from the high-temperature distillation of coal in the production of domestic 'town' gas, was used in UK roads. It had good adhesive and waterproofing properties that made it eminently suitable for use as a binder in tarmacadam mixes and also as a spray application for surface dressing (commonly termed 'tar-spray and chippings'). However an alternative – bitumen – derived from the refining of petroleum oil – became available in the early 1900s and increasingly gained market share.

Coal tar use continued on UK roads until the late 1970s/early 1980s when it became increasingly scarce due to the closure of town gas works, with the advent of natural gas and other sources such as coke ovens at steelworks.

Table **14.3** Effects of different maintenance treatments
Adapted from Warwickshire County Council (2009). Courtesy of Warwickshire County Council

Treatment	Thickness range	Increase pavement strength?	Texture depth	Improve skid resistance	Reduce permeability of pavement	Improve ride quality	Initial cost	Speed of construction	Re-profile	Noise reduction	Expected life	Level of sustainability
	mm	1–5	mm	1–5	1–5	1–5	1–5	1–5	1–5	1–5	years	–5 to +5
Patch (no other treatment)	Any	1	No	1	1	1	5+	1	1	1	0–3	–2 to –4
Retexturing	0	1	1.5	3	1	1	1	5	1	3	3 then re-do	+ 3 to + 4
Surface dressing	6–14	1	1–3	5	5	1	1	5	1	1	7–10	+4
Slurry surfacing	6–15	1	0.5–1.5	3	4	2	2	4	3	3	5	+2
Hapas thin surfacing	15–50	2	0.5–2	4	2	3	3	3	3	5	10–15	+2
55% hot rolled asphalt	30–70	4	0.3–1	4	5	4	4	3	5	3	10–15	+2
High friction systems	3–5	1	0.5–1	5	3	1	5+	2	1	1	3–10	–4
Structural overlay	80+	5	Depends on surfacing	4	5	5	5	1	5	Depends on surfacing	20+ for structure	+4
Haunching	80+	3	Depends on surfacing	3	3	3	3	3	4	Depends on surfacing	20+ for structure	–2 to +2
Retread with 2 surface dressings	75–100	3	1–3	5	4	3	3	4	3	1	10+ (as structure)	+3
Deep recycling with foamed bitumen	150–250	4	Depends on surfacing	4	4	4	5	3	3	Depends on surfacing	20+ for structure	+4

Numeric scale 1–5 [Low (No) (Slow) – 1 2 3 4 5 – High (Yes) (Fast)]

Table 14.4 Properties of footway surfacing materials
Data taken from Hampshire County Council (2010)

Material		Relative properties						
		Slip resistance	Durability	Surface unevenness		Structural contribution	Appearance	Unit cost
				Initial	Long-term			
Block Paving	Concrete	3	6	5	4	6	5	2
	Clay	2	6	5	4	6	5	2
Slabs	Concrete	3	5	5	3	4	3	3
	Natural stone	1–4	5	5	3	4	6	1
Asphalt concrete		4	4	6	6	6	4	4
Mastic asphalt		4	5	6	6	5	6	2
Surface dressing		5	3	2	2	0	4	6
Micro-asphalt		4	3	4	5	0	4	6

Table 14.5 Permeability of asphalt surfacing materials
Data taken from Daines (1995)

Material	Typical air void content %	Approximate water Permeability: m/sec
Mastic asphalt	<1	$<10^{-11}$
Rolled asphalt (30% stone)	2–8	10^{-11}–10^{-10}
Rolled asphalt (55% stone)	2–6	10^{-11}–10^{-10}
Asphalt concrete	3–5	10^{-10}–10^{-8}
Close graded bitumen macadam	4–7	10^{-8}–10^{-5}
Open graded bitumen macadam	12–20	10^{-8}–10^{-3}
Porous asphalt	15–25	10^{-4}–10^{-2}

Table 14.6 Coefficient of thermal expansion for various materials
Data taken from FHWA (2006). Information in the public domain

Aggregate	Coefficient of thermal expansion	
	$10^{-6}/°C$	$10^{-6}/°F$
Granite	7–9	4–5
Basalt	6–8	3.3–4.4
Limestone	6	3.3
Dolomite	7–10	4–5.5
Sandstone	11–12	6.1–6.7
Quartzite	11–13	6.1–7.2
Marble	4–7	2.2–4
Cement paste (saturated) w/c = 0.4, 0.5, 0.6	18–20	10–11
Concrete	7.4–13	4.1–7.3
Steel	11–17	6.1–6.7

Coal tar and bitumen are two entirely chemically different products and should not be confused. While tar has now been classified as carcinogenic, numerous studies have found no link between bitumen and cancer, and bitumen is not classified as carcinogenic anywhere in the world.

Until the mid-1980s tar was used as a binder in macadams, and as a grout in hand-pitched forms of construction. Tar was used as a surface dressing binder until the late 1980s, in many cases blended with bitumen. It is likely, therefore, to be present to some degree across the highway network in some part of the construction.

Records of construction materials were generally not kept in the past and in most local authorities there is no readily accessible,

reliable information about construction dates of parts of the network.

If any form of excavation in a bituminous pavement is required in a scheme then the designer or scheme compiler has a duty under the regulations to determine whether or not any of the materials encountered could be hazardous waste. The designer has a duty to minimise construction hazards, and inform the contractor of any remaining hazards, under the Construction (Design and Management) Regulations 2007.

If construction records show that no tar is present in the layers which are to be excavated, further investigation is unnecessary. If it is known that the layers to be excavated were laid after the mid-1980s and any surface dressing was laid after the late 1980s no further investigation is required.

In the case of a small project, if there is doubt, the designers have the choice; they can undertake no further investigation, accept that the excavated material contains tar, and follow the requirements of the CSS guidance note – 'Road materials containing tar' (Wilkinson and O'Farrell, 2008). For larger-scale works it may be more cost effective for the designer to determine whether all or some of the layers to be excavated contain tar. In this case, cores or else fragments of bituminous materials should be taken from each layer encountered in a trial pit.

A number of simple tests have been considered as screening tools to identify bituminous materials likely to contain tar. It is likely that a negative result in these tests confirms that the material is below the threshold level for use as an unbound material.

The simple tests identified are:

■ applying white spray paint (goes brown in the presence of tar, little affected by bitumen)

■ adding a drop of methylene chloride to a fragment of the material on a filter paper: tar gives a brown stain; bitumen gives a yellow stain.

If there is doubt, the samples should be tested by a laboratory with UKAS accreditation for specified polycyclic aromatic hydrocarbons (PAH). The detection limit for PAH should be specified as 1 ppm (parts per million) and the detection limit for phenol should be specified as 0.1 mg/kg.

If this test proves to be positive, at the present time the likely disposal cost will be of the order of £150/tonne: consequently the most economic course of action is either to leave the material in situ or to consider mixing it with other material to bring the resultant mixture below the threshold level. A further option is to consider reprocessing the arisings with a product such as Tarmac FoamMaster.

14.9. Enhanced performance using bitumen modifiers

The information in Table 14.7 is not exhaustive and is intended only as a guide. It has been adapted from Read and Whiteoak (2003), which in Chapter 5 thereof deals with this subject in detail.

Table 14.7 Effects of bitumen modifiers
Data taken from Read and Whiteoak, 2003

Modifier	Wheeltracking	Thermal cracking	Fatigue cracking	Moisture damage	Ageing
Elastomers, e.g. SBS	Yes	Yes	Yes		Yes
Plastomers, e.g. EVA	Yes				
Tyre rubber		Yes	Yes		Yes
Carbon black	Yes				Yes
Lime				Yes	Yes
Sulphur	Yes				
Chemical modifiers	Yes				
Antioxidants					Yes
Adhesion improvers				Yes	Yes
Hydrated lime				Yes	Yes
Polypropylene fibres			Yes		
Epoxy resin	Yes	Yes	Yes		

A 'Yes' in the box in Table 14.7 indicates that the modifier will improve a mixture's resistance to the relevant problem.

EVS and SBS are frequently used to modify bitumen's in thin asphalt concrete mixtures which have BBA/HAPAS approval.

Rubber is not easily combined with bitumen.

Lime is often specified for use in porous asphalts laid on airfields to replace limestone filler, and cement used in mixes with granite aggregate.

The use of asphalt containing rubber is increasing, particularly in the USA where it is seen as an environmental response to dealing with worn tyres. Discussions with colleagues in the USA suggest there is benefit in resistance to cracking.

14.10. Joints in asphalt

While the assumption is made that a bituminous layer is effectively continuous, in practice this is seldom the case because it is most unusual to find one without any joints.

All joints are a point of weakness and if poorly made are the first point at which deterioration occurs, this being due to lack of compaction or sealing, or a combination of both; either way a poor joint permits the ingress of water, with associated material degradation.

- All joints are a potential source of weakness.
- The number of longitudinal and transverse joints in the mat should be minimised.
- Longitudinal joints should not be in the wheelpath.
- Minimum distance between joints in adjacent layers should be 300 mm.
- All joints in all layers should be sealed.
- Joints are usually the first part of a pavement to show distress.
- Low density at the longitudinal joint is a major contributor to premature loss of pavement performance.

For such a critical subject there is little in the literature. The subject is dealt with briefly in BS 594987 (BSI, 2010).

14.11. Structural equivalence of various materials

The concept of structural equivalence, in pavements, was originally developed by the Asphalt Institute in the USA. It has also been used in the British Ports Federation heavy duty pavement design manual and in many other pavement design procedures.

Table 14.8 Materials equivalence factors
Data taken from BSI (2001) and Jacobs (2007)

Category of material	Material equivalence factor	
	Suggested value	Range
AC 100/150 dense and HRA base/binder course	1.0	0.95–1.05
AC 40/60 dense base/binder course	1.12	1.10–1.2
AC 30/45 HMB base/binder course	1.32	1.25–1.35
HRA surface course	1.0	0.9–1.1
Thin surface course	0.6	0.5–0.7
Cold mix asphalt storage grade and in situ stabilisation	0.75	0.7–1.0
Type 1 granular sub-base (150 MPa) over materials with a CBR of ⩾5%	0.3	0.2–0.4
Type 2 granular sub-base (75 MPa) over materials with CBR of >5%	0.2	0.1–0.25
Type 2 granular sub-base (75 MPa) over materials with CBR of ⩽5%	0.1	0.05–0.15
Dry bound macadam	0.45	0.3–0.6
Cement bound material 3 and 4	0.7	0.5–0.9
Pavement quality concrete	1.7	1.5–1.9
Concrete block paving	0.75	0.7–0.8

Condition factors for existing pavements
The equivalence factor should be multiplied by the above to give current equivalence

As new	1.0	
Slight cracking	0.8	
Substantial cracking	0.5	
Wide and frequent cracks and fretting	0.2	

Table 14.9 Site supervision checklist

Activity			Comment	
Site preparation			√	
1	Dip schedule on formation, previous layer or scarified surface available			
2	Ironwork positions and offsets referenced on kerb			
3	If previous layer is sub-base, is it properly compacted and free from coarse areas?			
4	If laying on rigid surface is it free from water/loose materials/foreign matter, i.e. swept properly?			
5	Joints in existing material to be cut vertically			
6	All joints to be painted			
7	All kerb faces to be painted (for surface course)			
8	All ironwork to be painted (for surface course)			
9	Bond coat on substrate – is it even and to correct spread rate?			
Materials				
1	Coated chippings – if used check for dustiness/coking/sticking together			
2	Visual check on asphalt materials for uniform mixing			
3	Time of arrival of delivery truck(s)			
4	Check delivery temperatures			
	1	Probe at least 225 mm long fully inserted and allowed to 'heat up' for first measurement		
	2	Minimum number of measurements 2no, 1 metre apart and 500 mm from edge of truck		
	3	Move probe quickly between test points		
	4	Take temperatures within 30 minutes of load arriving HRA 130°C min. AC 100 pen 120°C minimum AC 200 pen 110°C minimum		
5	Record tonnage Delivery ticket number Where laid on standard form			
6	Ensure 1 sample per 100 tonnes of material			
Laying				
1	Check surface temperatures Steady or falling <2°C stop laying Rising temperature ≥1°C laying may proceed if surface dry, unfrozen and ice free			
2	No standing water on surface			
3	Paving machine box set to max. practical laying width (i.e. minimum hand-lay)			
4	Minimum thickness Surface course 40 mm Binder course 60 mm Base course 105 mm minimum			
5	No dragging/tearing/segregation of material			

(*continued*)

Table 14.9 (*continued*)

	Activity	Comment	
6	Chipping spread rate OK 10 mm 4–8 kg/m^2 14 mm 5–10 kg/m^2 20 mm 6–13 kg/m^2		
7	150 mm channel boards placed for HRA with chippings		
8	Check rolling temperatures (average of 5 measurements) HRA 85°C min/AC 100 pen 95°C AC 200 pen 85°C		
9	Check roller(s) suitability (8–10 t dead weight; 450 mm width roll or approved vibrating roller)		
10	Check rolling procedure		
	1	Roll from restrained edge (e.g. kerb) to centre		
	2	Overlap on previous roll by half-width wide roller		
	3	Stagger reversing points		
	4	No standing on fresh asphalt		
11	Areas inaccessible to roller to be plate vibrated or hand rammed		
12	Joints between breeds to have good horizontal alignment/be cut vertical and painted		
13	Joints not adequately sealed by compaction to receive overband seal		
Miscellaneous			
1	Machine standing between loads – burners should be turned down if delay extensive		
2	Any residual material in hopper should be checked for temperature/condition before use		
Aftercare			
1	Excess materials/chippings to be removed from footways/verge		
2	Ironwork covers to be cleaned off/check covers can be removed		
3	Gullies checked for debris inside and cleaned out if necessary		
4	New bed protected from traffic until:		
	1	Material fully compacted		
	2	Material has cooled to atmospheric temperature		

Whilst it is possible to develop layer equivalences using Odemark's method, if one knows the layer modulus (dealt with elsewhere in these notes) Table 14.8 can be used if more detailed information is not available.

Table 14.8 is based on the concept that asphalt concrete 100/150 dense base/binder course (previously known as dense bitumen macadam) has a structural equivalence of 1.0.

This enables various different layers in a pavement to be assessed based on their equivalence, such that they could be replaced by another material depending on their stiffness.

14.12. Machine-laid bituminous materials site supervision checklist

See Table 14.9.

REFERENCES AND BIBLIOGRAPHY

BSI (British Standards Institution) (2010) BS 594987:2010: Asphalt for roads and other paved areas. Specification for transport, laying, compaction and type testing protocols. BSI, London.

BSI (British Standards Institution) (2001) BS 7533-1:2001: Guide to the structural design of heavy duty pavements constructed of clay pavers or precast concrete paving blocks. BSI, London.

Concise Oxford Dictionary of Current English (1964) Oxford University Press, Oxford.

Creegan PJ and Monismith CL (1996) *Asphalt-concrete Water Barriers for Embankment Dams*. ASCE.

Daines ME (1995) Tests for voids and compaction in rolled asphalt surfacings. Department of Transport, TRL Project 1978, Transport Research Laboratory, Crowthorne, UK.

DfT (Department for Transport) (1994) *Manual of Contract*

Documents for Highway Works, Vol. 1: Specification for Highway Works. DfT, London.

FHWA (2006) Portland cement concrete pavement research – thermal coefficient of Portland cement concrete. FHWA, Washington, DC. http://www.fhwa.dot.gov/pavement/pccp/thermal.cfm (accessed 21/07/2011).

Hampshire County Council (2010) Guidance document on surfacing options for highways: 2010 edn. Hampshire County Council, Winchester.

Hunter RN (2000) *Asphalts in Road Construction*. Thomas Telford, London.

Jacobs (2007) *Londonwide Asphalt Specification*, 2nd edn. Transport for London, London. http://www.lotag.com/attachments/article/23/London%20Asphalt%20Specification%20Revision.pdf (accessed 21/07/2011).

Linden RN, Mahoney JP and Jackson NC (1989) The effects of compaction on asphalt concrete performance. 1989 Annual Meeting of the Transportation Research Board, Washington, DC.

Nicholls JC, Hale MJ and Griffiths RD (2008) Road note 42: Best practice guide for the durability of asphalt pavements. TRL, Wokingham.

Oliveira JRM (2006) *Grouted Macadam – Material Characterisation for Pavement Design*. PhD thesis, University of Nottingham, Nottingham.

Oliveira JRM, Pais JC, Thom NH and Zoorob SE (2007) A Study of the Fatigue Properties of Grouted Macadams. *International Journal of Pavements* (IJP) **6(1-2-3)**: 112–123.

Read J and Whiteoak D (2003) *Shell Bitumen Handbook*, 5th edn. Thomas Telford, London.

Roberts FL, Kandhal PS, Brown ER, Lee DY and Kennedy TW (1996) *Hot Mix Asphalt Materials, Mixture Design, and Construction*. National Asphalt Paving Association Education Foundation, Lanham, MD.

TRB (2000) *Hot-mix Asphalt Paving Handbook 2000*. TRB, Washington, DC.

Warwickshire County Council (2009) Delivering a safe and sustainable highway network – County Surfacing and Structural Maintenance Strategy – 2009, Environment and Economy Directorate, Warwickshire County Council, Warwick.

Wilkinson D and O'Farrell D (2008) *Road Materials Containing Tar*. CSS, Durham County Council, Durham.

Deterioration and Maintenance of Pavements
ISBN: 978-0-7277-4114-1

ICE Publishing. All rights reserved
http://dx.doi.org/10.1680/dmp.41141.203

Chapter 15

Repair and Maintenance of Unpaved Roads

15.1. Introduction

15.1.1 Background

This section sets out to examine the problems and issues of unpaved roads, which in many countries form the major part of the highway network and are the only means of travel for wheeled vehicles. This chapter draws widely on publications by the South African Department of Transport, especially TRH 20:1990, 'The structural design, construction and maintenance of unpaved roads' (South African Department of Transport, 1990).

15.1.2 Definitions

Unpaved roads may be earth tracks, earth roads or gravel roads (Figures 15.1–15.8).

Earth tracks generally consist of parallel ruts separated by vegetation. They may well be impassable during wet weather.

Earth roads are those where there is no imported gravel but the material is cleared of vegetation and lightly compacted, generally by passing traffic. Often shaped by materials taken from the side

Figure 15.2 Rural Road – Congo
Courtesy of Ado Bagishire

drains, they are normally constructed by a road authority and are important to the economic and social development of the area.

Gravel roads have a designed layer of imported material, which is typically constructed to a specified standard and width and provides an all-weather surface. Maintenance is usually carried out on a regular and systematic basis. Roughness varies with time and depends significantly on the maintenance activity.

15.1.3 Traffic

Unpaved roads are nearly always lightly trafficked. Should the traffic exceed about 300 vehicles per day, it is usually economical to provide a bituminous seal (Table 15.1).

Construction thickness will typically be in the range 150–250 mm.

Figure 15.1 Typical problem of deterioration in rural areas
Courtesy of Peter Yawson

Table 15.1 Typical road widths
Data taken from South African Department of Transport (1990)

Traffic ADT	>200	100–200	50–100	<50
Width (m)	6.5–7.3	6.0–6.5	5.5–6.0	4.5–5.5

15.1.4 Basic economic principles

These relate to the comparison of the benefits and costs of providing alternative facilities. The benefits are the expression in economic terms of the advantages of the particular action, for example, fuel- and time-saving, with reduced roughness.

Many problems occur in the economic analysis of unpaved roads by comparison with paved roads. Unpaved roads need continual maintenance and their condition can be significantly affected by periods of excessive traffic or inclement weather.

15.2. Typical unpaved road defects

15.2.1 Dustiness

Dust is the fine material released from the road surface under the wheels of moving vehicles and turbulence caused by vehicles. Silt-sized particles (2–75 μm) are usually generated by vehicles. The quantity of dusts depends on the speed of the vehicle.

Dust is undesirable from a number of points of view

- safety
- comfort
- health
- vehicle damage
- vegetation
- environmental
- economic.

In many cases, it is necessary to apply dust palliatives in order to bind the dust particles. A number of the dust palliatives are commercially available but each one has to be tested individually in order to identify its suitability and cost-effectiveness for the materials under consideration.

Common dust palliatives may be bitumen-based, inorganic compounds (magnesium and calcium chlorides being the most popular), ligno-sulphate (a product of the sulphite timber pulping process) and various commercial products of variable effectiveness.

15.2.2 Potholes

Potholes play a significant role in the development of roughness on unpaved roads and may cause substantial damage to vehicles if they are allowed to develop and increase in size. The effect of potholes on vehicles depends both on the depth and diameter of the pothole. The potholes, which affect vehicles most are those between 250 mm and 1500 mm in diameter with a depth of more than 50–75 mm.

Potholes may arise from the following processes

- poor road shape and drainage
- poor grader operation practice
- compaction of material behind oversize stones under wheel loads
- enlargement of corrugation troughs
- deformation of weak subgrades and wearing courses
- subsidence of animal and insect burrows
- disintegration of highly cracked roads
- disintegration of soft oversize materials
- dispersive soils
- poor compaction
- material and moisture variability.

Once pothole formation has been initiated (irrespective of the cause), the surface drainage deteriorates, water ponds in the depression and the potholes are enlarged by traffic.

15.2.3 Stoniness

Stoniness is the relative percentage of material in the road that is larger than the commended maximum size (usually 37.5 mm). This is one of the few defects of an unpaved road, which can usually be controlled. Excessively stony roads result in the following problems

- unnecessarily rough roads
- difficulty with grader maintenance
- poor compaction of areas adjacent to stones (leading to potholes and ravelling)
- the development of corrugations
- the need for thick loose material to cover the stones.

15.2.4 Corrugations

Corrugations are one of the most disturbing defects of an unpaved road causing excessive roughness and poor vehicle stability. Corrugations are caused by wheel bounce, which becomes more pronounced as the roughness increases. Corrugations can either be 'loose' or 'fixed'. Loose corrugations consist of parallel crests of loose, fine sandy material at right angles to the direction of travel. While fixed corrugations consist of compacted parallel crests of hard, fine sandy material. The troughs are compacted by the force of the wheel regaining contact with the ground. Loose corrugations are easily removed by blading, whereas fixed corrugations need cutting or even tining with the grader before the material is re-spread. The wavelength of the corrugations is dependent on the modal speed (i.e. the most frequently occurring speed) of the vehicles using the road, with the longer wavelengths formed by faster traffic. Roads that have a low modal speed (less than 20 kph), such as haul roads, do not usually corrugate.

Roads susceptible to the formation of corrugations should be inspected regularly in order to programme the necessary maintenance required to avoid loose corrugations becoming fixed. On many sandy roads, regular grader blading (perhaps as often as once a week) is not economically viable, but simple towed drags have been used successfully for the removal of corrugations. These can be towed behind an ordinary light vehicle (or even a draught animal if necessary) to retain the road roughness at acceptable levels.

15.2.5   Ruts
Ruts are depressions of the surface parallel to the wheeltracks. They may form as a result of deformation (compaction) of the subgrade, compaction of the wearing course or loss of gravel from the wearing course. Under local conditions rutting is usually insignificant in terms of the overall unpaved road performance. The probable reason for this is the typically strong, free-draining, sandy subgrade prevalent over much of southern Africa, as well as the deep water tables. Routine blading of unpaved roads replaces gravel in the ruts and simultaneously compensates for any subgrade deformation which may have occurred.

15.2.6   Cracks
Cracks, as such, are not a major problem on unpaved roads but bad cracking may lead to the formation of potholes. Cracking of the wearing course (which usually occurs only during the dry season) is the result of the plasticity being too high or the material being very fine grained. The materials which crack badly also tend to become slippery when wet and should be avoided.

15.2.7   Ravelling
The generation of loose gravel under traffic, termed ravelling, is a significant economic and safety problem. Loose gravel may be distributed over the full width of the road but more frequently is concentrated in windrows between the wheeltracks or alongside the travelled portion of the road. The major problems with roads susceptible to ravelling are

- the windrows are a safety hazard
- stones from the loose gravel may damage vehicles or windscreens
- the rolling resistance of the vehicle is increased by loose material with associated increases in fuel consumption and vehicle operating costs
- problems with lateral drainage of the road may be caused by windrows of loose material.

15.2.8   Erosion
Erosion (or scour) is the loss of surfacing material caused by the flow of water over the road. The ability of the material to resist erosion depends on the shear strength under the conditions at which the water flow occurs. If the shear strength of the material is less than the tractive forces induced by the water flowing over the material, grains become detached and erosion will occur.

The result of erosion is runnels (run-off channels) which, when occurring transversely, result in extreme roughness and dangerous conditions, and when occurring longitudinally (on grades) form deep ruts. Associated with this deposit is a significant loss of gravel. Much of the gravel is deposited in drains and culverts, necessitating extensive labour intensive maintenance. Erosion can be prevented by

- increasing the shear strength of the wearing course material by improving the grading
- good compaction, which also increases the shear strength
- decreasing the grade and the cross-fall and ensuring that the length of the flowpath of water is minimised.

Erosion can be expected on most roads with grades or cross-falls greater than 5%, unless precautions are taken.

15.2.9   Shape
Poor cross-sectional shape of the road usually results in poor drainage, which accelerates the formation of potholes and ruts as well as erosion. Routine maintenance of unpaved roads should be carried out regularly to maintain the crown of the road and to ensure adequate cross-fall.

15.2.10   Slipperiness
Slipperiness of the surface of an unpaved road is a significant safety problem. In wet weather, slipperiness is caused by excessive fine or plastic material in the wearing course. Even materials with adequate coarse aggregate may become slippery if the fine silt and clay fraction become concentrated near the surface.

In dry weather, unpaved roads may become slippery if an excess of loose, fine gravel (between 2 and 7 mm in diameter) accumulates on the road surface through ravelling under traffic or poor blading practices. This layer behaves like a layer of ball bearings and the skid resistance is reduced to practically zero.

The only cure for roads that are slippery when wet, is to re-gravel with a better gravel. The practice of adding a gravel or sand to the existing material is recommended in some manuals but does not avoid the possibility of the fine material migrating to the surface.

15.2.11 Impassability

The primary objective of importing wearing course gravel during the construction of an unpaved road is to provide an all-weather surface. The objective is not met if the material becomes impassable in wet weather.

It is generally considered that an adequately high material strength (in terms of CBR) will provide a trafficable surface under all conditions. Values of CBR recommended in specifications vary from a minimum soaked value of 15 at 95% Proctor compaction. Very little failure of unpaved roads caused by inadequate material strength at depth has been observed.

Local experience indicates that a minimum CBR of 15 at the expected field compaction and moisture condition is adequate to prevent well-shaped roads from becoming excessively churned up, except in those regions where long spells (up to seven days) of wet weather occur and under excessive traffic.

15.2.12 Gravel loss

Although the loss of the wearing course material from the road surface under traffic and climatic conditions (rain and wind) is inevitable, the replacement of the lost material is the most costly maintenance operation. Materials which ravel are most likely to result in a high gravel loss.

Although the major contributor to gravel loss is traffic, significant reductions can be obtained by selecting material with a suitably high plastic factor (PF greater than 500) and percentage passing the 26.5 mm sieve. Well-graded and well-compacted gravels resist loss better than materials deficient in either fine or coarse fractions.

Erosion should be reduced as far as possible to avoid excessive gravel loss on longitudinal grades.

15.2.13 Excessive loose material

Excessive loose material in the form of non-compacted materials across most of the road width or thick windrows next to the trafficked portion of the road or between the wheeltracks results in increased user costs and unsafe driving conditions. This problem is typically a symptom of inadequate or ineffective grader maintenance and may be exacerbated by materials which are particularly susceptible to ravelling.

15.3. Design of unpaved roads

15.3.1 Geometric design

The geometric design is not considered in any great detail here since the road alignment will normally need to be adapted to the prevailing conditions. Where possible, construction along watersheds is recommended.

15.3.2 Thickness design

The structural design of paved roads has, in the last two or three decades, developed into a highly sophisticated branch of engineering. The design of unpaved roads, on the other hand, has received minimal attention. Unpaved roads may form an initial stage towards paved roads and designs should take this into consideration.

In general terms where the subgrade has a CBR >5 a thickness of 150 mm to 250 mm of wearing course construction will require some 10 000 truck repetitions to produce a rut of 75 mm, which is regarded as the failure criterion.

15.3.3 Materials selection

There are various specifications for the grading of ideal materials for gravel roads. This may well depend, to a large extent, on what is available within economic haul distances. An angular aggregate is to be preferred as experience indicates that a rounded river gravel is unsuitable (Table 15.2).

Technically these represent clayey gravels or clayey sands and it is desirable for the plasticity index of the fines to be varied according to the prevailing local climate, with materials of lower plasticity being used in wetter climates as indicated in Table 15.3.

Higher limits may be acceptable for some laterites or concretionary gravels that have a structure that is not easily broken down by traffic. Lower limits may be appropriate for some other gravel that is easily broken down by traffic. Any variation in these limits should be based on local experience.

An alternative form of specification for an unpaved rural road is set out in TRH 20:1990 (South African Department of Transport (1990) as follows:

Table 15.2 Particle size distribution for gravel surfacings
Data taken from South African Department of Transport (1990)

Sieve size: mm	Percentage passing sieve		
	Forest roads in UK	TRH 14 South Africa	Road building in the tropics (Millard)
40	100		
37.5		100	100
26.5		85–100	80–100
20	60–80	70–100	55–80
10	40–20		40–60
5	23–55	40–60	30–50
0.6	10–25		15–30
0.075	7–15	7–30	5–15

Table 15.3 Characteristics of natural materials
Data taken from South African Department of Transport (1990)

Climate	Liquid limit < %	Plasticity index range %	Linear shrinkage %
Moist tropical and wet tropical	35	4–9	2–5
Seasonal wet tropical	45	6–20	3–10
Arid and semi-arid	55	15–30	8–15

Maximum size   37.5 mm
Oversize index $(l_o)^a$ $\leqslant 5\%$
Shrinkage product $(S_p)^b$ 100–365 (max of 240 preferable)
Grading coefficient $(G_c)^c$ 16–34
CBR $\geqslant 15$ at $\geqslant 95\%$ Mod AASHTO compaction at OMC^d

(a) l_o = Oversize index (% retained on 37.5 mm sieve)

(b) S_p = Linear shrinkage × % passing 0.425 mm sieve

(c) $G_c = \dfrac{(\% \text{ passing } 26.5 \text{ mm} - \% \text{ passing } 2.0 \text{ mm}) \times (\% \text{ passing } 4.75 \text{ mm})}{100}$

(d)   tested immediately after compaction.

15.4. Construction

15.4.1 Subgrade

Many unpaved roads, however lightly trafficked at the time of construction, will with the passage of time capture more traffic and increase in use (and importance) as the local population increases. They may eventually be upgraded to higher standard unpaved roads or even relatively lightly trafficked paved roads. Good preparation of the subgrade for a new unpaved road is therefore extremely important, as this will often be the subgrade for a large part of the future improved road. The sequence of operations is summarised as follows.

- Clear brush and trees over full width.
- Remove all vegetable and organic matter.
- Road bed should be ripped and mixed, sprayed with water to about OMC.
- Compact to 90% Mod AASHTO (about 95% Proctor) max. dry density.
- Material of at least subgrade quality (CBR $\geqslant 5\%$) should be used for 300 mm above the natural ground: usually taken from side drainage ditches.
- Compact to 90% Mod AASHTO (about 95% Proctor) max. dry density.
- Formation level should be smooth and have adequate cross-fall to shed water which soaks through from wearing course.
- Wearing course is placed on the formation.
- In some cases additional sub-base may be required if the sub-

grade is poor or a large number of heavy vehicles are likely to use the road.

Drains should be wide and deep enough to take all expected surface water from the road.

15.4.2 Gravel operations

The location, winning and transportation of wearing course gravels is one of the most expensive operations associated with the development of unpaved roads. It is therefore important that the optimum material be located nearby and used to maximum advantage.

Stockpiles should be kept as low as possible to reduce segregation of the material and operations should be carried out in a manner, which ensures a consistent gravel of the required quality.

The use of a grid roller to break down oversize materials on the road is not always successful, accordingly care should be taken to remove as much oversize material as possible at the borrow pit. If the proportion of oversize material is significant it may be necessary to use a portable crusher to reduce this maximum size. Similarly, blending to produce the correct grading can also be done at the borrow pit.

Care should be taken that the newly constructed sections are not used to provide access to the works from the borrow pit as this may well lead to early damage.

One of the main problems with the construction of unpaved roads is lack off supervision. Greatly improved unpaved roads would result from close supervision by experienced personnel during the borrow pit working and actual construction.

15.4.3 Surface course construction

Good construction practices for surface courses will

- provide the correct thickness of material
- provide adequate compaction
- provide a smooth finish with a good cross-sectional shape
- ensure material is dumped at correct spacing to ensure correct thickness when spread
- ensure good compaction practices which produces a tightly bound gravel with optimum particle interlock, minimum permeability and porosity and significantly increased strength.

Poor compaction results in low-density, permeable materials.

15.4.4 Drainage

Unpaved roads are totally exposed to the elements and rainfall can result in significant maintenance problems. The importance of good drainage cannot be overemphasised. The moisture content of an unpaved road is one of the few problems, which can be controlled by the road maintenance team.

The water in an unpaved road can only come from two sources

■ surface water from precipitation (including flooding)
■ subsurface water from high water tables, seepage, springs and capillary suction.

15.4.4.1 Surface water

Surface water is predominantly in the form of rain (not necessarily in the specific area where the road is, as in the case of flooding). Infiltration of this water into the wearing course can be limited by ensuring a compact, tightly bound wearing course with an adequate cross-fall which removes the water rapidly from the road surface into the side drains without causing scour. The importance of the road surface being raised above the surrounding area is obvious. When the surrounding area is higher than the road surface, the road becomes the drain during periods of heavy rainfall and rapidly becomes deformed or even impassable if the water soaks in.

15.4.4.2 Subsurface water

Subsurface water is derived mainly from high-ground (temporary or permanent) and seepage, but occasionally springs beneath the road may be encountered, especially in cuttings. Capillary rise of water from relatively high-ground water levels may occur in clayey soil. Subsurface drainage problems are usually manifested as damp areas on the road surface that eventually result in potholes. The remedial action may require subsurface drains if the water is due to high water tables or capillary suction, or cut-off drains when the water seeps from areas adjacent to the road. These are, however, not recommended as they are expensive and often require careful maintenance. The use of rock-fill embankments is a possible alternative.

15.5. Maintenance

15.5.1 Maintenance management

The annual expenditure on maintenance of unpaved roads in southern Africa is of the same order as that on paved roads. The management of maintenance is therefore necessary to maximise the benefit from the available finance. Maintenance management should provide answers to questions such as the following.

■ What budget is required?
■ How many graders and staff are required?
■ How often should each road be bladed?
■ What is the resulting level of serviceability?
■ What volume of gravel needs to be replaced annually?
■ Which roads should be upgraded to bituminous standards?

Presently, the management of maintenance of unpaved roads is minimal over much of southern Africa. The frequency of grader

maintenance tends to be based primarily on the number of graders available with a systematic type of programme being followed to utilise each grader to maximum advantage. This may not result in optimal levels of maintenance.

15.5.2 Levels of serviceability

A level of serviceability acceptable for a remote, rural unpaved road with low traffic would generally be unacceptable for an unpaved feeder road to a densely populated developing area. The basis of a system may be as detailed in Table 15.4.

15.5.3 Practical aspects of maintenance

Despite all the programming and time spent on maintenance it is not worth doing if it is not delivered cost-effectively. The importance of sufficient maintenance carried out by experienced and conscientious machine operators and back-up staff cannot be overemphasised. Once the condition of a road deteriorates beyond a certain point restoration of the road to an acceptable condition can seldom be achieved with routine maintenance and requires a considerable mechanical and labour input.

Figure 15.3 Pothole rural road – Congo
Courtesy of Ado Bagishire

Table 15.4 Serviceability levels
Data taken from South African Department of Transport (1990)

Level of serviceability	Maximum roughness *	Required standards dustiness	Impassability
1	200	5	Frequently
2	150	4	< 5 days/yr
3	120	4	Never
4	100	3	Never
5	80	3	Never

* Quarter car index (QI) counts per km over 10% of the link. (IRI not defined)

Figure 15.4 Bush road – Congo
Courtesy of Ado Bagishire

Figure 15.6 Women spreading gravel for road construction – Uganda
Courtesy of Cyrus Swebato

15.5.3.1 Roadside maintenance

The roadside is generally defined as the first 3 m adjacent to the shoulder or pavement.

The main maintenance activity affecting the roadside is bush-clearing and grass-cutting. This procedure is carried out principally for safety reasons, but also to avoid damage to vehicles from vegetation overhanging the pavement edge and to reduce the fire hazard in some areas. The frequency of this maintenance depends on the relevant level of serviceability. Areas with a high rainfall and short-radius horizontal and vertical curves (i.e. short sight-line distances) will require considerably more vegetation control than long straight roads in arid areas.

Vegetation control on unpaved road reserves is best carried out

manually, although mechanised control may be cost-effective in some areas.

Collection of litter should also be programmed periodically, especially near built-up areas and on more heavily trafficked tourist routes. Debris from car accidents, discarded car parts (e.g. exhausts and silencers) that periodically litter the road, and dead animals should be removed as soon as possible.

Most of the roadside maintenance is labour intensive, and great scope exists for the contracting of this type of work to local residents in developing rural areas.

15.5.3.2 Drainage maintenance

In areas of heavy rain storms, drainage problems affecting unpaved roads are significant. Although the overall drainage systems are usually adequate, with time the drains often become eroded and/or silted up and free drainage of water from the road is impeded.

The first significant problem is to remove the bulk of the rainwater from the road surface without causing erosion of the gravel-wearing course. For this to occur effectively the surface of the road should be well maintained with a good shape (definite crown), no potholes, deep corrugations or ruts and an adequate cross-fall. Local experience shows that a cross-fall of about 4 or 5% is the optimum, which allows run-off without erosion. Steeper slopes are prone to erosion.

Maintenance of the side drains and mitre drains should take place as a matter of priority. These should be designed with widths and side slopes (1:2 or 1:3) which permit ready access of a motorised

Figure 15.5 Labour based construction – Uganda
Courtesy of Cyrus Swebato

grader so that maintenance can be carried out during the routine pavement surface maintenance.

Deep v-shaped drains are difficult to maintain (even manually), and are not always effective – even unsafe, for lightly trafficked roads.

In many cases it is cost-effective to clean drains of their silt and excessive vegetation manually. Drain maintenance should endeavour to retain the grass cover, which reduces the erosion potential. This is especially necessary during manual clearing around culverts and drains. It is important that silt excavated from drains is removed as far as possible from the drains and should under no circumstances be used to patch or repair the road surface as the material is usually uniformly graded (i.e. single-sized particles).

Excessive silting of drains is indicative of inadequate water-flow velocities while erosion is indicative of excessive velocities, which may need to be controlled. An ideal drain should be graded to provide the optimum velocity with no siltation or erosion.

The maintenance of culverts is necessarily a labour-intensive operation and should be carried out regularly to avoid damage to culverts and surroundings, as if they become blocked more intensive flooding will occur. It is important that the material removed from the culverts is not used to maintain the road and is disposed of as far away as possible from the road. Cleaning of the outlet of the culvert to ensure free-flow conditions on the downstream side should not be neglected.

15.5.3.3 Surface maintenance
The maintenance of the surface of unpaved roads is the major cost factor in the maintenance programme. Grader blading may be carried out at any frequency from one-week to six-monthly intervals, depending on the climate, traffic and required level of serviceability, while regravelling is necessary at intervals of between five and ten years depending on traffic.

15.5.3.4 Grader blading
The standard procedure for surface maintenance is grader blading. A grader is run across the surface of the road with the blade set to smooth and shape the surface. After grading, no potholes, corrugations, excessive loose materials, large boulders, ruts or erosion channels should be present and straight portions of the road should have a definite crown and cross-fall, while curves should have an adequate super-elevation for safety. Experience has, however, shown that cross-falls and super-elevations greater than 5% result in excessive erosion. A balance is required for the super-elevation not to result in erosion but be adequately safe.

Figure 15.7 Maintenance by grading – Uganda
Courtesy of Cyrus Swebato

15.5.3.5 Light blading
Light blading consists of a light trimming of the road surface on a routine basis. During the dry season, the loose material should be removed to the side of the road, while during the wet season the loose material should be graded towards the centre of the road. It must be remembered, however, that the fine material is slowly lost from the road surface in the form of dust, and the repeated return of the loose surface material which is deficient in fines may lead to the formation of corrugations. 'Sand blankets' are usually placed during light grading.

15.5.3.6 Heavy blading
Heavy blading should be carried out when inspection reports indicate excessive defects. The road surface is scarified and cut to the bottom of the deformations and reshaped. This should only be done when the material is moist and more than 75 mm of surfacing aggregate remains. Heavy grading is often necessary when 'fixed corrugations' have formed. These corrugations may need initial tining or deeper cutting to break them up before grading and recompaction.

15.5.3.7 General
Loose material is a significant problem on unpaved roads. Many single vehicle accidents on unpaved roads are caused by windrows of loose material on the road. These windrows interfere with the directional stability of the vehicles, which may eventually overturn: the higher the speed, the greater the interference. It is important that these windrows are not permitted to become higher than 50 mm. Additionally, high windrows often conceal large stones, which can cause extensive damage to tyres and the underside of vehicles. A common problem caused by poor grading practices is damming of water on the roads by windrows left at the edge of the road. The development of ruts should be

Figure 15.8 Culvert damaged by rainfall – Uganda
Courtesy of Cyrus Swebato

controlled during grader maintenance. Grading should occur before ruts have become deeper than about 25 mm, with ruts being filled with loose material. On excessively wide roads (more than 8 m) the vehicles tend to hollow out the centre of the road and the crown is totally lost. Particular care should be taken to restore and maintain this crown during grader blading. Instances have been seen where permanent corrugations with a 2.5–3 m wavelength occur in the road. These were caused by bouncing of the grader during blading, and once formed they cannot be removed by the same grader without tining, as their wavelength is the same as the distance between the front wheels and the blade of the grader. A carefully driven grader with a different wheel base to blade length is required to remove the corrugations.

The lowest class of surface maintenance is dragging. Many types of drag are available, ranging from steel bars, branches or small trees, tyres or other custom-made devices.

15.5.3.8 Regravelling

Regravelling is the most expensive single maintenance procedure for unpaved roads. It is carried out when the imported gravel on the road has been almost totally lost through erosion by rain and wind or abrasion by traffic, or when inappropriate materials are present in the road. Regravelling should take place before the subgrade is exposed in order to avoid

- deformation, which will necessitate reconstruction
- loss of strength which has been built up in the subgrade by traffic moulding over time.

Improvements to any drainage deficiencies should be made prior

to regravelling. The gravel should be to the grading procedure suggested earlier. The regravelling process should follow the same procedure as the construction process with respect to winning, hauling, spreading and compaction of the material set out previously.

15.5.3.9 Spot regravelling

Spot regravelling is carried out to replace the gravel over areas where it has become excessively thin or worn through, and for filling potholes, ruts, erosion channels and even corrugations. Although spot regravelling is the most common regravelling strategy in the USA, full regravelling is the norm in southern Africa with spot regravelling only being used for patching and repair of limited lengths of road.

Spot regravelling is predominantly a manual operation in southern Africa, restricted to potholes and subgrade failures. It should make use of the same materials as the wearing course. Potholes should be cleared out, the loose material should be removed from the sides, the potholes should be moistened with water, and then they should be back-filled with moist gravel in 50–100 mm layers. Each layer should be compacted (a hand rammer is adequate) until the hole is filled to about 1 cm above the surrounding road.

It is useful during the regravelling process to stockpile small supplies of wearing course aggregate in the borrow pit, at the maintenance depot/camp, or along the road at strategic places for maintenance purposes.

15.5.3.10 Dust control

Dust control is normally undertaken by the application of one of the following liquids to the road surface

- water
- deliquescent salts, such as calcium chloride
- organic compounds, including sulphite liquor, molasses, palm and other vegetable oils
- mineral oils, such as waste fuel oil.

The relief obtained by spraying water is normally short lived, particularly in hot climates. Deliquescent salts function by retaining moisture in the surfacing. Organic compounds and mineral oils function by coating and binding the dust particles. Use of such dust palliatives is only economical when they are available as waste materials and, in all cases, their effectiveness is only temporary. When the cost of repeated applications is taken into account, the application of palliatives is likely to be more expensive than a more permanent treatment, such as surface dressing. They may, however, be a useful expedient until more permanent action can be taken.

15.6. Safety

Poor safety conditions are likely to occur on unpaved roads during maintenance operations. The road is dusty, a windrow exists along the road, labourers are on and off the road, the grader moves at a low speed, potholes often occur and boulders may lie in the road during the operation.

It is important that the section being maintained is fully sign-posted with the correct warning signs. Many of the signs used are often in poor condition, as they are used under fairly severe conditions of dust, flying stones and exposure to the elements. The quality and condition of the signs should therefore be closely controlled and the signs regularly repaired where possible, or replaced. The grader should be clearly visible over adequate distances with a high quality rotating warning light, which must be kept clean and operating.

Windrows left temporarily on the road should not be allowed to become too high (greater than 100 mm) and should be left for as short a time as possible. Under no circumstances should a road be left partly graded overnight.

Labourers should all be supplied with high-visibility safety clothing, which should be kept clean. Wearing these garments during maintenance operations should be compulsory.

REFERENCES AND BIBLIOGRAPHY

Archondo-Callao R (2004) Transport note no. TRN-2: Economically justified levels of roads works expenditure on unpaved roads. World Bank, Washington, DC.

Austroads (2008) Austroads Technical Report AP-T97/08: Development of HDM-4 road deterioration (RD) model calibration for sealed granular and asphalt road. Austroads, Sydney.

DFID (Department for International Development) (2002) *Footpaths and Tracks: A Field Manual for their Construction and Improvement.* IT Transport Ltd, Wantage.

Donnges C, Edmonds G and Johannessen B (2007) SETP no. 19: Rural road maintenance – sustaining the benefits of improved access (SETP 19), International Labour Organisation, Geneva. http://www.ilo.org/public/english/employment/recon/eiip/download/setp/setp19.pdf (accessed 22/07/2011).

Gourley CS and Greening PAK (1997) Report PA3281/97: Use of 'substandard lateritic' gravels as roadbase materials in southern Africa. TRL, Wokingham.

Henning T, Kadar P and Bennett CR (2006) Transport note no. TRN-33: Surfacing alternatives for unsealed rural roads. World Bank, Washington, DC.

Houlsby GT and Burd HJ (2008) Understanding the behaviour of unpaved roads on soft clay. Department of Engineering Science, Oxford University, Oxford. http://www.civil.eng.ox.ac.uk/people/gth/c/c50.pdf (accessed 22/07/2011).

Intech Associates (2005) Seacap 4: Rural road gravel assessment programme module 4 – final report. Intech-TRL, Great Bookham. http://www.dfid.gov.uk/r4d/PDF/Outputs/SEACAP4.pdf (accessed 22/07/2011).

IRC (Indian Roads Congress) (2007) IRC:SP:72–2007: Guidelines for the design of flexible pavements for unpaved roads. IRC, New Delhi.

IRC (Indian Roads Congress) (2008) IRC:SP:77–2008: *Manual for the Design, Construction and Maintenance of Gravel Roads.* IRC, New Delhi, India.

Jackson BD (1992) *Guide to Permanent Unpaved Roads on Wet Soils.* University of Georgia, Athens, GA.

Johansson KS and Johansson FE (2007) Roadex III Task B publications B4: Policies for forest roads – some proposals. Roadex III Northern Periphery Programme. http://www.roadex.org/uploads/publications/docs-RIII-EN/Policies%20for%20Forest%20roads.pdf (accessed 22/07/2011).

Johansson S and Johansson K (2005) Road condition management policies for low volume roads– tests and development of proposals. Roadex II Northern Periphery Programme. http://www.roadex.org/uploads/publications/docs-RIII-EN/Road%20condition%20management%20policies%20for%20public%20roads.pdf (accessed 22/07/2011).

Jones TE (1984) TRRL Report 1111: The Kenya maintenance study on unpaved roads: research on deterioration. TRRL, Wokingham. http://www.transport-links.org/transport_links/filearea/publications/1_274_LR1111%20Kenya%20Maintenance%20study%20-%20research%20on%20deterioration.pdf (accessed 22/07/2011).

Louis Berger Group (2005) 4654RO/B.1./3a/3.5/010: Low cost design standards for rural roads projects in Romania. Lewis Berger Group Inc. for International Bank of Reconstruction and Development (IBRD), Washington, DC.

Millard RS (1993) *Road Building in the Tropics – State-of-the-Art Review.* TRL, Crowthorne.

Naidoo K and Purchase RB (2001) Managing unpaved roads in urban areas. 20th South African Transport Conference, Pretoria.

Nnanna OJ (2003) Research Department occasional paper no. 27: Highway maintenance in Nigeria: Lessons from other countries. Central Bank of Nigeria, Abuja.

Paige Green P (2007) New perspectives in unsealed roads in South Africa. Low Volume Roads Workshop, Nelson.

Pinard MI (2010) Working paper no. 90: Guidelines on vehicle overload control in eastern and southern Africa. Sub-Saharan Africa Transport Policy Programme, International Bank of Reconstruction and Development/World Bank, Washington, DC. http://siteresources.worldbank.org/EXTAFRSUBSAHTRA/Resources/1513929-1262811936256/SSATPWP90-Guidelines-Overload.pdf (accessed 22/07/2011).

Rabelland G, Macchi P and Petracco C (2010) *Rural Road Investment Efficiency, Lessons from Burkina Faso, Cameroon, and Uganda*. World Bank, Washington, DC.

Skorseth K and Selim AA (2000) *Gravel Roads – Maintenance and Design Manual*. FHWA, Washington, DC.

South African Department of Transport (1990) TRH 20: The structural design, construction and maintenance of unpaved roads. South African Department of Transport, Pretoria.

South African Department of Transport (1996) TRH 14: Guidelines for road construction materials. South African Department of Transport, Pretoria.

Southern African Development Community (2003) Guidelines to Low-volume sealed roads. Southern Africa Transport and Communications Commission, Gaborone.

Technical Committee 3 Roads in Developing Regions (1994) *Road Maintenance Handbook – Practical Guidelines for Rural Road Maintenance* (revised edition by Intech Associates). TRL, Wokingham.

TRL (Transport Research Laboratory) (1994) *International Road Maintenance Handbook: Practical Guidelines for Rural Road Maintenance* (revised by Intech Associates). TRL,

Wokingham. http://www.metschies.com/downloads/021-Road-Maintenace-4-Structures-Traffic-Control.pdf (accessed 22/07/2011).

Usace (US Army Corps of Engineers) (2005) Improved performance of unpaved roads during spring thaw. TRB, Washington, DC.

US Department of Agriculture (Usda) (2000) *Drainage Improvement Guide for Unpaved Roads*. Washington, DC. www.centralcoastrcandd.org/pdf/UnpavedRoads2.pdf (accessed 22/07/2011).

US Department of the Army (1995) TM 5–626: Unsurfaced road maintenance management. US Department of the Army. Washington, DC.

Villumsen A, Stuhr Jørgensen A, Barten A *et al.* (2007) Road construction in Greenland – the Greenlandic case. Roadex III Northern Periphery Programme. http://www.roadex.org/uploads/publications/docs-RIII-EN/The%20Greenlandic%20Case%20-%20RIII.pdf (accessed 22/07/2011).

Deterioration and Maintenance of Pavements
ISBN: 978-0-7277-4114-1

ICE Publishing. All rights reserved
http://dx.doi.org/10.1680/dmp.41141.215

Chapter 16
Elemental Paving

16.1. Introduction

This chapter is intended to cover the diverse range of elemental paving, where an element is defined as a single item of construction fabric used in conjunction with others to form the surface course of a pavement. Elements can be made from a broad range of materials, the main ones being

- natural stone
- concrete
- brick.

Figure 16.1 shows the typical construction of an elemental pavement.

The top layer represents two fundamentally different constructions, being either conventional concrete block paving or heavy-duty grouted natural stone. The base design is identical to that of any other pavement and depends on the expected traffic load and the bearing capacity of the formation.

Natural stone can be found in a range of sizes, from large slabs up to 3 m × 3 m × 100 mm thick used in prestige public concourses such as Trafalgar Square in London, to 100 mm × 100 mm × 100 mm cubes used largely for decorative paving. Despite its high cost, natural stone is the material of choice in shared surface feature areas, where vehicles and pedestrians interact.

Figure 16.1 Typical elemental pavement construction

Block paving (50 mm to 100 mm)
(may be up to 150 mm with grouted natural stone)
Bedding sand (30 mm to 50 mm)
(may be cementitious mixture if grouted stone)

Base (depends on traffic and subgrade)
Asphalt, granular or cement bound
(may be concrete slab if grouted natural stone surface
course elements are used)

Natural formation subgrade

In the Victorian era, almost without exception, constructed walking surfaces consisted of riven stone slabs in a range of sizes and thicknesses. There is currently an increasing amount of sawn imported natural stone, typically 125 to 150 mm in thickness and width and in random lengths, laid with a grouted joint, being used in pedestrian areas. In Europe and many Mediterranean countries natural stone setts are used in a range of pavements, both pedestrian and vehicular, but generally with granular joints to preserve flexibility and minimise relaying costs.

Concrete paving is available in a considerable range of shapes, sizes and colours but those used in highway and port/industrial pavements tend to measure 200 mm × 100 mm. They come in a range of thickness from 50 mm for domestic use to 100 mm for heavy-duty pavements. In some countries the use of irregular shapes is common, but less so in the UK. Concrete block paving is used extensively in central shared surface areas.

The recent move towards SUDS (sustainable urban drainage systems) exclusively uses concrete block paving. Concrete blocks can have either a square or a chamfered edge and can be a made in a broad range of surface textures and exposed aggregate finishes. In Germany, where block-makers tend to be smaller and more local, many towns have their own special exposed aggregate mix.

Brick paving is similarly available in a range of colours but tends to have a regular 200 mm × 100 mm plan size × 50 or 65 mm in thickness. Edges can be square or chamfered.

16.2. Natural stone sett paving

In urban areas in the UK, especially where heavy loads were generated from adjacent industry and particularly ports, the use of stone sett paving became normal. Setts had two major advantages: first, they were resistant to the imposed stresses from the iron tyres of carts; and, second, they provided some grip for the feet of the horses pulling the carts, which were the principal means of transporting goods at the time.

In some areas local hard stone was used where it was available, and these tended to be rectangular sections 6 × 10 inches deep

215

(150 mm × 250 mm) in plan and typically 8 inches (200 mm) deep, with the larger dimension laid across the road. In many port areas the use of smaller granite setts in the form of a 150 mm or 200 mm cube was the norm, these setts having usually arrived as ballast in returning trading ships.

Experience indicates that there are two different ways of constructing sett paving; it is convenient to refer to them as normal and heavy. In the latter case a concrete supporting layer will be found under the setts. The typical cross-section of heavy construction is shown in Figure 16.2 and it should be noted that the sett is not laid directly onto the concrete, but rather onto a 12–20 mm thick bed of tarred chippings. When laid, the sett construction is sealed with hot poured tar for the top half of the sett. This ensures a degree of flexibility and a very high resistance to moisture penetration, the latter being important in the days of horse-drawn traffic.

Clinker ashes can be found in the lowest layer, these being the product of coal-fired boilers and furnaces. From about 1850 onwards, most industrial processes needed steam-driven motive power, requiring coal-powered boilers and furnaces.

Consequently furnace clinker ashes were in ready supply and in many cases could be obtained at no cost, as the factory owners were very happy to have somebody take them away. For this reason many highway constructions between 1800 and 1920

contained ashes. In some cases they were stabilised by the use of about 5% of cement, which in the Manchester area was found to be especially suitable in reinstatements (utility cuts) because they ensured no settlement and were not too hard to excavate.

Setts are still widely used in Scandinavia, Germany and most Mediterranean countries, although it is normal for the top half of the joint to be filled with 3–6 mm nominal size crushed granite. Filling with a granular material has the great advantage that relaying is a straightforward affair, with very limited materials cost.

Figures 16.3 and 16.4 show the installation of tram tracks and associated sett paving in Barnsley circa 1900.

Figure 16.3 Sett paving construction, Barnsley, UK, c. 1900
Courtesy of Tasker Trust

Figure 16.2 Typical heavy sett construction, c. 1900

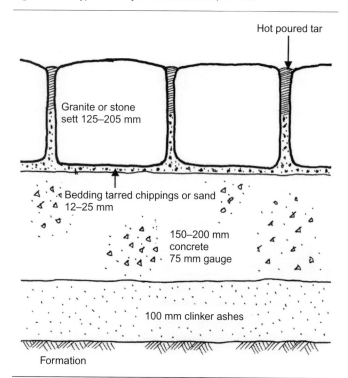

Figure 16.4 Sealing sett paved construction, Barnsley, UK, c. 1900
Courtesy of Tasker Trust

It can be seen that the setts are bedded in a granular material and are laid to a camber between the rails. An indication of the size of the setts can be seen by comparison with the man looking directly into the camera in Figure 16.3.

The dress code of the day was that the labourers wore flat caps and the foreman a bowler hat. On larger jobs it would not have been unusual to find a more senior person wearing a top hat.

In Figure 16.4, the foreman can be seen using a 'beetle', which is a heavy wooden tamping tool used for settling the sett into the granular bed prior to filling the joints with liquid tar, which was heated on site in the boiler, which can be seen in the right of the picture. In the situation seen here the tram lines clearly act as a robust edge restraint.

16.3. Block paving

Four types of block paving are identified as

- wood
- rubber
- concrete
- brick.

The first two were used in the early 1800s, particularly near hospitals where the noise of the horses' feet on the natural stone setts was found to be intrusive. In both cases the use of a concrete bed was normal and the setts were held in place by a bitumastic grout. While both surfaces were found to be quiet, in the days of horse-drawn transport they resulted in smelly, insanitary conditions and were only used for a short period. The author has encountered timber blocks in central urban road constructions, which had provided a robust formation to support a later asphalt layer which had lasted for many years. These blocks were found to be set in pitch.

In the latter two cases, concrete and brick, the size of the elements is the same and generally construction is the same, being either rigid or flexible. The pavers are laid on a 30 mm sand bed, supported at the periphery by a flexible or cement-bound base. If a robust pavement is required the latter is to be preferred.

As with all other pavements, the contribution to overall failure by the construction process exceeds that of the design process. This is especially true of all forms of elemental paving, where the expertise of the genuine artisan generally exceeds that of the designer.

One of the problems with elemental paving is that it is very difficult to demonstrate stability and bearing capacity by analytical calculation. Nevertheless, much worldwide experience supports the contention that, if properly constructed by skilled artisans, block paving provides a long-lasting surface course to a robust pavement.

Lilley (1991) suggests that failure is not easy to define, as requirements demanded by one profession may not be the priority of another profession. For example, an architect may concentrate his attention on the visual impact of the pavement. If this is not achieved the pavement will, in his estimation, have failed before it has been in service. Highway engineers are concerned about the longevity of a road, adequacy of riding quality and skid resistance. Maintenance engineers, who are responsible for the day-to-day function of an area, may consider the pavement a failure if extensive maintenance is required (Dowson, 2001).

The performance of block paving relies on interlock being achieved between the individual units. The concept of interlock relies on the transfer of load across the joint between adjacent elements. This is achieved by mobilising shear transfer in the joint sand as shown in Figure 16.5.

16.4. The laying procedure

After construction of the foundation, which follows conventional highway practice, a sand bedding course is placed and screeded accurately to the required level which should allow a surcharge for

Figure 16.5 Concrete block paving joint mechanics

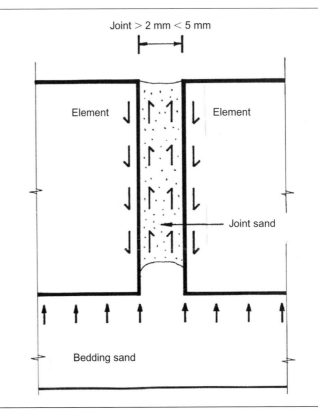

the effects of pre-compaction. In the process of pre-compaction a vibrating plate is run over the surface to ensure a consistent laying surface.

The blocks are laid on the bedding sand. Unless the area is very large this is usually done by hand, and it is important that no work should take place from the bedding sand, rather working out from the blocks already laid.

The blocks are then settled into the bedding sand by means of a vibrating plate or wheeled roller. Jointing sand is brushed over the area and further passes of the vibrating plate cause the sand to enter into the vertical joints between adjacent blocks. In the UK it is normal for this jointing sand to be a fine-grained dried sand to ensure penetration and filling of the full depth of the joint.

In continental Europe, however, the same sand that is used for the bedding is also employed in the joint and after the second pass of the vibrating plate passing traffic, either vehicular or pedestrian, is left to finish the process. As may be imagined, this leaves a very difficult surface, especially for pedestrians, until the surplus sand is removed.

Climatic and environmental factors begin to affect the pavement immediately. The daytime and night-time temperatures vary and rainfall modifies the moisture content of the sand in the joints and in the blocks themselves. Passing traffic changes the quantity and density of sand in the joints, either by wheel action or by the effects of wind, generated by the moving vehicle. Any sand thus removed from the joints adds to the detritus lying on the surface of the pavement. This detritus comprises particles of rubber, dust, organic matter and so forth. In time the detritus settles into the joints between the blocks and forms an upper plug over the jointing sand. Because of the complex nature of the detritus the plug formed helps to seal the joint, thereby improving its waterproofing characteristics.

In time a firm bond develops between the blocks and the jointing sand. The blocks themselves settle a little further into the bedding sand, which is also affected by its environment and absorbs moisture, if present. The combined effect of all this is to compact the bedding sand and the jointing material to a somewhat higher density than that achieved immediately after construction. In this way the bonding of block, bedding sand and jointing sand is improved. This is the condition of the block pavement after the initial settling-in period.

From the earliest use of pavers, it was observed that interlock between rigid components with a flexible joint formed a stable, flexible surface with inherent strength. The jointing material effectively prevents any block from moving horizontally, vertically or rotating, and consequently causes the concrete pavers to act in unison.

Knapton (1976) defined interlock as the ability of one block to transfer the load to its neighbours without deformation or loss of integrity and identified horizontal, vertical and rotational interlock as follows.

16.4.1 Horizontal interlock

Horizontal interlock is developed during the laying process. Blocks are laid on the sand layer and vibrated, causing some fine particles of sand to penetrate up between the blocks. Full interlock is achieved when the joints are filled with sand to their top. To achieve this it is necessary that robust lateral restraint is provided to ensure that the blocks cannot move horizontally.

16.4.2 Vertical interlock

When a load is applied to an individual block without vertical interlock, downward movement of the block can occur. Vertical interlock is achieved by vibrating the pavers, thus compacting the bedding sand layer. This action causes sand particles to penetrate up into the block joints, sometimes to 30% of the block depth.

16.4.3 Rotational interlock

If a vertical load is applied to one edge of a paver, a movement will be generated and the paver will rotate in the direction of the applied moment. The rotating paver requires more space since the distance between its diagonally opposite corners is greater than the distance between the two sides. If the neighbouring pavers are prevented from moving laterally by edge restraint, the individual paver is prevented from rotating, so rotational interlock is achieved.

Figures 16.6–16.9 attempt to clarify the mechanics of failure if interlock does not develop.

Figure 16.6 The interlock effect allows pavers to retain their integrity even when the underlying support is removed
Reproduced from Dowson, 2001, with permission

Figure 16.7 Inadequate sand interlock: individual unit settles relative to adjacent ones
Adapted from Dowson, 2001, with permission

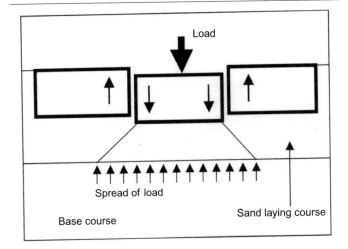

Figure 16.9 No rotational interlock, due to horizontal movement of units
Adapted from Dowson, 2001, with permission

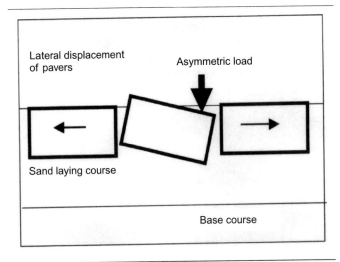

Figure 16.8 Adequate sand interlock: no relative settlement
Adapted from Dowson, 2001, with permission

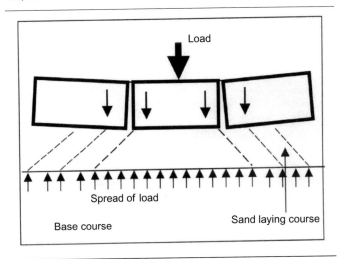

For both rigid concrete and asphalt pavements it is commonly required that the surface deflections be strictly limited to values that are usually less than 0.5 mm. This is to avoid load-associated cracking of the pavement surface.

The surface of a block pavement is dissected by a network of joints (cracks), because of which it can routinely tolerate much larger deflections than conventional pavements without becoming unserviceable. Because there is effectively no cumulative fatigue in the block course, recent mathematical models consider the pavement to be a series of rigid slabs supported both horizontally and vertically by springs.

Tests have shown that the efficiency of the block layer in distributing stress depends on the method of construction. In particular, it has been found that, by rolling a block pavement during construction using a pneumatic tyred roller, the stiffness of the block surface can be greatly increased. Indeed, following rolling, the stresses measured immediately below the blocks may be as little as 25% of the surface (contact) stresses.

Further evidence of the relative importance of the various pavement layers has been provided by studies of deflection profiles in block pavements. For example, the rate at which deflection diminishes with depth depends on the type of base material used. In this respect cement-bound materials are generally found to be associated with smaller deflections than bitumen-stabilised bases.

The fact that the block surface is a structural layer has been confirmed by FWD studies. These studies have established that the pavers may be characterised in terms of equivalent elastic moduli which are often higher than those measured in asphalt pavements. Typical values are given in Table 16.1. Other factors affecting pavement performance are listed in Table 16.2.

Table 16.1 Typical values of layer stiffness derived by FWD testing

Country	Block shape	Elastic modulus (MPa)
Australia	Dentated (crinkly)	mean 3400
Britain	Rectangular	2500–7200
Holland	Rectangular	mean 2975

Table 16.2 Factors affecting the performance of trafficked block pavement

Pavement component	Factors affecting response to traffic
Paving blocks	• Shape • Size • Thickness • Laying pattern
Sand	• Thickness • Grading • Angularity • Geological history • Moisture content
Base and sub-base	• Material type • Thickness
Subgrade	• Material type • Strength (bearing capacity)

16.5. Bedding sand

In some areas of the UK there have been problems for several years where strange failures have occurred. One of the most intriguing has been described as 'elephants' footprints'. This defect presents itself as local indentations of up to 2 m diameter. Investigation has found that there has in all cases been a serious degradation in the bedding sand.

It was originally believed that a good angular crushed rock bedding sand was to be preferred. For example, in Sweden a 3–6 mm crushed granite is extensively used without a problem. In the UK it has been found that on sites subjected to a high volume of heavy loads the angular sand grains were rubbing against each other to the extent that the sand was becoming worn, forming a paste of fine material which was susceptible to being washed out and leading to local settlement.

All sand used for bedding paving should be naturally occurring silica sand. Current guidance is based on a classification of the site related to usage, as shown in Table 16.3.

The categorisation of bedding sand was based on the parameters given in Table 16.4.

The grading for bedding and jointing sand is set out in Table 16.5.

16.6. Modes of failure of block paving

Investigating failure is important because it will determine the ultimate material performance and accurately assess factors of safety. Often the initial diagnosis is inaccurate owing to failure in the underlying levels that manifests itself in the surface profile. Replacement of failed pavements can be very costly, especially

Table 16.3 Bedding sand categories (Data taken from BS 7533-3)

Sand categories

Category	Application
1	Pavements subject to severe channelised traffic Industrial pavements Bus stations Loading bays
2	Adopted highways Petrol station forecourts Pedestrianisation projects with regular heavy traffic Car parks with occasional heavy vehicles Aircraft pavements
3	Pedestrianisation projects with occasional heavy traffic Car parks with no heavy vehicles Private driveways Public areas with pedestrian traffic only Footpaths likely to be overridden by vehicular traffic
4	Footpaths not likely to be overridden by vehicular traffic Private areas with pedestrian traffic only

Table 16.4 Bedding sand parameters (Data taken from BS 7533-3)

Category	% sand passing 75 µm sieve	% sand passing 600 µm sieve
1	< 0.1%	< 60%
2	0.1%–1.0%	< 60%
3	1.0%–3.0%	< 70%
4	> 3.0%	< 70%

when the pavement has been correctly designed and construction fails for no apparent reason.

The majority of structural failure manifests itself in the surface layer as depressions, as illustrated in Figure 16.10. Causes of failure of the surface can be categorised into inadequate design, sand degradation or construction methods.

As with other pavement constructions, failures can be categorised into four distinct types

■ design

■ construction

Table 16.5 Bedding and jointing sand grading (Data taken from BS 7533-3)

Sieve size	Percentage by mass passing through sieve	
	Bedding course sand	Jointing sand
10 mm	100	100
5 mm	90–100	100
2.36 mm	75–100	95–100
1.18 mm	55–90	90–100
600 μm	35–70	55–100
300 μm	8–35	15–50
150 μm	0–10	0–15
75 μm	0–3	0–3

- ■ materials
- ■ maintenance.

Table 16.6 sets out some of the principal reasons for the degradation or failure of concrete block paving.

This rationale may also be applied to burnt clay pavers if laid on a sand bed.

16.7. Heavy duty block paving

Examples of heavy duty block paving are shown in Figures 16.13, 16.14 and 16.15.

If a cement-bound base (CBM) has been specified, this will inevitably suffer from shrinkage cracking due to thermal movement. In these circumstances, especially with a heavy duty

Figure 16.10 Example of surface deformations in block paving
Reproduced from Dowson, 2001, with permission

Figure 16.11 Creep in pavers under traffic due to incorrect bonding
Reproduced from Dowson, 2001, with permission

Figure 16.12 Pushing of pavers due to sand bed being too thick
Reproduced from Dowson, 2001, with permission

Figure 16.13 Example of heavy duty pavers – Dallas Fort Worth, Texas, USA
Reproduced from Dowson, 2001, with permission

Table 16.6 Failures in concrete block paving: some causal factors
Reproduced from Dowson, 2001, with permission

Design

Inadequate evaluation of formation bearing capacity
Inadequate falls to facilitate drainage, resulting in ponding
Inadequate edge restraint
Inadequate detailing of surface course bonding, leading to creep under vehicle braking loading
Inadequate detailing of joints in base, leading to loss of fines in sand bed and resulting in localised settlement
Incorrect detailing of vertical alignment, causing impact by vehicles, especially buses in a pedestrianised area

Construction

Sand bed too thick, leading to uneven settlement
Sand bed too thin, leading to fracture of blocks
Irregular joint thickness to achieve straight lines in laid blocks
Incorrect bonding of elements; if trafficked, must be herringbone and not stretcher bond
Use of unskilled labour
Incorrect cutting adjacent to edge restraints
Incorrect cutting around access chambers
Variable open texture of formation allows migration of bedding course sand fines, leading to local settlement
Incorrect setting out of location of edge restraints, requiring small cuts
Irregular formation, especially on reconstruction or overlay
Not keeping sanding of joints up to laying
Edge restraint not sufficiently robust or inadequately anchored
Joint thickness inadequate, leading to spalling of elements

Materials

Incorrect bedding sand specification for usage
Degradation of bedding sand, leading to evacuation of fines and subsequent settlement due to loss of support – equivalent of mud pumping from formation of flexible construction
Faulty manufacture of pavers, mix constituents or curing

Maintenance

Progressive removal of joint sand by suction sweepers
Lateral movement of blocks due to inadequate support to sides of utility or other excavation
Surface degradation due to abrasion
Local overload due to transient point loads

pavement, there is a high probability that fines from the sand laying course will migrate into the base, leading to local surface depressions. This was particularly the case in one of the early airfield applications at Dallas Fort Worth Airport, where after a short time local transverse depressions were noted in the surface. On investigation, migration of fines into the crack in the underlying CBM was found (Soule, 1995) Consequently, if a CBM is used there is merit in considering the use of a geotextile layer to prevent this happening.

As with all pavements, the selection of a non-frost susceptible sub-base is essential.

If inadequate lateral restraint is provided the blocks will 'float' horizontally, resulting in a lack of rotational interlock with a serious loss of stability, which will destabilise the construction. Assuming lateral restraint to be adequate, deformation failure must be due to vertical movement caused by loss of support.

Figure 16.14 Use of spreader plate under jack to prevent local overload and depression in surface
Reproduced from Dowson, 2001, with permission

Figure 16.15 Heavy duty pavement in port container yard
Reproduced from Dowson, 2001, with permission

Figure 16.16 Natural stone setts laid on stabilised granular bedding, Blackpool, UK

Figure 16.17 Natural sawn stone laid on concrete bed, Leeds, UK

Local depressions approximately 1 m in diameter were reported by Lilley and Dowson (1986), which they christened 'elephants' footprints' and which on investigation were found to result from the evacuation of fines (<75 μm) from the laying course sand. This was particularly so in areas of bus traffic. The dilemma was that not all sands were affected and, as the result of Dowson's PhD dissertation (Dowson, 2001), the current standards categorise the geological source of sands in the UK and relate them to loading categories to ensure that the problem is under control. Nevertheless, until the problem was identified and controlled, there were doubts about the use of block paving in various applications.

16.8. Contemporary grouted natural stone paving

Figures 16.16 and 16.17 show contemporary examples of natural stone paving.

REFERENCES AND BIBLIOGRAPHY

BSI (British Standards Institution) (various years) 7533: Pavements constructed with clay, natural stone or concrete pavers. Guide for the structural design of trafficked pavements constructed of natural stone setts and bound construction with concrete paving blocks. BSI, London. Various parts as follows:

Part 1 (2001) Guide to the structural design of heavy duty pavements consisting of clay pavers or precast concrete paving blocks.

Part 2 (2001) Guide for the structural design of lightly trafficked pavements constructed of clay pavers or precast concrete paving blocks.

Part 3 (2005) Code of practice for laying precast concrete paving blocks and clay pavers for flexible pavements.

Part 4 (2006) Code of practice for the construction of pavements of precast concrete flags or natural stone slabs.

Part 6 (1999) Code of practice for laying natural stone, precast concrete and clay kerb units.

Part 7 (2010) Code of practice for the construction of pavements of natural stone paving units and cobbles, and rigid construction with concrete block paving.

Part 8 (2003) Guide to the structural design of lightly trafficked pavements of precast concrete flags and natural stone flags

Part 9 (2010) Code of practice for the construction of rigid pavements in clay pavers.

Part 10 (2010) Guide for the structural design of trafficked pavements constructed of natural stone setts and bound construction with concrete paving blocks.

Part 11 (2003) Code of practice for opening, maintenance and reinstatement of pavements of concrete, clay and natural stone.

Part 12 (2006) Guide to the structural design of trafficked pavements constructed on a bound base using concrete paving flags and natural stone.

Part 13 (2009) Guide to the design of permeable pavements constructed with concrete paving blocks and flags, natural stone slabs and setts and clay pavers.

DfT (Department for Transport) (2011) MCHW Series 1100: Kerbs, footways and paved areas. DfT, London.

Dowson AJ (2001) *Investigation into the performance and suitability of sand laying course and jointing material in modular pavements*. PhD thesis, University of Newcastle, Newcastle upon Tyne.

DWFS (Defence Works Functional Standard) (1996) Specification 035: Concrete block paving for airfields. HMSO, London.

Knapton J (1976) Technical report 42.515: The design of concrete block roads. Cement and Concrete Association, Slough.

Lay MG (1986) *Handbook of Road Technology: Vol. 1, Planning and Pavements*. Gordon and Breach, New York.

Lilley AA (1991) *A Handbook of Segmental Paving*. E & FN Spon, London.

Lilley AA and Dowson AJ (1986) Laying course sands for concrete block paving. *Proceedings of 3rd International Conference on Block Paving*, Rome: 457–462.

Shakel B (1990) *Design and Construction of Interlocking Concrete Block Pavements*. Elsevier, London.

Soule R (1995) Private communication.

Deterioration and Maintenance of Pavements
ISBN: 978-0-7277-4114-1

ICE Publishing. All rights reserved
http://dx.doi.org/10.1680/dmp.41141.225

Chapter 17
Concrete Pavements

17.1. Introduction

Concrete pavements appear in many guises including roads, airfield runways and taxiways, industrial yards and internal industrial floor slabs.

Concrete roads are less familiar in the UK than in some other countries, particularly the USA, where they form majority of the interstate network.

Concrete pavements are not maintenance-free as was originally believed and with roads they have been found to generate more traffic-induced noise that asphalt, and generally present a less comfortable ride. In the USA, for example, the permitted roughness for a concrete road is higher than for an asphalt one.

Deterioration of the surface in localised areas at joints is an ongoing process with a concrete road. At the present time in England, the Highways Agency, which manages the trunk road and motorway network, will not permit new carriageways to be constructed with a concrete running surface, due to their higher noise signature. Most recent major concrete roads in the UK have been continuously reinforced with an asphalt surface course, which can be removed and replaced as required.

Concrete pavements in the UK have generally been constructed as a series of discrete slabs both with and without dowels to enhance the shear transfer as a vehicle moves from one slab to the next. With discrete slabs one of the major problems is ensuring that there is no moisture penetration at the joint, consequently this is a major ongoing maintenance task. If there are dowel bars present between slabs this moisture ingress leads to corrosion and subsequent failure of the dowel. Moisture penetration also leads to void formation under the slab adjacent to the joint, which permits the slab to rock and the ride to become unacceptable.

In limited amounts it is possible to introduce a polymer grout under the slab adjacent to the joint to stabilise it, and part of these notes contain a summarised case study where this was done successfully to negate the 'slab bounce' in a newly constructed factory unit where the forklift truck driver complained about the discomfort he experienced while moving about the floor.

In a road where the incidence of rocking slabs is too great to consider under-slab grouting, then the option of crack and seat may be considered. With crack and seat the existing slabs are sheared into short lengths (Figure 17.4) of approximately 1 m and the subsequent sections are then seated with a heavy roller to dissipate any excess pore water pressure that may exist. Subsequent to this an asphalt overlay in the region of 150–200 mm is applied to enhance the ride quality. Part of these notes contains a case study where crack and seat was undertaken on a section of the UK motorway network.

17.2. General

- A well-built concrete road has a potentially infinite life.
- When overlaid with asphalt problems are more akin to those associated with flexible pavements.
- The general failure mode of concrete pavement is different to that of flexible pavement: essentially if it's cracked it is assumed to have failed.
- It used to be argued that concrete pavement did not need maintaining.
- Due to the materials used, lengthy maintenance site possessions may be needed.
- There is the need to commit to continuous inspection and joint repair.
- Emergency maintenance can be undertaken with bituminous materials.
- Concrete surface can be retextured.
- Reinforcement in ground slabs is only to control cracks – not for strength.
- Stresses in slab are a combination of thermal- and traffic-induced.
- Testing is best done at night when slab edges tend to lift.
- Dowel bars into adjacent slabs remove the free edge and add strength.
- Concrete pavement failure – with unreinforced construction 30% of bays are expected to have failed when design traffic loading is reached.
- Concrete pavement failure – with reinforced construction 50%

of bays are expected to have failed when design traffic loading is reached.

- Load transfer efficiency (LTE) of joints should be a minimum of 80%.
- LTE problems can be due to dowel bar corrosion and/or void under slab.
- The inspection sequence must be systematic and produce diagrammatic information.

There are six basic types of pavement:

- unreinforced without load transfer
- unreinforced with load transfer
- reinforced without load transfer
- reinforced with load transfer
- continuously reinforced concrete pavement
- continuously reinforced concrete roadbase.

There are four basic types of joint:

- construction joint
- expansion joint
- contraction joint
- warping joint.

17.3.   Non-structural maintenance

Non-structural maintenance comprises

- surface treatment (spalls and local deterioration)
- bush hammering
- grit blasting
- flailing – transverse
- high-pressure water jetting
- transverse grooving
- surface dressing
- restore ride – bonded repair
- restore ride – local inlay
- joint repairs.

Ongoing regular repair is needed to ensure

- no moisture penetration
- no lock-up due to grit in joint
- no arris spalling
- joint life of seven–ten years needs rolling replacement programme.

Drainage of gullies and over-run systems need regular maintenance.

17.4.   Structural maintenance

Classification of cracks

- narrow: less than 0.5 mm – full aggregate interlock
- medium: 0.5–1.5 mm – partial load transfer
- wide: greater than 1.5 mm – no load transfer.

Maintenance measures

- control cracks with stitching or freyssinet connectors
- full-depth replacement can be implemented locally where there is no alternative
- joint lock-up or poor load transfer may need full-depth strip repair
- replacement of full bays to original design specification
- limestone aggregate is preferred due to low coefficient of expansion.

For out-of-level/rocking slabs the following measures should be taken, as appropriate

- normal grouting
- vacuum grouting
- slab lifting.

When a bituminous overlay is used, all reflective cracking should be sealed.

Continuously reinforced concrete may result in possible punch-out, due to harmonic resonance.

17.5.   Problems in evaluation of a concrete pavement

(a)   The remaining life of concrete pavements cannot be assessed directly as it is affected by several factors other than the structural capability of the slab, some of which are
(i)   foundation support being kept dry to prevent loss of support
(ii) joint performance
(iii) ambient temperature range
(iv) joint load transfer
(v)   occasional very heavy loads
(vi) slab faulting.

(b)   It is first necessary to carry out a comprehensive visual survey and produce a record map of the defects which relate primarily to cracking, faulting and pumping.

(c)   Cores would be taken to allow:
(i)   measurement of slab thickness
(ii) DCP testing to assess the foundation support
(iii) samples to be subjected to laboratory testing to assess the compressive strength of the concrete.

(d)   Using a falling weight deflectometer, measurements are made at the slab centre and on the joint leave slab. This allows calculations to be made to:
(i)   calculate the foundation support under the slab centre
(ii) calculate the layer stiffness of the concrete
(iii) assess the load transfer at the joint

(iv) assess the total deflection at the joint (v) assess the probability of loss of support at the joint.

(e) The remaining life of the slabs can be calculated using TRL publication RR87 (Mayhew and Harding, 1987), which:

    (i) provides separate equations for reinforced and unreinforced concrete

    (ii) allows estimation of theoretical life in cumulative standard axles by input

    (iii) specifies standard thicknesses

    (iv) specifies 28-day mean cube strength

    (v) offers an equivalent foundation modulus.

The total traffic to date should be subtracted from the design life to calculate the residual life.

There are some reservations about this method as it was developed to relate to the design of new concrete roads; its use is, however, mandated by the UK DfT for use in the UK. In the USA different methods are used.

17.6. Options available for strengthening a concrete pavement

- The general philosophy in the design of an overlay is to increase the section properties sufficient to reduce the tensile stresses in the underside of the slab such that the ratio of working stress to ultimate stress is sufficiently low to allow the number of load repetitions required in the design life.

- The overlay can either be in bituminous material or concrete.

- If the overlay is bituminous the major problem is reflective cracking – assuming the existing is a jointed concrete pavement. If absolute deflection is more than 50 microns an asphalt overlay is not recommended.

- Reflective cracking can be minimised by the use of horizontal stress-absorbing layers or by stabilising the movement of the slabs by grouting.

- A minimum thickness of overlay greater than that required structurally may be used to retard the development of reflective cracking.

- A concrete overlay, usually of continuous reinforced form, can be used. It may be unbonded (separated from original by a bituminous layer) or bonded to the underlying concrete. Design methods are presented by the US Corps of Engineers, and AASHTO.

- There are several problems with a concrete overlay:
  - expansion provision at the tie-ins
  - possible local reconstruction at overbridges
  - sufficient space needed to work within the existing highway boundary.

- A further option is the use of the generic crack and seat process, which seeks to convert the slab into small sections in an attempt to prevent or significantly reduce reflective cracking. This involves the breaking up of the existing concrete slab and seating it with the use of large rollers. A range of techniques is available, from reducing the existing slab to a granular mass, to the use of small slabs about 0.5 m square. In all cases a bituminous overlay is used. The main practical problem is developing a sufficient degree of control to ensure consistency in the layer modulus of the broken concrete.

17.7. Design of overlays – can be concrete or bituminous

- Concrete:
  - FWD survey to assess equivalent foundation modulus.
  - Cores should be taken to assess thickness and concrete strength.
  - Use regression equations from RR87 to assess total needed thickness.
  - From this, assess additional thickness required.
  - Overlay design is related to practicality of laying and bonding to existing slab.
  - It can be unreinforced, but continuously reinforced is to be preferred.

- Bituminous:
  - Normal evaluation converts existing bituminous overlay to an equivalent thickness of concrete (100 mm bituminous = 15 mm concrete).
  - Use RR87 after FWD survey.
  - Develop needed thickness of concrete using RR87 and design needed overlay based on equivalence principles.
  - Minimum overlay of 180 mm needed to prevent reflective cracking.
  - Bituminous overlay permits rapid wearing course replacement.
  - Cracking and seating of concrete slabs should take place prior to bituminous overlay.

17.8. Reconstruction

This involves full-depth replacement, either in bituminous or concrete design, in accordance with HD 26/94 (DfT, 1994) and HD 26/06 (DfT, 2006) based on CBR and estimated traffic loading for the relevant design period.

17.9. Thickness design of concrete roads

TRL research report 87 (Mayhew and Harding, 1987) presents multiple regression equations relating pavement life in terms of msa (millions of standard axles), to various parameters: namely slab thickness, concrete strength, amount of reinforcement and foundation support. Performance data were obtained from a total of 29 types of unreinforced and 42 types of reinforced concrete pavement.

With the exception of corner loading, the most likely cause of concrete pavement failure is the horizontal tensile stress developed in the underside of the slab by the combined effects of wheel load and thermally induced internal and restraining warping stresses.

Shoulders abutting the carriageway reduce the traffic-induced stresses in the concrete slab and increase the service life of the pavement. Experience in the USA has shown that for the best performance shoulders should be tied and at least 1 m wide. The AASHTO design method, based on experimental observations and mechanistic stress analysis, provides a method for evaluating the improvement in performance in terms of reduced slab thickness.

The practical choice of foundation has been restricted by the need to provide a sub-base/subgrade combination that is non-erodible and provides an all-weather working platform for the road construction, while remaining stable throughout the predicted life of the pavement.

The life of unreinforced pavements is related to changes in slab thickness, concrete strength, and foundation support (listed here in order of sensitive significance). In reinforced pavements, the amount of reinforcing steel also has a considerable effect on life and is second in significance only to slab thickness.

17.9.1 Unreinforced concrete pavements

Multiple regression of the available data gave the following regression estimate of cumulative traffic (T) in msa that can be carried before failure as:

$$Ln(T) = 5.094 \, Ln(H) + 3.466 \, Ln(Rc) \\ + 0.4836 \, Ln(E) + 0.08718 \, Ln(F) - 40.78 \qquad (17.1)$$

where

Ln	is the natural logarithm
H	is the thickness of concrete slab in mm
Rc	is the 28-day mean cube strength in MPa
E	is the equivalent foundation modulus in MPa
F	is the % of failed bays.

Failure conditions are defined by:

(a) a crack width equal to or greater than 0.5 mm crossing the bay longitudinally or transversely
(b) a longitudinal and transverse crack intersecting both starting from the edge and greater than 0.5 mm wide and each longer than 200 mm
(c) corner cracking wider than 1.3 mm and more than 200 mm radius
(d) a bay with pumping at a joint or edge
(e) a replaced or structurally repaired slab.

In HD 26/06 (DfT, 2006) this equation has been modified to ignore the need to consider the number of failed bays and is given as follows:

$$Ln(H) = [Ln(T) - 3.466 \, Ln(Rc) - 0.484 \, Ln(E) \\ + 40.483] \times (1/5.094) \qquad (17.2)$$

The other principal difference being that two values of Foundation Class Stiffness E are given as:

200 MPa for Foundation Class 3
400 MPa for Foundation Class 4

The relevant Foundation Class values are as given in HD 26/06 (DfT, 2006).

In addition to design this equation can also be used as the basis of assessing the remaining life of the pavement, the major problem being that of establishing the 28-day cube strength of a concrete which may be many years old.

17.9.2 Reinforced concrete pavements

The regression estimate for cumulative traffic (T) in msa that can be carried before failure is given by (RR87)

$$Ln(T) = 4.786 \, Ln(H) + 1.418 \, Ln(R) + 3.171 \, Ln(R) \\ + 0.3255 \, Ln(M) - 45.15 \qquad (17.3)$$

where

Ln	is the natural logarithm
H	is the thickness in mm of concrete slab
R	is the amount of reinforcement in mm^2/m
Rc	is the 28-day mean cube strength in MPa
M	is the equivalent foundation modulus in MPa.

Failure conditions are defined when the amount of the crack length exceeds one lane width per bay.

In HD 26/06 (DfT, 2006), the above equation is again slightly modified and values of R are given for different amounts of steel reinforcement as follows:

$$Ln(H) = [Ln(T) - R - 3.171 \, Ln(Rc) - 0.326 \, Ln(E) \\ + 45.150] \times (1/4.786) \qquad (17.4)$$

where
R = 8.812 for 500 mm^2/m reinforcement
R = 9.071 for 600 mm^2/m reinforcement
R = 9.289 for 700 mm^2/m reinforcement
R = 9.479 for 800 mm^2/m reinforcement.

This equation assumes that the concrete slabs do not have a tied shoulder or 1 m edge strip.

If there is a tied shoulder or 1 m edge strip then $H_2 = 0.934 H_1 - 12.5$.

17.9.3 Relevance of RR87 for evaluating existing pavements

Research report 87 was produced by the TRL following a research project to develop a method of designing new concrete pavements.

It requires the use of the 28-day cube strength. If the evaluation is some 30 years after construction, it will be necessary to assess the original concrete strength. If cores are taken this may require the answers to be divided by a factor as high as 1.9.

The only thing which relates to the present-day condition is the equivalent foundation modulus.

17.10. Industrial concrete pavement

There is a considerable number of industrial pavements, both internal and external, where the maintenance issues are similar to those of road pavements.

Internal concrete pavements tend to be designed to conform with the advice contained in TR 34 (Concrete Society, 2003), which is generally consistent with the philosophy proposed by Meyerhof (1962) and where the concrete tends to contain fibres and must be laid to extreme tolerances, particularly in warehouse application where high racking and narrow aisle access is the norm.

External concrete pavements tend to be designed to conform with TR 66 (Concrete Society, 2007), which is based on the use of a 150 mm granular base and is understood to have been developed from RR 87 (Mayhew and Harding, 1987).

17.11. Industrial concrete ground slabs – case study

17.11.1 Introduction

This section follows an investigation carried out into the reasons for problems being experienced with a concrete ground slab due to movement at the joints when subject to vehicular loading from fork lift trucks, and is summarised from Pearson (1999).

17.11.2 The investigation

The investigation was undertaken using a falling weight deflectometer inside a recently constructed warehouse extension to a factory. The location of the tests was constrained by the position of racking and the assembly of machinery within the building. A total of 73 joint locations were tested.

17.11.3 Possibility of voids under the slab

The void data relate to the deflection of the slab under the three different load levels. If a void is present at the test point the deflection will not increase proportionally with the load level. Even a low load will close the void. By extrapolating from the test at different loads the deflection corresponding to a theoretical no load may be found. This may be taken as an indication of voids beneath the pavement. If a chart is plotted for load against deflection (Figure 17.1) where the latter is represented by the Y axis, then if the line joining the various tests forms an intercept greater than 25 microns there is the probability of a void. As the value of this intercept increases so does the probability of voiding (Cudworth, 1997).

There is no precise technique for determining the size of an under-slab void, rather a series of indicators that a void is present. If a void exists it may be possible to stabilise it by under-slab grouting introduced under a vacuum to minimise the possibility of causing the slab to lift if normal pressure grouting is used.

17.11.4 Remedial works

Target or intervention levels were defined for the various parameters as part of defining the contract performance.

The intervention level for slab deflection was determined as follows. It was argued that if the concrete is in a reasonable condition, which it was found to be in the investigation described here, then there ought to be a correlation between the concrete layer moduli and the deflection. The 95% confidence line based on mean + 1.96 std devn (standard deviation) was plotted and considered against the concrete moduli and corrected for the effects of load transfer, as shown in Figure 17.2.

This investigation was used to develop the specification for the vacuum grouting.

From this an intervention level of 310 microns was suggested.

Figure 17.1 Possibility of voids under slab joint
Reproduced from Cudworth, 1997, with permission

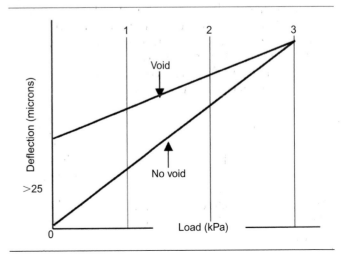

Figure 17.2 Evaluation of possible reduction in void
Pearson, 1999

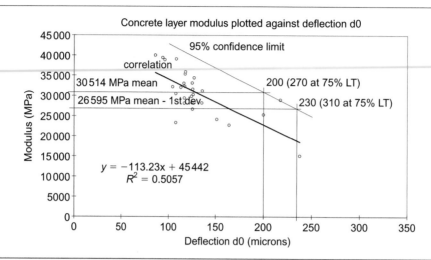

17.11.5 Conclusions from the project

The measured deflections achieved in microns (1000 microns = 1 mm) at the joints before and after grouting are shown in Table 17.1.

17.12. Concrete road slabs – crack and seat

17.12.1 Introduction

The following is taken from a design study for an alternative design for the reconstruction of a 4.5 km section of concrete slab pavement of a UK motorway.

The existing construction comprised concrete slabs, many of which were rocking and exhibiting faulting between adjacent slabs. The subgrade CBR was of the order of 2%, which is why the original pavement was constructed of concrete.

The tender design called for a reconstruction using a flexible pavement. The major problem was that with the design subgrade CBR in the region of 2%, and the design load of 80 msa, this resulted in a total pavement thickness of about 1 m, leading to a very considerable volume of excavated material to be disposed of and a similar volume of new material needed to replace it.

The alternative proposed was to crack and seat the existing slabs and overlay with a 150 mm thickness of bituminous material. In such cases, once the existing slabs have been seated and the layer stiffness of the resulting pavement reassessed, it is usual to find a concrete layer stiffness of about half of that prior to cracking. The accepted design process allows for this to be considered as a very stiff base and to examine strains at the bottom of the asphalt layer and the top of the subgrade, making the assumption that the pavement conforms to a flexible model.

17.12.2 Available information

The values displayed in Table 17.2 indicate there to be some deterioration in the concrete, with an acceptable degree of variation to allow consideration of the length of the project as a single reasonably homogeneous section. A plot of the layer stiffness is shown in Figure 17.3 to illustrate the variation along the section length.

The pavement evaluation report advised the following:

■ The results of the joint load transfer measurements indicated that 88% of the joints in the northbound direction fell below the desirable 75% threshold.

Table 17.1 Statistical comparison – before and after grouting

	Mean	Std dev.	Coefficient of variation %
Before	491.8	171.1	35
After	230.8	29.4	13
Reduction %	53	83	63

Table 17.2 Summary original layer stiffness data

Value	Stiffness modulus (MPa)	
	PQ concrete	Foundation
Mean	23 578	69
15th percentile	17 451	52

Figure 17.3 Layer stiffness plot for section under consideration

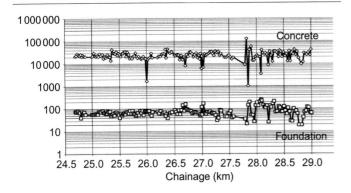

Chainage (km)

■ 31% of the joints tested displayed a void intercept in excess of 25 microns, indicating that there was a reasonable probability of voiding under the slab concerned.

■ As detailed in the inventory survey sheet for carriageway structures, headroom was in the range 5.26–6.44 m: consequently there were no headroom problems.

■ Coring and ground penetrating radar (GPR) investigations showed the construction of the pavement to be typically as shown below over the majority of the length:

> 300 mm PQC (pavement quality concrete)
> 100 mm unbound granular material
> clay subgrade.

The bearing capacity of the foundation is suggested to be in the range 2–3%. This is consistent with the FWD survey when the mean − 1 standard deviation FWD derived stiffness value is divided by factor of safety of 2 and converted to CBR using the following equation taken from LR 1132 (Powell *et al.*, 1984).

$$E = 17.6(CBR)^{0.64} \text{ MPa} \qquad (17.5)$$

17.12.3 Analytical pavement design model

Strictly speaking, cracked and seated concrete is neither a truly flexible nor truly composite design and may be considered to be a grey or hybrid design.

The UK literature recommends the use of a flexible design model using the strain transfer functions set out in LR 1132 (Powell *et al.*, 1984) for fatigue and deformation, which are respectively:

A two-layer model was selected with the layer stiffness of the individual layers being derived as follows:

The layer stiffness of the bituminous overlay is determined from

the type of material used, with guidance being set out in paragraph 4.11 of DMRB HD 26/01 (DfT, 2001a).

For the supporting layer the literature indicates that a threshold value should be established for the cracked and seated concrete layer. This depends both on the strength of the original concrete and the cracking pattern used.

Experience indicates that the layer stiffness of the concrete looses approximately 50% of its value during the cracking process. Additionally, it is considered prudent to use a factor of safety of 2 in deriving the threshold value of the supporting layer.

A conservative characteristic (15th percentile) layer stiffness was therefore selected.

The layer stiffness for the equivalent foundation can conveniently be derived assuming as 2% CBR, which is consistent with the FWD results when corrected for plate size.

17.12.4 Design loading and critical strains

Using a design load of 80 msa and the LR 1132 (Powell *et al.*, 1984) strain transfer functions set out in the preceding paragraph it can be seen that the critical strains are (see Table 20.10):

Tensile strain at the bottom of the asphalt layer

$$\varepsilon_t = 70 \text{ microstrain}$$

Compressive strain at the top of the subgrade

$$\varepsilon_z = 150 \text{ microstrain}$$

Table 17.3 Properties of materials considered

Material	MPa	Poissons ratio
Thin SCS	2000	0.35
DBM	3100	0.35
DBM50	5600	0.35
HMB35	7000	0.35
Cracked and seated concrete (threshold)	4000	0.20
Subgrade	27	0.45

Table 17.4 Layer thickness used for conventional design

Thickness	Material
30 mm	Thin system surfacing
50 mm	HMB35 binder course
235 mm	HMB35 roadbase
150 mm	Type 1 granular sub-base
600 mm	6F2 capping

Table 17.5 Layer thickness selected from crack and seat design

Thickness	Material
30 mm	Thin system surfacing
120 mm	DBM50
300 mm	Cracked and seated concrete

Figure 17.4 Concrete slab shearer

The strain calculations were made using Abatech ELSYS linear layered elastic software, which gives identical answers to Shell BISAR3 software.

Subsequently, strain calculations were made using the proposed layer thickness set out in Table 17.5, and were found to be lower than the design requirements.

17.12.5 Original layer stiffness along section
See Figure 17.3.

17.12.6 Concrete slab shearer
See Figure 17.3.

REFERENCES AND BIBLIOGRAPHY

Concrete Society (2003) TR 34: Concrete industrial ground floors – a guide to their design and construction. The Concrete Society, Slough.

Concrete Society (2007) TR 66: External in-situ concrete paving. The Concrete Society, Slough.

Cudworth DM (1997) An improved method for evaluating the condition of jointed concrete pavements based on deflection testing. MSc dissertation. University of Nottingham, Nottingham.

DfT (Department for Transport) (2001a) HD 26/01: Pavement design. *Design Manual for Roads and Bridges* vol. 7 Section 2 Part 3. HMSO, London.

DfT (Department for Transport) (1980) HA/6/80: Vacuum grouting of concrete road slabs. HMSO, London.

DfT (Department for Transport) (1992) MCHW(1): Specification for highway works. Vol. 1. *Manual of Contract Documents for Highways*. HMSO, London. http://www.dft.gov.uk/ha/Standards/mchw for further details (accessed 14/07/2011).

DfT (Department for Transport) (1994) HD 26/94: *Design Manual for Roads and Bridges*. DfT, London.

DfT (Department for Transport) (2001) Notes for guidance on the specification for highway works Vol. 2, Clause NG716 (05/01): Cracking and seating of existing jointed unreinforced concrete pavements and CBM roadbases. HMSO, London.

DfT (Department for Transport) (2006) HD 26/06: DMRB Vol. 7, Section 2, Part 3. DfT, London. http://www.dft.gov.uk/ha/standards/dmrb/vol7/section2/hd2606.pdf (accessed 23/07/2011).

DfT (Department for Transport) (2009) MCHW(1) 716 (11/07): Clause 716 (05/01) Cracking and seating of existing jointed unreinforced concrete pavements and hydrolically bound mixture (hbm) bases. Specification for highway works. Vol. 1. *Manual of Contract Documents for Highways*. HMSO, London.

DSIR (Department of Scientific and Industrial Research) (1955) Road note 19: The design thickness of concrete roads. HMSO, London.

Langdale PC, Potter JF and Ellis SJ (1999) TRL 590: The use of the crack and seat treatment in the refurbishment of airfield pavements. HMSO, London.

Mayhew HC and Harding HM (1987) Research report 87: Thickness design of concrete roads. TRL, Crowthorne.

Meyerhof GG (1962) Load-carrying capacity of concrete pavements. *Journal of the Soil Mechanics and Foundation Division, ASCE* **88**: 89–116.

Pearson DI (1999) Industrial floor slabs: towards a performance specification. *Proceedings of the 3rd European Symposuium on Performance and Durability of Bituminous Materials and Hydraulic Stabilised Composites*, University of Leeds. Aedificatio, Zurich.

Potter JF, Dudgeon R and Langdale PC (2000) Implementation of crack and seat for concrete pavement maintenance. 4th Rilem International Conference on Reflective Cracking in Pavements, Ottawa.

Powell WD, Potter JF, Mayhew HC and Nunn ME (1984) LR 1132: The structural design of bituminous roads. TRL, Crowthorne.

Deterioration and Maintenance of Pavements
ISBN: 978-0-7277-4114-1

ICE Publishing. All rights reserved
http://dx.doi.org/10.1680/dmp.41141.233

Chapter 18
Pavement Design

18.1. Introduction

While the principal purpose of this text is not pavement design, it is relevant to consider it as it affects maintenance activities. This chapter does not set out to be a detailed examination of the subject; rather it sets out to examine briefly the general principles and practices relating to pavement design both in the UK and in some countries outside the UK.

For the purpose of maintenance design it is necessary that the principles are proven and tested and able to be applied on a range of pavements, the majority of which will carry utility apparatus, which is 98%+ of the asset stock. In these circumstances the sophistication of analytical design is substantially irrelevant as any reinstatement will be undertaken in 'standard' rather than 'special' materials.

For this reason pavement design related to maintenance should be empirical – in other words it must be based on proven experience of what has worked successfully in the past and this leads to the relatively simplistic use of design catalogues and charts.

Empirical design is where the design is based solely on observations of performance; mechanistic design is where the design is based solely on mathematical principles; and mechanistic-empirical design is where the design is based on mechanistic principles but calibrated by empirical observations.

18.2. Design process

The process of designing a pavement may be defined in five fundamental steps

- to assess the design load, in msa, based on life, traffic flow and vehicle type
- to assess the bearing capacity of the foundation and any needed reinforcement
- to assess the required thickness and specifications of the asphalt layers
- to ensure the serviceability of the pavement for its design life
- to define the maintenance profile to ensure the required serviceability level(s).

18.3. Failure of a pavement

Any design must take place against some assumed failure or serviceability criteria. In the case of a pavement, failure is usually considered to be a combination of surface deformation (rutting), generally taken as 20 mm, and cracking when this affects 50% of the wheelpath.

Even in this 'failed' condition the pavement will still be serviceable, to a degree, in the context that its capability to carry traffic is still viable and the traffic may only have to reduce speed of travel by a small amount to maintain safe passage. In the case of a pavement it must be understood that the term 'failure' is not used in the context that it will no longer be unserviceable. In other words, failure of a pavement is a defined state of deterioration and not an inability to allow the passage of traffic.

18.4. Loads, stresses and strains

As with any structure the permissible stresses and strains to which it may be subjected are governed by the magnitude of load and the number of repetitions of that load. In the design of pavements the load is defined as a 'standard axle', which is dealt with in detail in Chapter 7.

The limiting design load is the cumulative product of standard axles over a defined time period (the design period), expressed in units of million standard axles (msa). While the design period is usually fixed during the design process, use of the term design life is confusing since it does not recognise the continual mix, variation and inevitable ongoing increase in traffic. Consequently, it should be appreciated that a pavement has a design load and not a design life – because this latter term presupposes constant traffic per unit of time and this is very unlikely.

The need to understand the concept of design load in msa is because there is an increasing tendency to place implicit belief in the notion that the statistic residual life means (X) years of life. Since this calculation is based on assumed traffic flows, growth predictions and traffic mix it must be understood that these three parameters are totally outside the control of the pavement engineer.

18.5. Design load in units of msa not life in units of years

In the UK, and many other countries, the 'standard' axle load is 80 kN, so care must be exercised when comparing UK practice against another country. For example, in France the standard axle is 130 kN (seven times the damaging effect) so at first sight the French designs appears to produce considerably thinner pavements than does the UK curve – for the same loading in msa! The 80 kN axle derives from the 18 kip (18 000 lb or 8160 kg in metric) axle load used in the AASHO Road Test in the late 1950s. See Chapter 7 for a detailed explanation.

18.6. Development of pavement design in the UK

18.6.1 Road note 29 (TRL, 1960)

The basis of UK pavement design was described in 1960 by the publication of Road note 29 (RN 29 – TRL, 1960). This document effectively pulled together diverse documentation, generally prepared by county councils and developed progressively, as the result of successful in-service experience. RN 29 has been used as the basis of several publications issued for use in the UK and extensively used internationally. It was based on the empirical evaluation of pavement performance data. It also proposed a method for the calculation of traffic loading, based on vehicle usage at the time.

The advice in RN 29 comprised a series of charts which related traffic load to asphalt thickness on the assumption that a defined level of foundation support was available.

18.6.2 LR 1132 (1984)

Following several editions of RN 29, and the result of considerable monitoring, measuring and analytical analysis of existing pavements, the Transport Research Laboratory published LR 1132 in 1984 (Powell *et al.*, 1984).

It went forward where Road note 29 stopped, and introduced the basis of modern analytical design by proposing transfer functions for permissible strains for a range of materials.

Based on these criteria a series of design curves were developed, and a more sophisticated method of calculating traffic loading was proposed. The transfer functions, relating permissible strains in the asphalt and foundation to traffic load, were proposed, based on calibration with 30 trial pavements. Assuming the use of a dense bitumen macadam (the generic UK grading) the transfer functions proposed, which were based on an 85% probability of failure, are as follows:

(*a*) tensile strain at the bottom of the asphalt layer:

$$\text{Log } N = -9.38 - 4.16 \log \varepsilon_t \qquad (18.1)$$

(*b*) compressive strain at the top of the subgrade or foundation:

$$\text{Log } N = -7.21 - 3.95 \log \varepsilon_v \qquad (18.2)$$

where
  N is the number of load applications in msa
  ε_t is the horizontal tensile strain
  ε_v is the vertical compressive strain.

This set out the opportunity to engage in a mechanistic or analytical design procedure; however, while the principles appeared similar to other forms of design, the characterisation of materials construction processes proved to be extremely difficult and, as reported by Brown (1998), there have been no official developments since 1984. This is substantially still true in 2011.

The notes on total asphalt thickness curves published in LR 1132 to supersede those of RN 29 made the assumption that the surface course comprised 40 mm of HRA – a stiff impermeable material, which until fairly recently was the 'standard' UK material.

When LR 1132 was published in 1984, most asphalt materials were mixed using 100 pen or softer binders and, as will be seen later, an allowance was made for the progressive use of stiffer binders. In addition to the use of a different system for calculating design load in msa, compared with RN 29 the report made an interesting move forward related to the estimation of formation CBR, concerning which the following table was proposed. This table has been widely quoted in various literature worldwide.

18.6.3 Foundation CBR

A high water table is one within 300 mm of the formation level and is consistent with effective subsoil drainage; a low water table is one which is at least 1 m below the formation level. The differentiation between thick (1200 mm including a 650 mm capping layer), which is typical of a motorway construction, and thin (which assumes a 300 mm deep layer) relates to the benefit in bearing capacity resulting from a higher surcharge or overburden loading. Good conditions result in subgrades never getting wetter than their equilibrium moisture content beneath the finished road.

DMRB HD 26/94 (DfT, 1994b) was a development of previous guidance notes, all of which were based on LR 1132. It was the first attempt to deal with asphalt materials of different aggregate grading (strength?) (stiffness?) and is shown in Figure 18.1.

18.6.4 UK pavement asphalt design

Design curve relating total asphalt thickness to traffic load is shown in Figure 18.1.

Table 18.1 Estimation of CBR from soil classification
From LR 1132 © TRL

Table C1
Equilibrium suction-index CBR values

Type of soil	Plasticity index	High water table						Low water table					
		Construction conditions						Construction conditions					
		Poor		Average		Good		Poor		Average		Good	
		Thin	Thick	Thin	Thick	Thin	Thick	Thin	Thick	Thin	Thick	Thin	Thick
Heavy clay	70	1.5	2	2	2	2	2	1.5	2	2	2	2	2.5
	60	1.5	2	2	2	2	2.5	1.5	2	2	2	2	2
	50	1.5	2	2	2.5	2	2.5	2	2	2	2.5	2	2.5
	40	2	2.5	2.5	3	2.5	3	2.5	2.5	3	3	3	3.5
Silty clay	30	2.5	3.5	3	4	3.5	5	3	3.5	4	4	4	6
Sandy clay	20	2.5											
	10	1.5	3.5	3	6	3.5	7	2.5	4	4.5	7	6	>8
Silt*	—	1	1	1	1	2	2	1	1	2	2	2	2
Sand (poorly graded)	—	← 20 →											
Sand (well graded)	—	← 40 →											
Sandy gravel (well graded)	—	← 60 →											

* Estimated assuming some probability of material saturating

Figure 18.1 Design curve relating total asphalt thickness to traffic load
Reproduced from DfT (2001) © Crown copyright 2001

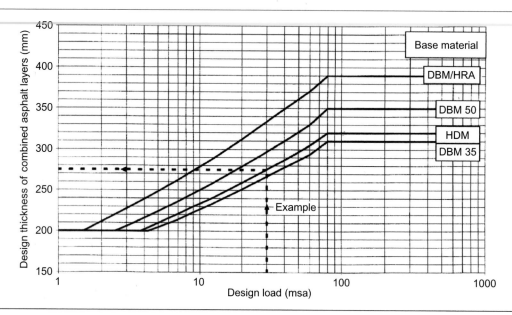

In Table 18.2, which relates to the use of DBM125 with both HRA and TSCS, the rate of increase in pavement thickness can be seen to be fairly constant with an additional 30–40 mm thickness being required for every doubling of cumulative traffic load. This format may be found to be helpful when considering first order rehabilitation thoughts.

Above 20 msa it would be normal to use a more robust mix such as DBM 50 so long as there is no utility apparatus present.

DMRB HD 26/06 (DfT, 2006) introduces the concepts of much higher stiffness asphalt (EME2) and more robust foundations.

Table 18.3 is based on the use of a class 2 (>100 MPa) stiffness granular sub-base formation.

Table 18.3 Typical construction arrangement in UK in 2001

Wearing course	40 mm HRA – 50 pen (BS 594)
Base course	60 mm DBM binder course – 125 pen (BS 4987)
Roadbase	XXX mm DBM roadbase – 125 pen (BS 4987)

Table 18.2 Tabular version of Figure 18.1 for DBM 125
Data taken from DfT, 2001, 2006

Traffic load (msa)	Thickness (mm) [HRA] HD 26/01	Thickness (mm) [TSCS] HD 26/06	Traffic load (msa)	Thickness (mm) [HRA] HD 26/01	Thickness (mm) [TSCS] HD 26/06
1	190		9	280	
2	220	250	10	290	330
3	230		15	310	
4	240		20	320	350
5	250	290	25	340	
6	260		30	350	
7	270		40	360	380
8	280		50	370	400

It will also be seen that the use of a TSCS leads to a pavement in overall generally 30–40 mm thicker than if a HRA surface course had been used. This is due to the lower stiffness of TSCS (typically 1800–2200 MPa) compared with HRA (typically 3500–4500 MPa) and, consequently, the lower structural contribution it makes to the overall pavement.

In the UK, asphalt moduli are always quoted at a reference temperature of 20°C and rate of loading of 5 Hz.

18.6.5 UK pavement foundation design

The starting point for current UK foundation design may be considered to be HD 25/94 (DfT, 1994a) (Figure 18.2). This is consistent with foundation class 2 granular sub-base in HD 26/06 (DfT, 2006).

HD 26/06 (DfT, 2006) contained a fundamental change in design procedure for the HA road network. The foundation had until then been assumed to attain a 30% CBR, which, with proper drainage design and good construction control is normally possible with a granular base and capable of providing a level of support consistent with a surface modulus of 100 MPa. There began a progressive move, however, towards more robust foundations, such as are used in France, where hydraulically bound bases are more readily accepted. The premise here was that if one wishes to generate a higher stiffness (and hence bearing

capacity) in the pavement then it is necessary for the foundation to be sufficiently robust to permit this.

HD 26/06 (DfT, 2006) defines four foundation classes

- Foundation Class 1 ⩾ 50 MPa
- Foundation Class 2 ⩾ 100 MPa
- Foundation Class 3 ⩾ 200 MPa
- Foundation Class 4 ⩾ 400 MPa.

18.7. Pavement design outside the UK
18.7.1 France

An English language translation of the French design manual for pavement structures, which became available in 1997 (Setra and LCPC, 1997), contains much interesting information and highlights the French methods of evaluation and design, which use the Alize software (www.itech-soft.com/en/alize.htm) and are much more mechanistic and laboratory focused than those used in the UK.

In France, the reference axle is a dual wheel isolated axle weighing 130 kN which is equivalent to 6.9 times the damaging effect of an 80 kN axle – so care must be exercised in making direct comparisons. The basis of the mechanistic calculations is the load applied from two discs 125 mm diameter at 375 mm centres exerting a uniformly distributed load of 662 kPa (0.662 MPa).

Figure 18.2 Foundation design
Reproduced from DfT, 1994a © Crown copyright 1994

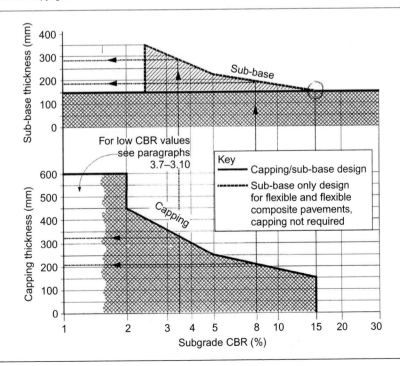

The design stiffness for asphalt in France is quoted at a reference temperature of either 10°C or 15°C and a loading rate of 10 Hz.

Bearing in mind that one might reasonably expect France to have a warmer climate than the UK, it is interesting to note that the asphalt design temperatures are actually lower than in the UK and the rate of loading is also different. For this reason it is difficult to make straightforward direct comparison of the various designs.

18.7.2 Germany

In Germany the system of design is firmly based in a formal catalogue – Richtlinien für die Standardisierung des Oberbaues von Verkehrsflächen (RStO 01) (Forschungsgesellschaft für Straßen- und Verkehrswesen [FGSV], 2001) which relates to a series of traffic classes and build classes.

The German guide is based on the principle of design classes rather than individual discrete designs, which is sensible and is similar to the concept set out in Chapter 1.

The groups are shown in Table 18.4.

What is interesting is that the SV (special class – Autobahn) is to all intents and purposes identical to the UK upper design load of 80 msa, above which the layer thickness does not alter.

Table 18.4 German standard design classes
Data taken from FGSV, 2001

Number		$10^6 \times$ 10t axle (UK equivalent msa)		$10^6 \times$ 10t axle (UK equivalent msa)	Bauklasse (Build class)
1	>	32 (78)			SV
2	>	10 (24)	<	32 (78)	I
3	>	3 (7.5)	<	10 (24)	II
4	>	0.8 (2.0)	<	3 (7.5)	III
5	>	0.3 (0.7)	<	0.8 (2.0)	IV
6	>	0.1 (0.2)	<	0.3 (0.7)	V
7			<	0.1 (0.23)	VI

Again it is interesting to note that the assumption is made that the level of support provided for the pavement by the foundation is equivalent to 120 MPa.

Because of the range of climate in Germany, the country is split into three climate zones and there are rules governing the thickness of insulation support for each climate zone. An examination of Figure 18.3 indicates that the overall construction thicknesses are fairly similar to those used in the UK.

18.7.3 Australia

In Australia the published Austroads procedure is mechanistically based, although the subgrade strain criterion is significantly different from other countries. The current edition, *Guide to Pavement Technology Part 2: Pavement Structural Design* (Austroads, 2010) can be purchased either as hardback or as a .pdf from www.austroads.com.au. An earlier edition used by the author is *A Guide to the Structural Design of Road Pavements*, which was issued in 1992, from which the following paragraphs are taken. It takes an interesting approach, presenting a series of tables from which an initial design can be drafted for subsequent examination using Circly, a linear elastic software program used extensively in Australia.

Demonstration copies of Circly can be obtained from www.mincad.com.au/circly.htm.

A granular layer placed on a subgrade should be confined to 100–150 mm thick layers, and each subsequent layer is assumed to have a positive modular ratio of 2: for example 2 × 150 mm granular layers on a foundation of CBR = 5 would have a equivalent CBR of 20 at the asphalt interface.

Table 18.5 sets out typical values for the value of asphalt layer stiffness at various temperatures and traffic loading speed.

The relationship for asphalt fatigue is given as

$$N = \left(\frac{K}{\mu\varepsilon}\right)^{7.14} \tag{18.3}$$

Table 18.5 Modulus E and fatigue constant K for asphalt with representative speed values
Data taken from Austroads (2010)

Traffic speed	Asphalt temperature								
	20°C			25°C			30°C		
	E (MPa)	K	Chart	E (MPa)	K	Chart	E (MPa)	K	Chart
50 kph	3500	4161	EC33	1600	5515	EC31	750	7245	EC29
80 kph	4500	3801	EC34	2800	2800	others	1000	6532	EC30

Figure 18.3 German construction thickness catalogue
Courtesy of FGSV Verlag GmbH

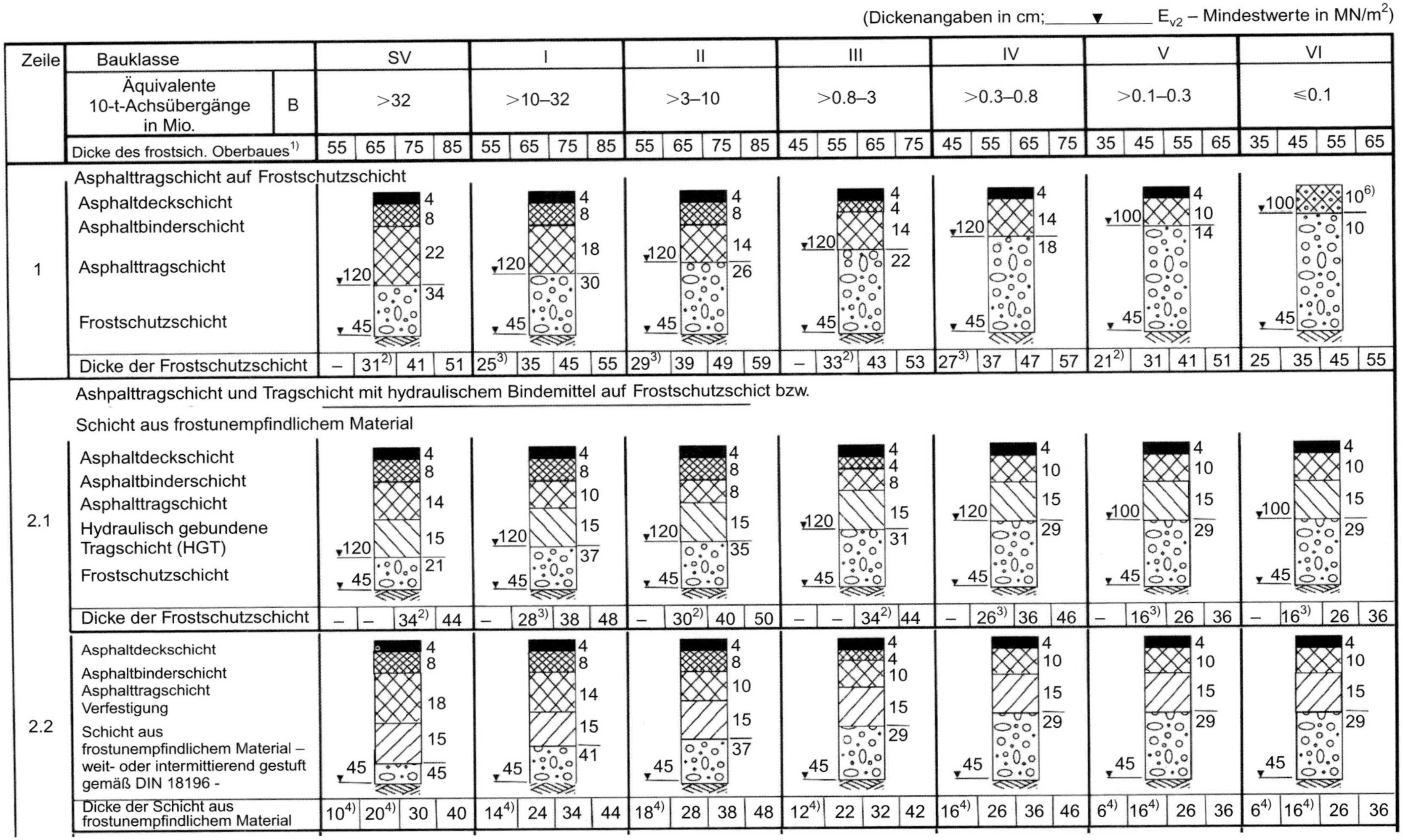

(Dickenangaben in cm; ▼ ——— E_{v2} – Mindestwerte in MN/m²)

Zeile	Bauklasse	B	SV >32	I >10–32	II >3–10	III >0.8–3	IV >0.3–0.8	V >0.1–0.3	VI ≤0.1
	Äquivalente 10-t-Achsübergänge in Mio.								
	Dicke des frostsich. Oberbaues[1]		55 65 75 85	55 65 75 85	55 65 75 85	45 55 65 75	45 55 65 75	35 45 55 65	35 45 55 65
1	Asphalttragschicht auf Frostschutzschicht								
	Asphaltdeckschicht		4	4	4	4	4	4	
	Asphaltbinderschicht		8	8	8	8			
	Asphalttragschicht		22 / 34	18 / 30	14 / 26	14 / 22	14 / 18	10 / 14	10[6] / 10
	Frostschutzschicht		▼120 ▼45	▼120 ▼45	▼120 ▼45	▼120 ▼45	▼120 ▼45	▼100 ▼45	▼100 ▼45
	Dicke der Frostschutzschicht		– 31[2] 41 51	– 25[3] 35 45 55	29[3] 39 49 59	33[2] 43 53	27[3] 37 47 57	21[2] 31 41 51	25 35 45 55
2.1	Asphalttragschicht und Tragschicht mit hydraulischem Bindemittel auf Frostschutzschicht bzw. Schicht aus frostunempfindlichem Material								
	Asphaltdeckschicht		4	4	4	4	4	4	4
	Asphaltbinderschicht		8	8	8	8			
	Asphalttragschicht		14	10	8	8	10	10	10
	Hydraulisch gebundene Tragschicht (HGT)		15 / 45	15 / 37	15 / 35	15 / 31	15 / 29	15 / 29	15 / 29
	Frostschutzschicht			▼120 ▼45	▼120 ▼45	▼120 ▼45	▼120 ▼45	▼100 ▼45	▼100 ▼45
	Dicke der Frostschutzschicht		– 34[2] 44	– 28[3] 38 48	– 30[2] 40 50	– 34[2] 44	– 26[3] 36 46	– 16[3] 26 36	– 16[3] 26 36
2.2	Asphaltdeckschicht		4	4	4	4	4	4	4
	Asphaltbinderschicht		8	8	8	10	10	10	10
	Asphalttragschicht Verfestigung		18 / 45	14 / 41	10 / 37	10 / 29	15 / 29	15 / 29	15 / 29
	Schicht aus frostunempfindlichem Material – weit- oder intermittierend gestuft gemäß DIN 18196 –		▼45	▼45	▼45	▼45	▼45	▼45	▼45
	Dicke der Schicht aus frostunempfindlichem Material		10[4] 20[4] 30 40	14[4] 24 34 44	18[4] 28 38 48	12[4] 22 32 42	16[4] 26 36 46	6[4] 16[4] 26 36	6[4] 16[4] 26 36

239

The relationship for permanent deformation of subgrade is given as

$$N = \left(\frac{8511}{\mu\varepsilon}\right)^5 \qquad (18.4)$$

The loading for mechanistic design using Circly is assumed to be

twin plates of equal diameter, 330 mm centres-apart diameter, calculated from a 20 kN load on each and a contact stress in the range 550–700 kPa.

18.7.4 The USA

In the USA, the empirical AASHTO 1993 *Guide for the Design of Pavement Structures* (AASHTO, 1993) is still the official

Table 18.6 Washington State DOT pavement design catalogue
Information in the public domain

WSDOT flexible pavement layer thicknesses design table for new or reconstructed pavements (metric version)

Design period ESALs	Subgrade condition	Layer thickness[1]: mm											
		Reliability = 75%				Reliability = 85%				Reliability = 95%			
		HMA surface course	HMA base course	ATB	Crushed stone[2]	HMA surface course	HMA base course	ATB	Crushed stone[2]	HMA surface course	HMA base course	ATB	Crushed stone[2]
0.5–1 million	Poor	105	–	–	380	120	–	–	400	135	–	–	440
	Average	105	–	–	200	120	–	–	215	135	–	–	230
	Good	105	–	–	75	120	–	–	75	135	–	–	75
1–5 million	Poor	105	90	90	90	105	105	90	90	105	135	90	90
	Average	105	90	–	90	105	105	–	90	105	135	–	90
	Good	75	75	–	90	75	75	–	90	105	75	–	90
5–10 million	Poor	105	120	90	105	105	135	90	105	105	165	90	105
	Average	105	120	–	105	105	135	–	105	105	150	–	105
	Good	75	90	–	105	105	75	–	105	105	90	–	105
10–25 million	Poor	105	150	90	135	105	165	90	135	105	210	90	135
	Average	105	135	–	135	105	150	–	135	105	180	–	135
	Good	105	75	–	135	105	90	–	135	105	120	–	135
25–50 million	Poor	105	180	90	135	105	210	90	135	105	245	90	135
	Average	105	165	–	135	105	180	–	135	105	230	–	135
	Good	105	105	–	135	105	120	–	135	105	150	–	135
50–75 million	Poor	105	210	90	135	105	230	90	135	105	260	90	135
	Average	105	180	–	135	105	210	–	135	105	245	–	135
	Good	105	120	–	135	105	135	–	135	105	165	–	135

1. Based on the 1993 AASHTO *Guide for Design of Pavement Structures* for flexible pavements with the following inputs:

ΔPSI = 1.5	$a_{surfaceHMA}$ = 0.44	Subgrade condition (effective modulus):
S_0 = 0.50	$a_{baseHMA}$ = 0.44	Poor: M_R = 35 MPa (5,000 psi)
m = 1.0	a_{ATB} = 0.30	Average: M_R = 70 MPa (10,000 psi)
	$a_{crushedstone}$ = 0.13	Good: M_R = 140 MPa (20,000 psi)

2. Gravel borrow may be substituted for a portion of crushed stone when the required thickness of the crushed stone is at least 210 mm. The minimum thickness of crushed stone is 105 mm when such a substitution is made.
3. Shaded areas indicate unlikely combinations of ESALS and reliability for mainline roadways.

procedure. In 1997, AASHTO appointed a team to develop a mechanistic method of pavement design by 2000. In 2011, however, there is still considerable debate about many aspect of detail, which is symptomatic of the complexity of mechanistic pavement design.

AASHTO (1993) is the basis of current pavement design in the USA, with the AASHTO base design equation reproduced below relating the predicted number of 80 kN ESALS to various attributes of the pavement. It utilises the concept of structural number, which is itself based on the assessment or assumption of layer coefficients. One benefit of this method is that it takes account of the effects of drainage on the pavement structure, among other factors.

More details may be found at WSDOT (2011).

AASHTO base design equation (Equation 18.5)

$$\log_{10}(W_{18}) = Z_R \times S_o + 9.36 \times \log_{10}(SN+1) - 0.20$$
$$+ \frac{\log_{10}\left(\dfrac{\Delta PSI}{4.2 - 1.5}\right)}{0.40 + \dfrac{1094}{(SN+1)^{5.19}}}$$
$$+ 2.32 \times \log_{10}(M_R) - 8.07$$

$$(18.5)$$

where

W_{18} = predicted number of 80 kN (18,000 lb) ESALS

Z_R = standard normal deviate

S_o = combined standard error of the traffic prediction and performance prediction

SN = Structural number (an index that is indicative of the total pavement thickness required)
$\qquad = a_1 D_1 + a_2 D_2 m_2 + a_3 D_3 m_3 +$

a_i = i^{th} layer coefficient

D_i = i^{th} layer thickness (inches)

m_i = i^{th} layer drainage coefficient

ΔPSI = difference between the initial design serviceability index, p_o, and the design terminal serviceability index, p_t

M_R = subgrade resilient modulus (in psi).

These variables are further explained in 'Inputs' in Section 3.1.2 of WSDOT (2011).

18.7.4.1 Washington State DOT – the alternative catalogue approach

Table 18.6 can be seen to show a very sensible user-friendly approach, which allows a degree of decision-making by the designer regarding materials and general subgrade condition. It

also has the benefit that the Washington State DOT has confidence that pavements built using this design catalogue will have an acceptable degree of reliability.

18.7.5 TRL overseas road note 31

Overseas road note 31 – A guide to the structural design of bitumen-surfaced roads in tropical and sub-tropical countries

Table 18.7 Basis of design catalogue
Data taken from TRL (1993)

Traffic classes			Subgrade strength class		
Class	Loading msa		Class	CBR %	
	From	To		From	To
T1		<0.3	S1		<2
T2	0.3	0.7	S2	3	4
T3	0.7	1.5	S3	5	7
T4	1.5	3.0	S4	8	14
T5	3.0	6.0	S5	15	29
T6	6.0	10	S6	30+	
T7	10	17			
T8	17	30			

Figure 18.4 Graphics used in design catalogue
Reproduced from TRL (1993) © TRL

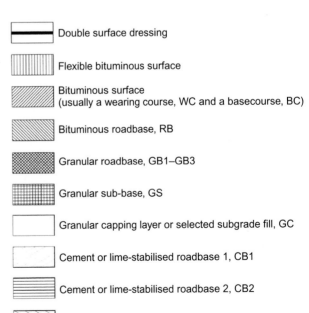

Material definitions

Double surface dressing

Flexible bituminous surface

Bituminous surface
(usually a wearing course, WC and a basecourse, BC)

Bituminous roadbase, RB

Granular roadbase, GB1–GB3

Granular sub-base, GS

Granular capping layer or selected subgrade fill, GC

Cement or lime-stabilised roadbase 1, CB1

Cement or lime-stabilised roadbase 2, CB2

Cement or lime-stabilised sub-base, CS

(TRL, 1993) is now in its fourth edition, published in 1993. It is the result of much work in temperate climates, which has been adapted to take account of different climatic factors, materials, uncontrollable vehicle loading and unreliable road maintenance. At the same time the level of technology available for construction and maintenance can be relatively low. The fourth edition extends the designs of previous editions to cater for traffic up to 30 msa.

As a single source the document is much more comprehensive than the normal DMRB chapters and more fundamental considerations are made. Considerable emphasis is placed on drainage, with the following observation: drainage within the pavement layers themselves is an essential element of structural design because the strength of the subgrade used for design purposes depends on the moisture content during the likely adverse conditions. It is impossible to guarantee that road surfaces will remain waterproof throughout their lives, hence it is important to ensure that water is able to drain away quickly from within the pavement layers.

Table 18.8 ORN 31 design catalogue for higher traffic classes
Reproduced from TRL (1993) © TRL

Chart 7 Bituminous roadbase/semi-structural surface

Layer thicknesses (mm), given top to bottom within each cell.

	T1	T2	T3	T4	T5	T6	T7	T8
S1				SD / 150 / 200 / 350	50 / 125 / 225* / 350	50 / 150 / 225* / 350	50 / 175 / 225* / 350	50 / 200 / 250* / 350
S2				SD / 150 / 200 / 200	50 / 125 / 225* / 200	50 / 150 / 225* / 200	50 / 175 / 225* / 200	50 / 200 / 250* / 200
S3				SD / 150 / 250	50 / 125 / 250	50 / 150 / 275*	50 / 175 / 275*	50 / 200 / 275*
S4				SD / 150 / 175	50 / 125 / 200	50 / 150 / 200	50 / 175 / 200	50 / 200 / 200
S5				SD / 150 / 125	50 / 125 / 125	50 / 150 / 125	50 / 175 / 125	50 / 200 / 125
S6				SD / 150	50 / 125	50 / 150	50 / 175	50 / 200

Notes:

* Up to 100 mm of sub-base may be substituted with selected fill provided the sub-base is not reduced to less than the roadbase thickness or 200 mm whichever is the greater. The substitution ratio of sub-base to selected fill is 25 mm:32 mm.

1. A cement or lime-stabilised sub-base may also be used but see section 7.7.2.

A series of catalogue designs are presented, based on the data in Table 18.7.

The catalogue for the higher traffic classes is shown in Table 18.8.

It is interesting to note that conceptually Table 18.8 is very similar to the German approach and the format could reasonably be adapted for use in the UK, in a similar manner to the National Utilities reinstatement specification (DfT, 2010), in an attempt to get a more regular approach than the one presently used.

REFERENCES AND BIBLIOGRAPHY

AASHTO (American Association of State Highways and Transportation Officials) (1993) Guide for design of pavement structures, 4th edition with 1998 supplement. AASHTO, Washington, DC.

Austroads (1992) *Guide to the Structural Design of Road Pavements*. Austroads, Sydney.

Austroads (2010) *Guide to Pavement Technology, Part 2: Pavement Structural Design*. Austroads, Sydney.

Brown SF (1998) Pavement design and maintenance. *Proceedings of the Institution of Civil Engineers, Transport*, **November**: 201–206.

CSIR (1996) TRH 4: Structural design of flexible pavements for interurban and rural roads. DoT, Pretoria.

DfT (Department for Transport) (1978) Technical memorandum H6/78: Road pavement design. HMSO, London.

DfT (Department for Transport) (1987) HD 14/87: Structural design of new road pavements. HMSO, London.

DfT (Department for Transport) (1994a) HD 25/94: Foundation design. *Design Manual for Raoads and Bridges* vol. 7. HMSO, London.

DfT (Department for Transport) (1994b) HD 26/94: Pavement design. *Design Manual for Raoads and Bridges* vol. 7. HMSO, London.

DfT (Department for Transport) (2001) HD 26/01: Pavement design. *Design Manual for Raoads and Bridges* vol. 7 Section 2 Part 3. HMSO, London.

DfT (Department for Transport) (2006) HD 26/06 Pavement design, *Design Manual for Raoads and Bridges*, vol. 7. Highways Agency, London.

DfT (Department for Transport) (2010) New Roads and Streetworks Act 1991 Specification for the Reinstatement of Openings in Highways – Code of Practice Third Edition (England) April 2010.

FGSV (Forschungsgesellschaft für Straßen- und Verkehrswesen) (2001) Richtlinien für die Standardisierung des Oberbaues von Verkehrsflächen, RStO 01. FSGV Verlag Gmbh, Köln, Germany.

Nunn ME and Smith T (1994) PR 66: Evaluation of enrobé à module élevé (EME): A French high modulus roadbase material. TRL, Crowthorne.

Nunn ME and Smith T (1997) TRL report 231: Road trials of high modulus base for heavily trafficked roads. TRL, Crowthorne.

Nunn ME, Brown D, Weston D and Nicholls JC (1997) TRL report 250: Design of long-life flexible pavements for heavy traffic. TRL, Crowthorne.

Powell WD, Potter JF, Mayhew HC and Nunn ME (1984) LR 1132: The structural design of bituminous roads. TRL, Crowthorne.

Setra and LCPC (1997) French design manual for pavement structures: guide technique. LCPC, Paris.

Sinhal R (1998) IAN 12/98: Indeterminate life flexible pavements (withdrawn; superseded by IAN 29). Highways Agency, London.

TRB (Transportation Research Board) (1995) TRR 1482: Transport research record no. 1482, Pavement design and analysis. National Academy Press, Washington, DC.

TRL (Transport Research Laboratory) (1960) Road note 29: A guide to the structural design of pavements for new roads, HMSO, London.

TRL (Transport Research Laboratory) (1993) Overseas road note 31: A guide to the structural design of bitumen surfaced roads in tropical and sub-tropical countries, 4th edn. TRL, Crowthorne.

Williams J (2000) IAN 29/00 (HD 26): Indeterminate life flexible pavements (withdrawn (9/6/06) superseded by HD 26/06). Highways Agency, London.

WSDOT (Washington State Department of Transport) (2011) Pavement Guide. Available at: www.training.ce. washington.edu/wsdot/(accessed 23/07/2011).

Useful information is also available from:
http://www.pavementinteractive.org/index
Design software:
BISAR 3 (Shell Bitumen)
SPDM (Shell Pavement Design Method: Shell Bitumen)
LEAPS (Layered Elastic Analysis of Pavement Structures) see http://www.Abatech.com for further details (accessed 23/07/ 2011).
Circly: see http://www.mincad.com.au/circly.htm for further details (accessed 23/07/2011).
Alize: see http://www.itech-soft.com/en/alize/alize.htm for further details (accessed 23/07/2011).

Deterioration and Maintenance of Pavements
ISBN: 978-0-7277-4114-1

ICE Publishing. All rights reserved
http://dx.doi.org/10.1680/dmp.41141.245

Chapter 19

Mechanistic-empirical Pavement Design Principles

19.1. Introduction

This chapter explores the concept of mechanistic-empirical design, whereby a mechanistic approach can be moderated by calibration resulting from empirical experience (FHWA (1995) and Ullidtz (1987, 1998)).

19.2. Basic concepts

In mechanics there is a fundamental relationship between stress and strain when a load is applied to an engineering material. Since both foundation soil and the various components from which a pavement is built may be considered to be engineering materials, this relationship can also be applied to pavement design. This may be set out simply:

$$Stress = \frac{Load}{Area} \tag{19.1}$$

$$Strain = \frac{Change\ in\ length}{Original\ length} \tag{19.2}$$

The fundamental relationship between stress and strain is characterised by the elastic modulus, which has in the past generally been referred to as Young's Modulus and is denoted by the symbol E. This may be set out in the form:

$$Stress = E \times Strain \tag{19.3}$$

Stress and strain may be either

- tensile
- compressive
- shear.

Whatever the form, the basic principles and relationship set out above hold good.

19.3. Reasons for using mechanistic-empirical principles

Mechanics is the science of motion and the action of forces on bodies. When engineers refer to a mechanistic approach in engineering they are alluding to the application of elementary physics to determine the reaction of structures to loading. The primary concern in pavements is how the structure distributes vehicle loads to the underlying soil layers.

Weak pavements concentrate the load over a smaller area of the subgrade than strong pavements, resulting in higher stresses as shown in Figure 19.1. In order to quantify how the load is being distributed, certain fundamental principles of materials must be known along with the thickness of the pavement layers and the load characteristics (Figure 19.1).

The empirical approach is based on results of experiments or experience. Generally it requires a number of observations to be made to ascertain the relationship between the variables and the outcomes of trials. It is not necessary to firmly establish the scientific basis for the relationships as long as the limitations are

Figure 19.1 Load distribution characteristics of strong versus weak pavements
Reproduced from FHWA (1995). In the public domain

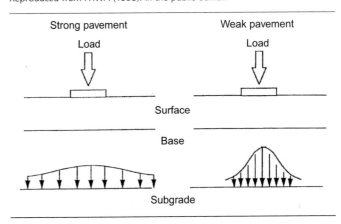

recognised. In some cases, it is much more expedient to rely on experience than to try to quantify the exact cause and effect of certain phenomena.

Most of the pavement design procedures used in the past have been empirical in that their failure criteria were based on a given set of conditions: traffic, materials, layer configurations and the environment.

The mechanistic-empirical approach to pavement design incorporates elements of both approaches. The mechanistic component is the determination of pavement structural response such as stresses, strains and deflections within the pavement layer through the use of mathematical models. The empirical portion relates these responses to the performance of the pavement structure.

For example, it is possible to calculate the deflection of the surface of a pavement, using some of the tools discussed later. If these deflections are related to the life of the pavement then an empirical relationship has been established between the mechanistic response of the pavement and its expected performance.

There are currently no pure mechanistic approaches to pavement design.

The basic advantages of mechanistic-empirical pavement design procedure are:

(i)   the ability to accommodate changing load types and quantify their impact on pavement performance
(ii)   the ability to utilise available materials in a more efficient manner
(iii) the ability to accommodate new materials
(iv)   more reliable performance predictions
(v)   a better evaluation of the role of construction
(vi)   the use of materials properties in the design process, which relate better to actual pavement behaviour and performance
(vii) an improved definition of existing pavement layer properties
(viii) the ability to accommodate environmental and ageing effects on materials.

Currently, the primary means of mathematically modelling a pavement is through the use of layered elastic analysis. Although more complicated techniques are available (e.g. dynamic, visco-elastic), this discussion is restricted to basic linear models subjected to static loading. Layered elastic computer programs can easily be run on PCs and do not require data, which may not be realistically obtained.

19.4.   Layered elastic systems

19.4.1   Assumptions and input requirements

The modulus of elasticity and the Poisson's ratio of each layer define the material properties required for calculating the stresses, strains and deflections in a pavement structure using layered elastic or finite element models. Typical values for moduli and Poisson's ratio are given later in this chapter.

In addition to the material properties of the layers, the thickness of each pavement layer must be known. For calculation purposes, the layers are assumed to extend infinitely in the horizontal direction, and the bottom layer (usually the subgrade) is assumed to extend infinitely downwards. Given the typical geometry of pavements these assumptions are considered to be fairly representative of actual conditions, except when analysing jointed PCC (Portland cement concrete) pavements in the vicinity of the joints or edges, as well as edge loadings on asphalt pavements.

It is assumed that the material behaviour is perfectly linearly elastic, homogeneous and isotropic. Homogeneous refers to pavement layers, which are composed of the same materials throughout. Isotropic means that the material will possess the same properties along all axes (as opposed to wood, which possesses different material properties with respect to the direction of the grain). If non-linear or stress-sensitive behaviour is modelled, iterative procedures are usually involved. In real life, unfortunately, pavement materials do not exhibit these idealised characteristics. This can result in problems during the evaluation of deflection basins leading to unrealistic values of moduli.

The loading conditions must be specified in terms of the magnitude of load, the geometry of the load, and the number of loads to be applied to the structure. The magnitude of the load is simply the total force (P) applied to the pavement surface. In pavement analysis, the load geometry is usually specified as being a circle of a given radius (r or a), or the radius calculated knowing the contact pressure of the load (p) and the magnitude of the load (P). Although most actual loads more closely represent an ellipse, the effect of the differences in geometry becomes negligible at a very shallow depth in the pavement.

Summing the effects of individual loads can approximate the effects of multiple loads on a pavement surface. This is known as the Law of Superposition and is considered valid so long as the materials are not stressed beyond their elastic ranges (subject to plastic or permanent deformation).

To summarise, the following information must be available to calculate the response of a pavement to loading

(a)   materials properties of each layer
      (i)   modulus of elasticity (E)
      (ii) Poisson's ratio (μ)
(b)   thickness of the pavement layer(s)
(c)   loading conditions
      (i)   magnitude of load

(ii) geometry of load

(iii) number of loads.

Figure 19.2 shows how these inputs relate to a layered elastic model of a pavement structure.

The use of a layered elastic analysis computer program will allow calculation of the theoretical stresses, strains and deflections anywhere in the pavement. There are, however, only a few locations, in a practical sense where the calculation of the critical responses is relevant. These are set out in Table 19.1.

The horizontal tensile strain at the bottom of the bituminous layer is indicative of potential cracking of the surfacing (fatigue failure).

Fatigue in PCC is related to tensile stress.

Rutting failure in the subgrade can be predicted using the vertical compressive strain at the top of the subgrade.

Deflections under load at the pavement surface may be used to

impose load restrictions during spring thaw and for determining overlay design.

19.4.2 One-layer system with point load (Boussinesq)

The origin of layered elastic theory is credited to Joseph Valentin Boussinesq, based on his classic work in 1885. He developed solutions for calculating stresses and deflections in a half space (soil) composed of homogeneous, isotropic and linearly elastic material. Boussinesq-influenced charts are still widely used in soil mechanics and foundation design. The governing differential equations for a point load on an elastic half space had previously been suggested by Kelvin in 1848. Boussinesq developed the closed form mathematical solution in 1885 for a point load, while Love extended this work to a circular load in 1928.

In this approach, the stresses and deflections are calculated for a point load applied to the surface of a deep soil mass. Distance variables are expressed in terms of cylindrical coordinates, in which the distance from a point on the surface may be represented as:

$$R^2 = r^2 + z^2 = x^2 + y^2 + z^2 \tag{19.4}$$

as shown in Figure 19.3.

The vertical stress, radial stress, and vertical deformation, u, can be calculated using the following formula for a point load:

Vertical stress

$$\sigma_z = \frac{-3Pz^3}{2\pi R^5} \tag{19.5}$$

Figure 19.2 Layered elastic pavement model
Reproduced from FHWA (1995). In the public domain

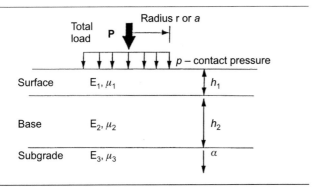

Figure 19.3 Cylindrical coordinates for a one-layer system
Reproduced from FHWA (1995). In the public domain

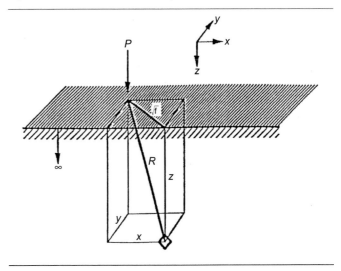

Table 19.1 Location of critical strain responses
Data taken from FHWA (1995). Information in the public domain

Location	Response
Pavement surface	Deflection
Bottom of asphalt layer	Horizontal tensile strain
Bottom of PCC layer	Horizontal tensile strain
Top of PCC slab (corner)	Horizontal tensile strain
Top of intermediate layer (base or sub-base)	Vertical compressive strain
Top of subgrade	Vertical compressive strain

Radial stress

$$\sigma_{r,z} = \frac{P(1+\mu)}{2\pi R^2}\left[\frac{-3r^2 z}{R^3} + \frac{(1-2\mu)R}{R+z}\right] \tag{19.6}$$

Vertical deformation below the surface:

$$u_{z,r} = \frac{P(1+\mu)}{2\pi E}\left[\frac{2(1-\mu)}{R} + \frac{z^2}{R^3}\right] \tag{19.7}$$

Surface deflection at a distance, r, away from the load (i.e. Equation 19.3 with $z = 0$ and $R = r$):

$$u_r = \frac{(1-\mu^2)P}{(\pi)(E)(r)} \tag{19.8}$$

For all practical purposes, the equation for a point load can be used for a distributed load at points more than about two radii from the load.

The deflection beneath the centre of a rigid, circular load of radius a, can be **estimated** by the equation:

$$u_0 = \frac{(1-\mu^2)P}{(2)(E)(a)} \tag{19.9}$$

Example 1

A load of 40 kN (9000 lb) is placed on a 300 mm (11.8 inches) diameter plate. The plate is resting on a subgrade which has an elastic modulus 51.7 MPa (7500 psi) with a Poisson's ratio of 0.4. What is the deflection at the centre of the plate?

$\mu = 0.40$
$P = 40,000$ N
$a = 150$ mm
$E = 51.7$ MPa

$$u_0 = \frac{(1-\mu^2)P}{(2)(E)(a)}$$

$$u_0 = \frac{(1-0.4^2)40,000}{(2)(51.7)(150)} = 2.17 \text{ mm (0.085 inches)}$$

Example 2

Given the loading conditions above, what is the modulus of elasticity of the subgrade if the deflection at the centre of the plate is 0.72 mm (0.028 inches)?

$$E = \frac{(1-\mu^2)P}{(2)(u_0)(a)}$$

$$E = \frac{(1-0.4^2)40,000}{(2)(0.72)(150)} = 155 \text{ MPa}$$

It can be seen from the examples that for a one-layer system pavement, modelling is straightforward. It should be noted from the examples that modulus and deflections are inversely, linearly related so that if the modulus increases by a factor of three the deflection will decrease by a factor of three.

In the Boussinesq equations below the following symbols are used:

$\sigma =$ Stress at surface (MPa)
$E =$ Elastic modulus (MPa)
$a =$ Plate radius (mm)
$z =$ Depth below surface (mm)
$\mu =$ Poisson's ratio

The Boussinesq equations were modified through mathematical integration to approximate the effects of a circular distributed load on the pavement surface. The equations for stress, strain, and displacement **below** and **along the centreline** of a **circular** load are as follows:

Vertical stress at depth z:

$$\sigma_z = \sigma_0\left[1 - \frac{1}{\left(1+\left[\frac{a}{z}\right]^2\right)^{3/2}}\right] \tag{19.10}$$

Radial and tangential stresses at depth z:

$$\sigma_r = \sigma_t$$

$$= \sigma_0\left[\frac{1+2\mu}{2} - \frac{1+\mu}{\sqrt{1+\left[\frac{a}{z}\right]^2}} + \frac{1}{2\left(\left(1+\left[\frac{a}{z}\right]^2\right)^{3/2}\right)}\right] \tag{19.11}$$

Vertical strain with depth z:

$$\varepsilon_z = \frac{(1+\mu)\sigma_0}{E}$$

$$\times \left[\frac{\left[\frac{z}{a}\right]}{\left(1+\left[\frac{z}{a}\right]^2\right)^{\frac{3}{2}}} - (1-2\mu)\left(\frac{\left[\frac{z}{a}\right]}{\sqrt{1+\left(\frac{z}{a}\right)^2}} - 1\right)\right] \tag{19.12}$$

Deflection with depth z:

$$d_z = \frac{(1 + \mu)\sigma_0 a}{E}$$

$$\times \left(\frac{1}{\sqrt{1 + \left[\frac{z}{a}\right]^2}} + (1 - 2\mu)\left(\sqrt{1 + \left[\frac{z}{a}\right]^2} - \left[\frac{z}{a}\right] \right) \right)$$

$$(19.13)$$

19.4.3 Odemark's method

In 1949, Odemark developed an approximate solution to the calculation of stresses, strains and displacements in a layered system. Since then a number of exact solutions to the same problem have been devised

- ELSYM5
- BISAR
- ALIZE III
- CIRCLY.

These 'exact' solutions are only close to 'exact' in a mathematical sense related to the numerical integration procedures. The assumptions made with respect to equilibrium, compatibility, and constitutive equations (Hook's law) are not correct for pavement structures.

Loads are dynamic, materials are not continuous – some are even particulate (granular) – and deformations are not only elastic, but also plastic, viscous and visco-elastic, and they are mostly non-linear and anisotropic. In a physical sense, therefore, all solutions are approximate.

There are two advantages with the use of Odemark's method.

(a) It is simple and very fast, it may be included in a spreadsheet or used in a pavement management system, where millions of calculations must be made.
(b) A non-linear elastic sub-grade (or a subgrade where the modulus, or apparent modulus, varies with the distance from the load) may easily be included. This may be extremely important for the interpretation of deflection data.

Odemark's method is based on the assumption that the response below a given layer will depend on the stiffness of that layer only. The stiffness of a layer is:

$$\frac{E \times I}{(1 - \mu^2)} \qquad (19.14)$$

where

E = elastic modulus
I = moment of inertia
μ = Poisson's ratio.

This assumption is used to change a layered system into a semi-infinite halfspace, for which Boussinesq's equations may be used.

Consider a two-layer system as shown below:

h_1, E_1, μ_1
E_2, μ_2

A layer of thickness h_1, modulus E_1, and Poisson's ratio, μ_1 rests on a material with a modulus E_2, and a Poisson's ratio μ_2.

The stiffness of the upper layer is

$$\frac{I \times E_1}{1 - \mu^2} = \frac{\left(\frac{1}{12}\right) \times b \times h_1^3 \times E_1}{1 - \mu^2} \qquad (19.15)$$

where b is the width under consideration (this can, in many cases, be assumed to be unity to simplify the process).

If the system is transformed to the following:

h_e, E_2, μ_2
E_2, μ_2

Where h_e is the equivalent thickness and the stiffness will be:

$$\frac{I \times E_2}{1 - \mu_2^2} = \frac{\left(\frac{1}{12}\right) \times b \times h_e^3 \times E_2}{1 - \mu_2^2} \qquad (19.16)$$

For the new stiffness to be identical to the original stiffness then:

$$h_e = h_1 \sqrt[3]{\frac{E_1}{E_2} \times \frac{1 - \mu_2^2}{1 - \mu_1^2}} \qquad (19.17)$$

The new system is a semi-infinite half space where Boussinesq's equation can be used.

With a multi-layer system the method can be used successively. The first layer is changed to the elastic parameters of layer two and the equivalent thickness, h_{e1}, is calculated. Any materials below layer two are assumed to have the same elastic parameters as layer two. Then layer one and two are changed to the elastic parameter of layer three, etc.

It has been found that the best argument with the 'exact solutions normally is obtained when Poisson's ration is assumed to be the same for all layers' (Ullidtz, 1987). The equation for the equivalent thickness may then be written as:

$$h_{e,n-1} = F \sum_{i=1}^{n-1} \left[h_1 \sqrt[3]{\frac{E_1}{E_2}} \right] \qquad (19.18)$$

To get a better argument with the exact solutions, then, equivalent thickness is normally multiplied by a factor F. For the first structural interface (e.g. between surfacing and base) F is 0.9 for a two layer system and 1.0 for a multi-layer system. For all other interfaces F is 0.8.

19.4.3.1 Example

A 300 mm diameter plate is loaded to 40 kN (9000 lb) on a bituminous pavement over a subgrade. The bituminous layer is 15 cm (6 inches) thick and has a modulus of elasticity of 3450 MPa (500 000 psi); and a subgrade modulus of 69 MPa (10 000 psi). Assuming Poisson's ratio to be 0.35.

(a)   What is the deflection of the centre of the loaded area?
(b)   What is the vertical stress at the top of the subgrade?

19.5.   Some thoughts

The total deflection of the pavement surface is the sum of the subgrade deflection and the compression of the bituminous layer.

First calculate the deflections at the surface and at a depth of 150 mm from the bituminous half space.

Calculate the compression of the asphalt layer by subtracting the deflection at the bottom of the layer from the deflection at the surface.

Convert the asphalt layer to an equivalent subgrade thickness using Odemark's method and calculate the subgrade deflection at this depth.

The sum of the bituminous compression and the deflection of the subgrade at this point can be summed to obtain the overall deflection.

The stress at the top of the subgrade can also be calculated at a depth equal to the equivalent bituminous thickness.

(a)   Calculate the plate pressure, then the deflection at the surface of the bituminous half space using Equation 19.11 (note since $z = 0$, most terms drop out).

$$\sigma_0 = \frac{load}{area} = \frac{40\,000\ \text{N}}{\pi(150)^2} = 0.56\ \text{MPa}\ \ (81.2\ \text{psi})$$

$$d_0 = \frac{2(1-\mu^2)\sigma_0 a}{E}$$

$$= \frac{2(1-0.35^2)(0.56)(150)}{3450}$$

$$= 0.043\ \text{mm}$$

Note the above equation is an algebraic simplification of Equation 19.9 for the case where $z = 0$

(b)   Calculate deflection at 150 mm (Equation 19.11)

$$d_{150} = \frac{(1+0.35)(0.56)(150)}{3450}$$

$$\left(\frac{1}{\sqrt{1+\left[\frac{150}{150}\right]^2}} + (1-2(0.35)) \left(\sqrt{1+\left[\frac{150}{a150}\right]^2} - \left[\frac{150}{a150}\right] \right) \right)$$

$$d_{150} = 0.027\ \text{mm}$$

(c)   Bituminous compression
$$= d_0 - dz$$
$$= 0.043\ \text{mm} - 0.027\ \text{mm}$$
$$= \textbf{0.016 mm A}$$

(d)   Calculate equivalent thickness of bituminous layer (as subgrade) using Equation 19.16

$$h_{e,n-1} = F \sum_{i=1}^{n-1} \left[h_1 \times \sqrt[3]{\frac{E_i}{E_h}} \right]$$

$$= (0.9)(150) \sqrt[3]{\frac{3450}{69}} = 497\ \text{mm}$$

(e)   Calculate the deflection at h_e using Equation 19.11

$$dh_e = \frac{(1+0.35)(0.56)(150)}{69} \left(\frac{1}{\sqrt{1+\left[\frac{497}{150}\right]^2}} + (1-2(0.35)) \right.$$

$$\left. \times \left(\sqrt{1+\left[\frac{497}{150}\right]^2} - \left[\frac{497}{150}\right] \right) \right)$$

$$= \textbf{0.547 mm B}$$

(f)   **Total deflection = A + B =**
0.016 mm + 0.547 mm = **0.563 mm**

(g)   Stress at the top of the subgrade

Using equation 19.8, stress at the top of the subgrade

$$\sigma_z = 0.56 \left[1 - \frac{1}{\left(1 + \left[\dfrac{150}{497} \right]^2 \right)^{3/2}} \right]$$

$$= 0.069 \text{MPa} = \textbf{69 kPa (10 psi)}$$

REFERENCES AND BIBLIOGRAPHY

FHWA (1995) FHWA-HI-95–021: Pavement analysis and design checks. NHI course no. 13130, *Participant's Manual*. National Highway Institute, Washington, DC.

Thompson WS (Lord Kelvin) (1848) Note on the integration of the equations of equilibrium of an elastic solid, *Cambridge and Dublin Mathematical Journal*. February.

Ullidtz P (1987) *Pavement Analysis*. Elsevier, Amsterdam.

Ullidtz P (1998) *Modelling Flexible Pavement Response and Performance*. Polyteknisk Forlag, Lyngby, Denmark.

Deterioration and Maintenance of Pavements
ISBN: 978-0-7277-4114-1

ICE Publishing. All rights reserved
http://dx.doi.org/10.1680/dmp.41141.253

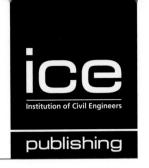

Chapter 20
Analytical Pavement Design – General Principles

20.1. Introduction

This chapter sets out the basis of the analytical design procedure. It is relevant here since pavement evaluation uses backcalculation, which is essentially the same process as forward calculation, but used iteratively until a sensible judgement can be made from the data available. The overall objective of the analytical design process is to determine the required thickness for a chosen asphalt mix to satisfy the design conditions, such that it does not fail due to fatigue and the formation does not fail due to deformation.

The method of design may be applied for service lives for either of the two terminal conditions used in the UK. These are **Failure**, corresponding to a 20 mm rut with extensive wheeltrack cracking and **Investigatory,** corresponding to a 10 mm rut or the first signs of wheeltrack cracking. TRL road note 29 (TRL, 1960) and LR 1132 (Powell *et al.*, 1984) used the terms 'failure' and 'critical'.

One major advantage with analytical design is that the process can be used with any materials, providing their fundamental characteristics can be defined. This is especially beneficial with the increasing desire to use recycled and hitherto marginal materials.

Figures 20.1 and 20.2 set out the basis of the design methodology. This procedure may be used to calculate the service life of

Figure 20.1 Basic procedure for fatigue design
Reproduced from Brown (1986), with permission

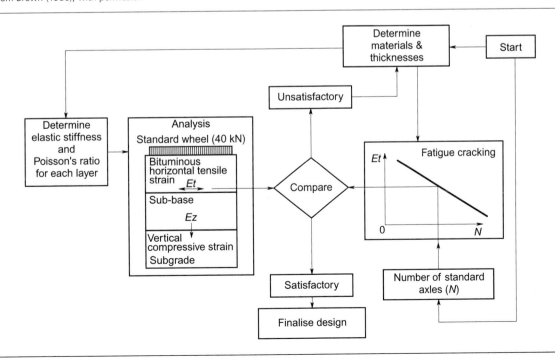

Figure 20.2 Calculation of pavement life
Reproduced from Brown (1986), with permission

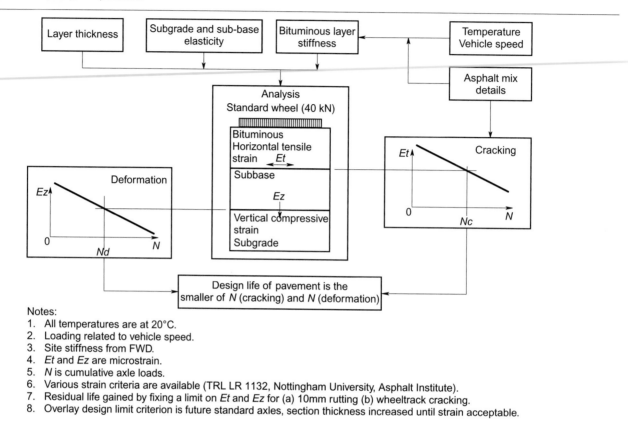

Notes:
1. All temperatures are at 20°C.
2. Loading related to vehicle speed.
3. Site stiffness from FWD.
4. *Et* and *Ez* are microstrain.
5. *N* is cumulative axle loads.
6. Various strain criteria are available (TRL LR 1132, Nottingham University, Asphalt Institute).
7. Residual life gained by fixing a limit on *Et* and *Ez* for (a) 10mm rutting (b) wheeltrack cracking.
8. Overlay design limit criterion is future standard axles, section thickness increased until strain acceptable.

a given pavement structure. The only difference between forward and back-calculation is as follows:

Forward calculation – the required life is specified
   Back calculation – the remaining life is calculated

20.2. Design criteria

20.2.1 Asphalt fatigue strain

The development of this criterion, which is sometimes referred to as a strain or fatigue transfer function, originally took place in the laboratory, but considerable scaling has to be done to make the results applicable to site operating conditions. The research used to establish the strain criterion involves cyclic loading of test specimens to failure.

In the 'real life' pavement, 'rest periods' between load applications occur, even on heavily trafficked roads, and a finite time is required for a crack, once initiated at the bottom of the base, to propagate upwards through the asphalt layer to the surface.

20.2.2 Comparison of asphalt strain criteria

Selection of the relevant strain criterion is the single most important decision to be made when using the analytical design process.

The TRL equations below (Powell *et al.*, 1984) have been set out below and relate, in the case of asphalt, to a generic rolled asphalt roadbase mix. A further equation has been proposed for a DBM roadbase mix, which from a pavement evaluation standpoint is probably more relevant than the rolled asphalt. The two equations are similar and are:

TRL rolled asphalt roadbase

$$\text{Log } N = -9.38 - 4.32 \log \varepsilon_r \tag{20.1}$$

TRL DBM roadbase

$$\text{Log } N = -9.38 - 4.16 \log \varepsilon_r \tag{20.2}$$

These equations, presented by Nottingham University (Brown,

1986), take account of specific features of the bituminous mix and may consequently be used in a more discriminating manner, since in the evaluation process it is possible to take samples of the bound layer and subject them to laboratory tests to gain the necessary data to use in the following equation:

$$Log\ N = 15.8 \log \varepsilon_t - 46.82$$
$$- (5.13 \log \varepsilon_t - 14.39) \log V_B \qquad (20.3)$$
$$- (8.63 \log \varepsilon_t - 24.2) \log SP_i$$

where

V_B = percentage of binder by volume (typical DBM 10%)
SP_i = initial softening point of bitumen (50 pen binder = 50)

Using the various options for asphalt strain the options set out in Table 20.1 can be deduced.

Table 20.2 sets out the traffic loading in msa needed to generate a strain of 100 microstrain and assuming an annual traffic loading of 5 msa the design life can be calculated.

It is interesting to see that while initially there appeared to be a very significant difference in the microstrain values, when the design life is considered the variation may be considered to be almost within the margin of error.

20.2.3   Subgrade strain
The subgrade strain relationship is based on less precise data than that for asphalt fatigue cracking. It is used to ensure that excessive rutting caused by deformation due to loss of foundation

support does not occur within the pavement's design life and is based on the back-calculation of various pavements of known performance. In these circumstances it is an indication rather than a direct measure of rutting.

TRL (Powell et al., 1984) subgrade strain – deformation

$$Log\ N = -7.21 - 3.95 \log \varepsilon_z \qquad (20.4)$$

The equation presented by Nottingham (Brown, 1986) for subgrade strain at critical conditions is as follows:

$$N = f_r \left(\frac{7.6 \times 10^8}{\varepsilon_z^{3.7}} \right) \qquad (20.5)$$

where f_r is a rut factor and is usually set at 1.0

The effect of different subgrade deformation strains is shown in Table 20.3.

Considering an acceptable strain level of 200 microstrain the respective design lives derived using the different guidance would be as follows (Table 20.4).

20.2.4   Temperature correction
When carrying out pavement evaluation surveys it is normally necessary to correct for the effects of temperature since all considerations and available statistics in the UK are at a standard 20°C.

A relationship between temperature and asphalt modulus is required. There are many factors involved and for the purpose of evaluation a robust approach is appropriate.

Table 20.1 Difference in fatigue strain for various loading

Source	1 msa	10 msa	20 msa	30 msa	50 msa	100 msa
Asphalt						
TRL rolled asphalt	224	131	112	102	91	77
TRL DBM	201	116	98	89	78	66
Nottingham	150	84	70	64	56	47
Asphalt Institute	211	105	85	75	64	52

Table 20.2 Effect of different transfer functions

Source	Loading (msa) at 100 μstrain	Design Life (yrs) at 5 msa/yr
TRL rolled asphalt	30	6
TRL DBM	20	4
Nottingham Vb 10%	5.02	1
Asphalt Institute	10	2

Table 20.3 Effect of different subgrade deformation strains

Source	1 msa	10 msa	20 msa	30 msa	50 msa	100 msa
Subgrade						
TRL	453	253	212	191	168	141
Nottingham	451	237	195	174	151	124
Asphalt Institute	482	288	247	226	201	172

Table 20.4 Effect of different subgrade transfer functions

Source	Loading (msa) at 200 μstrain	Design life (yrs) at 5 msa/yr
TRL	25	5
Nottingham	18	3.6
Asphalt Institute	51	10

Ullidtz (1987) suggests that to get more realistic moduli at high temperatures a back analysis of deflection data from the AASHO Road Test was carried out. Asphalt moduli were calculated from deflections corresponding to a vehicle speed of 35 mph at temperatures ranging from 0°C to 40°C. The following semi-logarithmic relationship was found: t°C

$$E_1(t) = 15000 \text{ MPa} - 7900 \text{ MPa} \times \log(t°C) \qquad (20.6)$$

where $E_1(t)$ is the asphalt modulus in MPa at a temperature of t_{ref} °C and $t = 1$°C

HD 29/08 (Highways Agency, 2008) mandates the following temperature correction for asphalt moduli on the HA network in the UK:

$$E_{20} = E_T \times 10^{(0.0003(20-T)^2 - 0.022(20-T))} \qquad (20.7)$$

For convenience both the above equations are presented in tabular format in Table 20.11.

20.3.   E moduli

Table 20.5 shows typical FWD measured values of E moduli at 20°C.

In Table 20.5, the required stiffness of the bitumen, the ambient temperature and the traffic speed influence the bound layer. The latter affects the rate of loading.

20.4.   Poisson's ratio

The other material parameter used in the elastic analysis of pavement systems is Poisson's ratio. This is defined as the ratio of transverse to longitudinal strains of a loaded specimen.

HD 29/08 (Highways Agency, 2008) mandated use of the values set out in Table 20.6 when undertaking back analysis. They will be seen to be slightly different from those given previously.

Table 20.6 Poisson's ratio
From Highways Agency, 2008 © Crown copyright 2008

Material	Poissons
Asphalt	0.35
Hydraulically bound	0.35
Pavement quality concrete	0.20
Crushed stone	0.45
Soil (fine grained)	0.45

Table 20.5 Typical E modulus values at 20°C

Material	Range of stiffness (MPa)
Bitumen bound	
HRA wearing course	4500–7500
Dense bitumen macadam basecourse	4500–7500
HRA basecourse	8000–10 000
Dense bitumen macadam roadbase	7000–10 000
Typical design value for bituminous layer <250 mm	3500
Evidence of cracking in layer possibly not visible	2450–3000
Serviceability of layer in question	1750–2450
Layer regarded as unserviceable	<1750
Typical design value for bituminous layer >250 mm	6500
Evidence of cracking in layer possibly not visible	4500–6000
Serviceability of layer in question	3000–4000
Layer regarded as unserviceable	<3000
Cement bound	
Concrete pavement quality slab	30 000–70 000
Cement-bound granular (intact)	10 000–30 000
Cement-bound granular (some cracking)	5000–15 000
Cement-bound granular (serviceability in question)	500–5000
Fractured pavement quality concrete slab	700–21 000
Granular	
Granular base (some cementing action)	300–2000
Granular base (no cementing)	200–500
Granular sub-base	50–200
Rockfill	100–400
Stone pitching	250–1000
Subgrade	
General comparator 10 x CBR	35–200

20.5.   Analytical pavement design in the UK (Highways Agency)

This section sets out to review the various inputs needed for analytical pavment design in the UK. They consist of several factors, the most important of which are listed below and are based on current UK practice to ensure Highways Agency compliance.

As with other structural design practice it is normal to specify or assume a structure and check the stresses, strains and deflections at various places. In the case of a pavement it is usual to consider the tensile strain at the bottom of the asphalt layer and the compressive strain at the top of the sub-grade. Conventionally these are estimated using a linear elastic model, of which there are several, but the most widely used is the Shell BISAR 3 (Shell, 1998) software.

In the UK the design guidance is set out in LR 1132 (Powell *et al.*, 1984) Appendix E. This takes a global approach to UK conditions and uses the assumptions and inputs set out in Table 20.7.

The use of this methodology was first allowed on Highways Agency roads in HD 26/01 (DfT, 2001).

20.6. Loading time

Loading time influences the stiffness of an asphalt layer. In general, the longer the loading time the lower the layer stiffness. Ultimately, an infinite loading time, such as is caused by a static load, leads to creep and indentation of the loaded areas.

Table 20.7 LR 1132 guidance relating to analytical design in the UK

Data taken from LR 1132

Asphalt materials

Loading frequency	5 Hz
Equivalent temperature	20°C
Modulus of DBM (100 pen)	3.1 GPa
Modulus for HRA (50 pen)	3.5 GPa
Poisson's ratio	0.35
Fatigue criteria DBM	Log Nf = −9.38−4.16 log εr
Fatigue criteria HRA	Log Nf = −9.78−4.32 log εr
Deformation criterion	Log Nd = −7.21−3.95 log εz

Sub-base (Type 1)

Modulus	Depends on number of layers but generally taken in the range 100–150 MPa
Poisson's ratio	0.45

Capping layer

Modulus	Range between 80 and 100 MPa
Poisson's ratio	0.45

Subgrade (cohesive)

Modulus	E = 17.6 (CBR) $^{0.64}$ MPa
Poisson's ratio	

Standard wheel load

Load	40 kN single wheel
Contact radius	0.151 m

The following equation relates loading time to layer thickness and vehicle speed:

$$\log t = 5 \times 10^{-4} h - 0.2 - 0.94 \log V \qquad (20.8)$$

In the Nottingham literature (Brown *et al.*, 1982) the position sets out the following approximation, which is suggested to be accurate for a range of thickness between 100 mm and 350 mm.

$$t = \frac{1}{V} \qquad (20.9)$$

where V = vehicle speed in kph.

Not only is the modulus of asphalt related to loading time and temperature, the latter being dealt with separately, but various tests and literature based on different testing regimes, which have been adopted by different organisations, refer to loading time in Hz.

For example, the Nottingham asphalt tester (NAT) operates at 2.5 Hz, and asphalt modulus values quoted in DMRB are based on loading at 5 Hz, with both being reported at a reference temperature of 20°C. In the *French Design Manual* (Setra and LCPC, 1997), however, asphalt modulus values are related to a loading speed of 10 Hz and a reference temperature of 15°C. Austroads uses the range 20°C, 25°C and 30°C.

Based on the above Table 20.8 shows the loading time for a range of vehicle speeds and how that relates to the various test/national reference data. While accurate consideration of the comparative data is fairly complex the table attempts to present a pragmatic comparison. A separate correction (shift) factor for temperature difference is set out in Table 20.11.

With an FWD the load pulse duration is generally 25–60 milli-secs. The load sizes and times correspond well with those of fast-moving freight traffic (CROW, 1998).

Table 20.8 Effect of loading speed

mph	kph	't' secs	Hz	Source	Temp. °C	Multiplier
15	24	0.041	2.5	NAT	20	1.0
20	32	0.031				
30	48	0.021	5	DMRB	20	1.5
50	80	0.125				
60	96	0.010	10	France	15	1.6
80	130	0.0076				
100	161	0.0006				

With the exception of asphalt, all pavement materials have a stiffness that is independent of loading speed and temperature; consequently the results of laboratory tests can be used directly in the design process.

20.7. Additional effect

Typical laboratory tests on asphalt will be carried out using the ITSM test in a NAT (Nottingham asphalt tester). If this is done two corrections need to be applied.

First for the effects of early life strength gain and second for the effects of confinement and loading speed. The following (Table 20.9) have been suggested by Al-Hakiem (2001).

Table 20.9 Effect of ageing, confinement and loading time
Data taken from Al-Hakiem (2001)

Initial binder pen	Ageing hardening	Confinement and loading time	Combined multiplier
100	1.75	1.65	2.9
50	1.5	1.32	1.98
35	1.15	1.25	1.44

Table 20.10 Permissible fatigue strain in asphalt

Load plotted against strain (µstrain)

Design load msa	Asphalt			Subgrade		
	LR 1132 DBM	Nottingham DBM	Asphalt Institute	LR 1132	Nottingham	Asphalt Institute
0.1	347.0	256	483.2	814.9	859.9	805.7
0.2	293.8	210	391.4	683.8	708.2	690.3
0.3	266.6	187	346.1	617.1	632.2	630.7
0.4	248.8	172	317.1	573.8	583.3	591.5
0.5	235.8	162	296.3	542.3	548.0	562.8
0.6	225.7	153	280.3	517.9	520.7	540.3
0.7	217.5	147	267.5	498.1	498.7	522.1
0.8	210.7	141	256.8	481.5	480.4	506.8
0.9	204.8	137	247.8	467.4	464.8	493.6
1	199.7	133	240.0	455.1	451.3	482.2
2	169.1	109	194.4	381.9	371.7	413.1
3	153.4	97	171.9	344.7	331.8	377.4
4	143.2	89	157.5	320.5	306.1	353.9
5	135.7	84	147.1	302.9	287.6	336.8
6	129.9	80	139.2	289.2	273.3	323.3
7	125.2	76	132.8	278.2	261.7	312.4
8	121.2	73	127.6	268.9	252.1	303.2
9	117.9	71	123.1	261.0	243.9	295.4
10	114.9	69	119.2	254.2	236.8	288.5
15	104.3	61	105.4	229.4	211.4	263.6
16	102.7	60	103.3	225.7	207.6	259.8
17	101.2	59	101.4	222.2	204.1	256.3
20	97.3	56	96.6	213.3	195.1	247.2
25	92.2	53	90.2	201.6	183.2	235.2
30	88.3	50	85.4	192.5	174.1	225.8
35	85.1	48	81.5	185.1	166.8	218.2
40	82.4	46	78.2	179.0	160.6	211.8
45	80.1	45	75.5	173.7	155.4	206.3

(continued)

Table 20.10. (*continued*)

Design load msa	Asphalt			Subgrade		
	LR 1132 DBM	Nottingham DBM	Asphalt Institute	LR 1132	Nottingham	Asphalt Institute
50	78.1	43	73.1	169.1	150.9	201.5
60	74.7	41	69.1	161.5	143.4	193.5
65	73.3	40	67.5	158.3	140.2	190.1
70	72.0	40	66.0	155.3	137.3	187.0
75	70.9	39	64.6	152.7	134.7	184.1
80	69.8	38	63.4	150.2	132.3	181.5
85	68.8	37	62.2	147.9	130.1	179.0
90	67.8	37	61.1	145.8	128.0	176.8
95	66.9	36	60.1	143.8	126.1	174.6
100	66.1	36	59.2	141.9	124.3	172.7

In HD 29/94 (Highways Agency, 1994, pp. 5–7) the conversion from NAT to FWD is given as:

$$ITSM \times 1.5 = FWD \qquad (20.10)$$

TRL Report 636 (Sanders and Nunn, 2005) at paragraph 10.2 also suggests that a multiplier of $1.5 \times ITSM$ will give a good estimate of the long-term design stiffness value.

20.8. Permissible strains

For convenience, the following permissible fatigue strain plotted against load (msa) are shown in Table 20.10.

20.9. Asphalt temperature correction

For convenience the temperature correction coefficients recommended by TRL and Dynatest are set out in Table 20.11.

Table 20.11 Temperature correction coefficients

Temp. °C	TRL	Elmod
1	2.0403	4.0240
2	1.9898	3.3243
3	1.9378	2.8918
4	1.8845	2.6246
5	1.8302	2.3994
6	1.7750	2.2154
7	1.7191	2.0597
8	1.6626	1.9249
9	1.6058	1.8061
10	1.5488	1.6997
11	1.4918	1.6035
12	1.4348	1.5157
13	1.3782	1.4349
14	1.3219	1.3600
15	1.2662	1.2904
16	1.2112	1.2253
17	1.1569	1.1641
18	1.1036	1.1064
19	1.0512	1.0518
20	1.0000	1.0000

(*continued*)

Table 20.11. (*continued*)

Temp. °C	TRL	Elmod
21	0.9499	0.9508
22	0.9012	0.9039
23	0.8537	0.8589
24	0.8076	0.8160
25	0.7630	0.7748
26	0.7198	0.7352
27	0.6781	0.6971
28	0.6380	0.6603
29	0.5994	0.6249
30	0.5623	0.5908
31	0.5269	0.5576
32	0.4929	0.5255
33	0.4606	0.4945
34	0.4297	0.4644
35	0.4004	0.4351
36	0.3726	0.4067
37	0.3462	0.3790
38	0.3212	0.3521
39	0.2976	0.3328
40	0.2754	0.3003

REFERENCES AND BIBLIOGRAPHY

Al-Hakiem B (2001) Seminar Nottingham University, 17th September 2001, discussion.

Brown SF (1980) *An Introduction to The Analytical Design of Bituminous Pavements*. Department of Civil Engineering, University of Nottingham.

Brown SF, Brunton JM and Pell PS (1982) The development and implementation of analytical pavement design for British conditions. *Proceedings of the 5th International Conference on the Structural Design of Asphalt Pavements*, Delft.

Brown SF (1986) Structural design of pavements, Lecture G, Bituminous Pavements: Materials, design and evaluation, lecture notes for a residential course. University of Nottingham, April 1986.

Brunton JM, Brown SF and Pell PS (1987) Developments to the Nottingham analytical design method for asphalt pavements. *6th International Conference on Structural Design of Asphalt Pavements*, University of Michigan.

CROW (1998) Deflection profile – not a pitfall anymore, Record 17, CROW, EDE, The Netherlands.

DfT (2001) HD 26/01: Pavement design. DMRB Vol. 7 Section 2 Part 3. HMSO, London.

ELMOD (2010) ELMOD 6 user's manual. Dynatest International A/S, Glostrup.

Highways Agency (1994) DMRB HD 29/94: Traffic speed conditions survey. *Design Manual for Roads and Bridges*. Highways Agency, London.

Highways Agency (2008) DMRB HD 29/08: Data for pavement assessment, *Design Manual for Roads and Bridges*. Highways Agency, London.

Kedah P and Nilsson R (2005) How may the variation of traffic loading effect measured asphalt strains and calculated pavement service life? 7th International Conference on the Bearing Capacity of Roads, Railways and Airfields (BCRA), Trondheim.

Powell WD, Potter JF, Mayhew HC and Nunn ME (1984) LR 1132: The structural design of bituminous roads. TRL, Crowthorne.

Sanders PG and Nunn M (2005) TRL 636: The application of enrobé à module élevé in flexible pavements. TRL, Crowthorne.

Setra and LCPC (1997) *French Design Manual for Pavement Structures: Guide Technique*. LCPC, Paris.

Shell (1998) *Bisar 3 – Bitumen Stress Analysis in Roads, User Manual*. Shell International Oil Products, The Hague, The Netherlands.

TRL (1960) Road note 29: A guide to the structural design of pavements for new roads, 3rd edn. HMSO, London.

Ullidtz P (1987) Pavement Analysis. Elsevier, Amsterdam.

Deterioration and Maintenance of Pavements
ISBN: 978-0-7277-4114-1

ICE Publishing. All rights reserved
http://dx.doi.org/10.1680/dmp.41141.261

Chapter 21

Strengthening of Pavements

21.1. Overlay design principles based on FWD data

This section considers pavement strengthening options following an FWD survey.

The results of the back-calculation output from most commercially available software programs are generally as shown in Table 21.1.

E1 (MPa) relates to the stiffness of the asphalt layer and the modulus is temperature sensitive; consequently a correction may need to be applied. In the UK the standard reporting temperature is 20°C, so it is necessary to correct for any variance between the site collection temperature and 20°C, using Table 20.13 in Chapter 20.

Where T is the pavement temperature at 100 mm depth below the surface.

It is generally accepted that the two supporting layers, the granular sub-base and the subgrade, are not temperature sensitive; consequently no correction to these moduli are required.

Once the corrected value of E1 has been calculated using the above equation, it is possible to calculate the two critical strain values $\varepsilon_{t(a)}$, the actual tensile strain at the base of the asphalt layer, and $\varepsilon_{z(a)}$, the actual compressive strain at the top of the subgrade.

This calculation can be done using any available forward design linear elastic software.

The permissible strains can be derived from the following strain transfer equations, and in the UK it is normal to use those set out in LR 1132 (Powell *et al.*, 1984), namely:

Table 21.1 Typical FWD moduli output

Chainage (m)	E1 (MPa)	E2 (MPa)	E3 (MPa)
1000	6500	215	98

Fatigue

$$\text{Log } Nf = -9.38 - 4.16 \log e_{t(p)} \tag{21.1}$$

Deformation

$$\text{Log } N_d = -7.21 - 3.95 \log e_{z(p)} \tag{21.2}$$

When these values have been calculated, the residual life of the pavement can be estimated by comparing the calculated strain with the permissible strain for both the tensile and compressive conditions.

$$\text{If } e_{t(a)} \geqslant e_{t(p)} \tag{21.3}$$

it will be necessary to increase the section properties by iteratively adding an overlay of an increasing thickness and defined stiffness value and recalculating the actual strains until such time as:

$$e_{t(a)} \leqslant e_{t(p)} \tag{21.4}$$

The bearing capacity of the pavement can be estimated by calculating the difference in the number of load repetitions, using the strain transfer equations set out above.

This process is illustrated in Figure 21.1.

As can be seen from Figure 21.1, if the actual (calculated) strain based on the existing pavement is higher than the permissible strain, then the section properties must be increased. The simplest way of achieving this is by applying an overlay.

Conceptually this is the same as strengthening a timber beam by the addition of a steel plate. The calculations are similarly straightforward, as is demonstrated in the following pages.

Reference to Figure 21.1 shows the overall concept. It should be remembered that the governing case will be whichever gives the shorter life: either the asphalt or the subgrade transfer function.

Figure 21.1 Calculation of strengthening (overlay) need

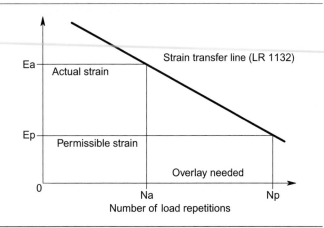

21.2. Translating theory into reality

Once the various layer stiffnesses and the overlay needed to provide the required bearing capacity for the design load have been determined, a number of practical issues must be considered, as set out below.

A typical data output format is given in Table 21.2.

It can be seen that the dataset is volatile. There is a large range in variation, which may cause problems with a normal statistical analysis.

Table 21.2 Typical post-processed FWD results

Chainage	E1 (MPa)	E2 (MPa)	Life, yrs	O/Lay,mm
2100	42 434	254	20	0
2125	39 821	197	2	82
2150	21 115	159	20	0
2175	3591	73	1	117
2200	1873	104	2	78
2225	10 684	54	6	43
2250	19 981	34	2	87
2275	3398	47	7	44
2300	2391	81	10	26
2325	1827	57	5	59
2350	4540	86	1	88
2375	26 370	98	7	48
2400	5445	65	5	58
2425	2527	60	4	73
2450	6793	103	14	14
2475	1275	48	4	76
2500	1555	53	10	26

21.3. Segmenting into reasonably homogeneous sections

The first problem is to segment the overall structure into reasonably homogeneous sections. This can be done by inspection of either the construction, the deflection data or the needed overlay data. Alternatively, it can be done statistically, and a convenient method is to use a Cusum (cumulative sum control chart) approach, which involves the use of an Excel or other spreadsheet where the setup shown in Table 21.3 may be used.

Figure 21.2 is an actual plot of a Cusum analysis, which was necessary to segment a 13 km section of road into reasonably homogeneous sections.

The beginning of a reasonably homogeneous section can be deduced from where the gradient of the line changes. It is the data within these individual sections which would then be subjected to a detailed statistical analysis.

When a shorter section is examined it may well be found that there are differences in the section lengths between the foundation and the bound layers. This may well point towards some of the problems that need to be addressed in the rehabilitation proposals.

21.4. Statistical analysis

Having arrived at reasonably homogeneous sections for the purpose of treatment, the next problem is to calculate the characteristic values for each section.

The statistical analysis of a group of numbers is normally undertaken to describe the mean and the standard deviation of the set. When doing so, it is usual to make the assumption that the data can be defined by a normal distribution. The normal analysis can be carried out as follows.

For a normal distribution, calculation of the mean and standard deviation can be made using the usual formulae as follows:

Table 21.3 Cusum method of segmenting into sections

	C	D	E
1	Chainage	Data	Ave col (D)
2			E1 − D2
3			E$1 − D3 + E2
4			E$1 − D4 + E3
5			E$1 − D5 + E4
6			E$1 − D6 + E5

Figure 21.2 Typical Cusum analysis

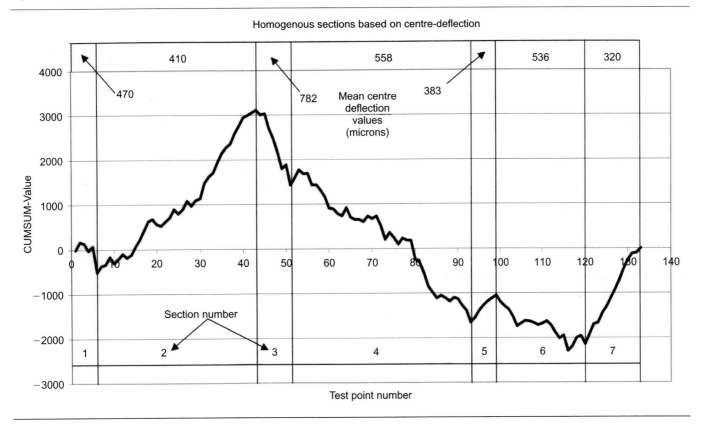

Homogenous sections based on centre-deflection

Mean or average

$$m = \sqrt{\frac{\sum x}{n}} \qquad (21.5)$$

Standard deviation

$$\sigma = \sqrt{\frac{\sum (x - m)^2}{n}} \qquad (21.6)$$

Coefficient of variation

$$\mu = \frac{\sigma}{m} \qquad (21.7)$$

The coefficient of variation is also a useful statistic as it characterises the variance of one section against another and is an indicator of volatility.

The standard deviation is useful in that it describes the variation in the numbers within a section under consideration and allows a close approximation to be made of the 15th and 85th percentiles. These are usually described in pavement evaluation as the 'design' values and are derived as follows:

15th percentile = mean − 1 standard deviation   (21.8)

85th percentile = mean + 1 standard deviation   (21.9)

In the context of pavement evaluation the design values are applied as shown in Table 21.4.

21.5.   Dealing with a volatile numbers set
The next issue to be considered is the volatility of the number set.

A volatile number set is defined as one in which there is a substantial variation between the upper and lower limits of the group. It is fairly normal when working with asphalt layer stiffness, particularly where there is a considerable difference in the visual condition within the overall length under examination, to find volatile numbers.

Table 21.4 Design values from statistical analysis

Parameter	Design value
Layer moduli	Mean − 1 std dev.
Life	Mean − 1 std dev.
Overlay	Mean + 1 std dev.

Table 21.2, which sets out the results of a survey carried out using a falling weight deflectometer to determine existing condition and examine possible maintenance options of a section of urban pavement, can be seen to contain a volatile set of numbers which will not conform to a normal distribution.

It is necessary to consider from these numbers what is to be done and it is usually preferred, from a construction aspect, that a section be treated as a whole; consequently the average and the 'design' values of the set are required.

The average (or mean) is well understood and should present few problems as it is usually considered to be the 50th percentile value.

The design value is that which is considered to be the 'characteristic' of the set and is a value where no more than 15% of the observations are outside these limits (either above or below).

With numbers such as those set out in the E1 column of Table 21.2 problems may be experienced when calculating the standard deviation by normal methods such as described previously, as it is possible to derive a standard deviation numerically greater than the mean – which is theoretically impossible.

Ullidtz (1987) proposed that with numbers of this volatility the set may be considered to conform to a logarithmic normal distribution. The problem can then be dealt with by calculating the mean and standard deviation on the logarithms of the numbers in the set.

When the antilog of the standard deviation is calculated, this is described as the standard deviation factor (sdf) and the design values are then calculated as follows:

$$\text{Mean} - 1 \text{ std dev.} = \frac{\text{mean}}{\text{sdf}} \tag{21.10}$$

$$\text{Mean} + 1 \text{ std dev.} = \text{mean} \times \text{sdf} \tag{21.11}$$

21.6. Presentation of FWD-derived data

FWD-derived data for a volatile set are presented in Figures 21.3, 21.4 and 21.5.

The practical problem now is how to translate the above data into a realistic rehabilitation proposal, making best use of existing structures and their condition.

21.6.1 Interpretation of FWD layer stiffness results

In pavement evaluation the value of individual layer stiffness within a reasonably homogeneous section is not in itself a measure of strength, rather of relative condition.

Table 21.5 shows a range of stiffness for various materials in varying conditions.

Figure 21.3 Layer moduli

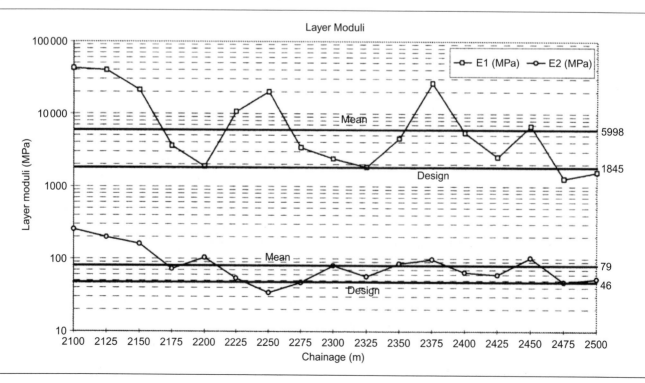

Figure 21.4 Residual life

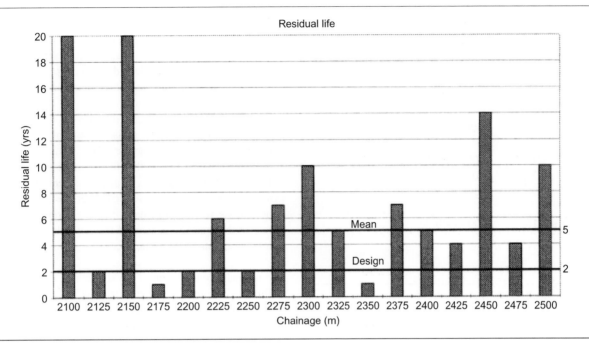

Figure 21.5 Overlay needed

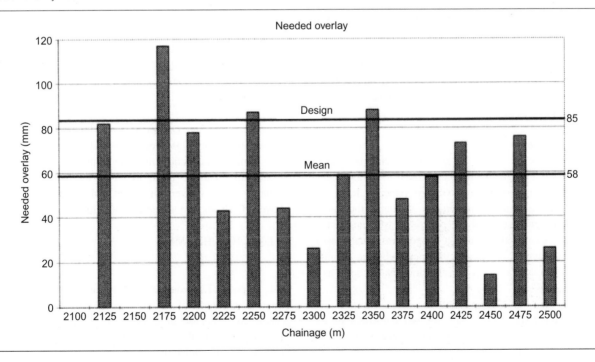

It is against the layer stiffness in Table 21.5 that a judgement can be made on whether it is feasible to use any or all of the existing structure in the rehabilitation.

21.6.2 Asphalt layer

When estimating the required strengthening, a figure of 3500 MPa is normally used for the overlaid bituminous layers.

Table 21.5 Typical layer stiffness, MPa

Stiffness at 20°C	Condition of layer		
Material	Poor integrity	Some deterioration	Good integrity
Bituminous < 250 mm	<2000	2000–4000	>4000
Bituminous > 250 mm	<4000	4000–7000	>7000
Lean concrete	<10 000	10 000–15 000	>15 000
PQC	<20 000	20 000–30 000	>30 000
Setts – ash Bedding	<500	500–1000	>1000
Setts – concrete bedding	<1000	1000–3000	>4000
Granular			>100
Subgrade			>70

When examining the adequacy of the existing structure, the following considerations are made.

Where the design value falls to 30% below the figure given above, to 2450 MPa, it may reasonably be assumed that significant cracking or degradation has taken place and it is sensible to remove the layer.

In the event of the value being more than than 50% below (<1750 MPa), it is possible, for the purpose of a rehabilitation design, to consider the material to be a good sub-base of stiffness 500 Mpa, should this be appropriate.

21.6.3 Sub-base layer

For granular foundation layers of existing pavements a layer stiffness of 100 MPa or greater has been found to be associated with good performance of fully flexible pavements. It is also thought to be a reasonable criterion for unbound foundation layers of flexible composite and PQ concrete pavements. Large variations in the measured foundation support are usually associated with a change in drainage efficiency, sub-base capping layer or sub-base material, or a construction change such as a cut/fill line.

In interpreting the FWD information for sett constructions the major problem is the range of E2 modulus values that may be found. Between 500 MPa and 2000 MPa it is possible to use either type of construction, depending on its condition, and direct visual inspection by trial hole is required to assist in the interpretation. Without direct inspection it becomes a balance of probabilities, requiring consideration of the value and consistency of the E2 modulus horizon.

21.6.4 Relationship between subgrade stiffness and CBR

It is generally accepted that the use of a falling weight deflectometer is one of the most appropriate and accurate ways of determining the elastic stiffness of the subgrade. The problem is that this characterises the in situ confined layer stiffness, which may become substantially degraded once excavation, and exposure to the atmosphere and construction traffic, takes place.

The extent of this degradation depends on various factors, the predominant ones being the moisture content of the soil and its geological history. For example, most natural clays are over consolidated, which means that their natural moisture content is lower than their equilibrium moisture content. This variation is generally described as the sensitivity of the clay and there are various tests which will allow it to be estimated. In practical terms, as the moisture content of the clay increases its capability to tolerate construction traffic decreases.

The normal representation of the strength of a subgrade is by the California Bearing Ratio (CBR) test, which involves comparison of the extent to which a soil will accept the penetration of a plunger compared with a sample of 'standard' crushed rock. The relationship is expressed as a percentage and, in general terms, a subgrade with a CBR of <5% may be regarded as weak and unable to support construction traffic, whereas one with a CBR >10% would not be expected to cause problems.

The problem then becomes a matter of converting a reasonably precise assessment of the elastic layer stiffness to an equivalent CBR since the strength of a soil is usually understood in these terms. Various relationships have been suggested, which are set out briefly below.

The *Shell Pavement Design Manual* (Shell, 1978) suggests that the sub-grade modulus should preferably be determined in situ from dynamic deflection measurements. Alternatively, dynamic triaxial tests can be used. In cases where such data are not available it is convenient to use the empirical relationship between CBR and the sub-grade modulus E3

$$E3 = 10 \, (CBR) \, \text{MPa} \tag{21.12}$$

TRL Report 1132 comments at some length, in Appendix C, about the problems of determining the soil strength. Generally it recommends the use of CBR as a determinant but makes the observation that the strength of the subgrade is critically dependent on its moisture content.

It also goes on to discuss the relationship between CBR and layer stiffness and indicates that the following equation is considered to be a lower bound relationship when the CBR is in the range 2 to 12%.

$$E = 17.6 \, (\text{CBR})^{0.64} \, \text{MPa} \tag{21.13}$$

21.7. Practical considerations

This section describes briefly some of the practical considerations associated with the process of rehabilitation. They are collected together to minimise the amount of repetition in the individual discussions, which follow.

(a) The recommendation that a section has a low residual life and requires a thick overlay does not automatically mean that the works should be put in hand immediately as it may be more appropriate to deal with other problems elsewhere on the network. Residual life is an estimate of the elapsed time from the present state to the onset of critical conditions, which is defined as the appearance of a crack in the wheeltrack or of rutting in excess of 10 mm, at which point the prediction of the rate of further deterioration becomes very difficult.

(b) Prior to the onset of critical conditions a pavement can usually be strengthened by an overlay at a cost index of 1.00. Subsequent to the critical stage being reached, current thinking suggests that the pavement requires to be reconstructed at a cost index of between 4 and 5. In the post-critical stage, however, the pavement will continue to provide useful service although the functional (ride) condition may be expected to decrease progressively until such time as it becomes unacceptable. From an economic point of view it will be seen that strengthening in the pre-critical stage provides a better investment strategy but may not be possible due to available budgets being inadequate to deal with all identified problems. Consequently, once a pavement enters this post-critical phase there is merit in prolonging any expenditure as long as possible. While this is a sensible technical decision it must be accompanied by a vigilant monitoring of the condition of the pavement, which can best be done by establishing the trend of increase in overt defectiveness and decrease in ride quality to prevent a position being reached where the section suddenly becomes impassable. The relative prioritisation of pavements in the post-critical stage can, therefore, readily be undertaken by regular comparison of the gradient of the trend lines of defectiveness and ride.

(c) Where a thin overlay (<50 mm) is to be used it is not advised that this be placed immediately on an existing surfacing without that course first being roughened with a planer. If the parent material shows any degradation it is advisable to plane 50 mm off and then replace 100 mm to ensure a reasonably robust layer.

(d) When any overlay is being considered, any cracking should first be removed. In the event of wheeltrack cracking this may be confined to the surface course or go deeper into the construction. If the latter is the case then local reconstruction may be required. This can only be confirmed by the use of trial holes at the contract preparation stage. Depending on the amount of cracking, planing is the preferred method of removing the asphalt layer.

(e) When the mean modulus of the existing asphalt layer is less than 1500 MPa its replacement is indicated. Its removal should preferably be undertaken by planing as this is more controllable than other methods and it also allows inspection of the underlying layers. This is particularly important when the second layer is of sett construction.

(f) When setts have been exposed, any breaches caused by previous excavations should be removed and replaced using a 20 N concrete to the thickness of the sett and its bedding.

(g) If setts with a low modulus are the subject of an investigation and it is found that they are loose, consideration should be given to their removal. In the event of there being a concrete bed more than 150 mm thick there is merit in leaving this in place unless it appears to be physically degraded, which can be assessed at the time the condition of the setts is examined. As a minimum, it will provide a working platform and be more robust than a granular layer, which may replace it.

(h) In the event of reconstruction being considered, a physical examination of the subgrade is advised to assess the sensitivity of the material to the effects of moisture or exposure, which may significantly degrade its physical characteristics when subjected to site traffic. Construction represents the most severe loading condition for the subgrade, where in the case of a clay soil stresses equal to and in excess of the shear strength can be applied, causing rupture of the layer. This evaluation should include laboratory testing of samples to determine the Atterberg limits of the material.

(i) When a wet subgrade is encountered which cannot be explained by malfunctioning drainage or a semi-permeable surface course, then consideration should be given to the use of deep side drains or a geotextile drainage blanket.

(j) The advice contained in this section assumes the use of normal recipe mixes (HRA/DBM) with a minimum of 70 pen bitumen. In some cases outside the urban area there may be merit in the use of HD 50 binders or sophisticated additives. Where it may reasonably be expected, within the service life of the asphalt layer, that it will be affected by statutory undertakings then there is little or no benefit to be gained from the use of more robust asphalt mixes.

(k) A bond coat should always be used between any two adjacent layers to ensure that interlayer bonding occurs, since without this the assumption made of composite action will not be valid as the several layers are likely to act either partially or wholly independently, with a reduction in the service life of the pavement.

21.8. What are the possible maintenance options?

A series of alternatives present themselves, which may be considered in the form of a hierarchy where the final option becomes reconstruction. This hierarchy may be set out as follows.

(*a*) Overlay as recommended by FWD processing software.
(*b*) Replace part of existing asphalt layer, with no overlay.
(*c*) Replace all of existing asphalt layer, with no overlay.
(*d*) Replace part or all of asphalt layer, together with an overlay.
(*e*) Replace part of or the entire second layer with asphalt material.
(*f*) Reconstruct the pavement structure.

In many cases the use of option (*f*) will most probably present the most practical option but this will depend on its existing construction, which will need to be proved by trial pits. In the event of the second layer being setts or stone pitching which cannot be reduced in level, then it will be necessary to consider whether an overlay of 50 mm is practical. With a full kerb face, normally 125 mm, a 50 mm overlay may be possible as it will retain the minimum advised 75 mm kerb face.

If it is not possible either to reduce the thickness of the sub-base or to use a thin overlay, coupled with replacement of the bituminous layer, then a full-depth reconstruction using existing surface levels will be the only alternative.

One of the significant benefits of an FWD analysis is that the back-calculation associated with the evaluation derives the elastic stiffness of the several layers in the pavement. Using this information in the following manner facilitates the development of an iterative process to consider a range of possible rehabilitation options, which can then be subjected to economic evaluation.

In this way the most economic rehabilitation treatments can be derived from a range of possibilities, when in the past full-depth reconstruction may have appeared to be the only solution. The further advantage of this technique is that it allows maximum use to be made of the potential of the existing construction. This iterative analysis is not possible using any other pavement evaluation methodology.

When carrying out any strengthening investigation it is useful to consider the reasonableness of what is being proposed. A useful starting point is to look at the recommended thickness of asphalt layer for a new pavement thickness, as shown in Chapter 18, Table 18.2, and consider the recommended overlay against that.

For example, if the design traffic load is 10 msa and the FWD analysis recommends an overlay exceeding 300 mm, then there is reason to be suspicious of the validity of the survey.

21.9. Strengthening by partial reconstruction

Once the calculation has been made for the overlay needed on each reasonably homogeneous section, there is the need to translate this into a practical project. Because there is detailed information on layer stiffness this can be done in the following

manner. The following revision, taken from a typical strength of materials course and illustrated in Figure 21.6, is relevant.

For the purpose of the present discussion the surface of the overlaid road may be considered, in the first calculation, to be the *x–x* axis. If an overlay is applied to the existing carriageway, then so long as the section properties between that surface and the formation are maintained the vertical compressive strain at the formation interface, which is usually critical, will not be exceeded. The elastic stiffness of the section below the surface considered is given by the expression:

$$\text{Elastic stiffness modulus} = \sum I \times E \qquad (21.14)$$

21.9.1   The principle

In the following example a section of carriageway has been evaluated and requires a 100 mm overlay to provide the required structural enhancement. This is not possible for practical reasons, and alternatives are examined, namely

(*a*) Is a replacement of the existing bituminous layer with new material adequate?

Figure 21.6 Section properties

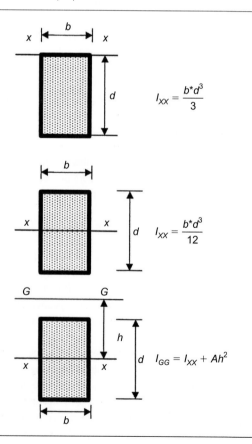

(b) How thick would the bituminous layer have to be, assuming no increase in the surface levels is possible?

The existing construction and layer moduli are

| Bituminous layer | 200 mm thick | E1= 1500 MPa |
| Sub-base layer | 300 mm thick | E2 = 250 MPa |

The existing construction comprises 200 mm asphalt on 300 mm sub-base and its existing elastic stiffness modulus can be calculated as follows:

Layer 1

$$I_{XX} = \frac{bd^3}{3}$$

Layer 2, etc.

To work systematically, a tabular form as shown in Table 21.6 is recommended. This permits clarity of calculation and ease of checking. First calculate the modulus needed.

Second, consider the effect of replacing all the existing asphalt layer with new material with a modulus of 3500 MPa (Table 21.7).

It can be seen that this is not sufficient.

The next step, therefore, is to consider whether the iterative replacement of an additional 50 mm of sub-base will be sufficient (Table 21.8).

The option shown in Table 21.9 is acceptable as $35.66 > 29.90$.

With presently available planing machinery the notion of removing and replacing sub-base has become a very practical option. Unless there are some practical reasons why this is not feasible, this would be the recommended treatment.

The above example is fairly straighforward, since in practice it will be found that there will be a different need for the various homogeneous sections on both sides of the centreline of the road. Consequently it will be found beneficial to identify the critical section and consider that first.

21.9.2 A practical format

Table 21.10, taken from an actual project, shows the results of an FWD survey carried out on a section of major urban highway. From the available data the section has been segmented into reasonably homogeneous lengths.

A practical format of data presentation is shown in the figure, where the various data have been entered into a table and the critical section identified.

Table 21.6 Required section elastic stiffness modulus with 100 mm overlay

Component	I_{xx}			E	$I_{xx}E$
Asphalt overlay 100 mm	$\frac{bd^3}{3} = \frac{1 \times 0.1^3}{3} = 0.00033$			3500	1.16
Asphalt original 200 mm	$I_{gg} + Ah^2 = \frac{bd^3}{12} + Ah^2$			1500	12.99
	$= \frac{1 \times 0.2^3}{12} + (1 \times 0.2 \times 0.2^2)$				
	$= (0.000666) + (0.008) = 0.0086$				
Sub-base 300 mm	$I_{gg} + Ah^2 = \frac{bd^3}{12} + Ah^2$			250	15.75
	$= \frac{1 \times 0.3^3}{12} + (1 \times 0.3 \times 0.45^2)$				
	$= (0.00225) + (0.06075) = 0.063$				
Total section modulus needed based on 100 mm overlay					29.90

Table 21.7 Calculation of modified section elastic stiffness modulus

Component	I_{xx}	E	$I_{xx}E$
Asphalt 200	$\dfrac{bd^3}{3} = \dfrac{1 \times 0.2^3}{3} = 0.00266$	3500	9.31
Sub-base 300	$I_{gg} + Ah^2 = \dfrac{bd^3}{12} + Ah^2$ $= \dfrac{1 \times 0.3^3}{12} + (1 \times 0.3 \times 0.35^2)$ $= (0.00225) + (0.03675) = 0.039$	250	9.75
Total elastic stiffness modulus if asphalt replaced			**19.06**

Table 21.8 Replacement of all asphalt + 50 mm sub-base

Component	I_{xx}	E	$I_{xx}E$
Asphalt 250	$\dfrac{bd^3}{3} = \dfrac{1 \times 0.25^3}{3} = 0.009$	3500	18.22
Sub-base 250	$I_{gg} + Ah^2 = \dfrac{bd^3}{12} + Ah^2$ $= \dfrac{1 \times 0.25^3}{12} + (1 \times 0.25 \times 0.375^2)$ $= (0.001302) + (0.03515) = 0.03645$	250	9.11
Total elastic stiffness modulus if asphalt replaced			**27.33**

Table 21.9 Replacement of all asphalt and 100 mm sub-base

Component	I_{xx}	E	$I_{xx}E$
Asphalt 300	$\dfrac{bd^3}{3} = \dfrac{1 \times 0.3^3}{3} = 0.00523$	3500	31.5
Sub-base 200	$I_{gg} + Ah^2 = \dfrac{bd^3}{12} + Ah^2$ $= \dfrac{1 \times 0.2^3}{12} + (1 \times 0.25 \times 0.400^2)$ $= (0.000666) + (0.016) = 0.0166$	250	4.16
Total elastic stiffness modulus if asphalt replaced			**35.66**

Table 21.10 Practical format for data presentation

Chainage, m	0	100	250	425	525
E1, MPa	4710	900	1110	2610	
E2, MPa	692*	106	221	68*	
E3, MPa	98	45	85	85	
Construction		225 mm bituminous on 250 mm loose stone			
Overlay, mm Proposals	0	160	60	0	
		Critical			
Proposals Overlay	0	100	85	0	
Construction		225 mm bituminous on 250 mm loose stone			
E1, MPa	2120	1200	1395	2820	
E2, MPa	650*	185	240	505*	
E3, MPa	86	67	75	81	
Chainage, m	0	90	235	360	525

Note: * self cementing

Once the critical section has been considered, the remaining sections can be examined to see if there are any further problems.

It should be remembered that different overlays on each side of the central line are not possible, so if an overlay is selected this thickness must be applied to all sections.

In an urban area, an overlay exceeding 50 mm may cause many costly problems and should be avoided if at all possible.

REFERENCES AND BIBLIOGRAPHY

FWHA (Federal Highway Administration) (1995) NHI course no. 13130, *Participant's Manual*, Publication no. FHWA-HI-95-021: Pavement analysis and design checks. National Highway Institute, FHWA, Washington, DC.

Powell WD, Potter JF, Mayhew HC and Nunn ME (1984) LR 1132, The structural design of bituminous roads TRRL, Crowthorne.

Shell (1978) *Shell Pavement Design Manual: Asphalt Pavements and Overlays for Road Traffic*. Shell, London.

Ullidtz P (1987) *Pavement Analysis*. Elsevier, Amsterdam.

Deterioration and Maintenance of Pavements
ISBN: 978-0-7277-4114-1

ICE Publishing. All rights reserved
http://dx.doi.org/10.1680/dmp.41141.273

Chapter 22
Glossary of Terms

AASHTO

American Association of State Highways and Transportation Officials.

AASHO Road Test

American Association of State Highway Organization major project in 1930s to test to destruction a large number of pavements. Much data have come from this and it has influenced pavement engineering worldwide.

Aggregate

Any particulate inorganic material, usually crushed rock, gravel, sand and slag which, when held together by a binding agent, forms the substantial part of such materials as concrete, asphalt and coated macadam.

Anionic bitumen emulsion

Bitumen emulsion in which the emulsifying agent coats the droplets of bitumen with a negatively charged organic ion.

Asphalt

A mixture of mineral aggregate and bitumen.

Asphalt concrete

The new preferred (EU harmonised) term for an asphalt mixture. In the UK DfT (HA) and TRL literature the term dense bituminous macadam (DBM) has previously been used.

Authority

Any authority (organisation) having responsibility for road maintenance.

Base (Roadbase)

A load-spreading layer, placed over the sub-base and required to support heavy vehicles.

Basecourse (see also binder course)

Layer forming part of the surfacing immediately below the surface course (wearing course).

Bedding course

A layer of sharp well-graded sand into which fired clay, natural stone or concrete pavers are compacted during the construction of 'block' paving. It must be kept as thin and even as possible to prevent differential settlement.

Benchmark

A parameter of data, process or function used for comparison.

Benkelman beam

A lightweight slender beam with an articulated joint which is capable of passing between the dual tyres of a standard loaded truck and which can be used to measure the amplitude of deflection caused by a slow-moving rolling load on the pavement.

Best value

Assurance that services are responsive to the needs of citizens, not to the convenience of the service providers. Securing continuous improvement having regard to a combination of economy, efficiency and effectiveness.

Binder

Bituminous, tar- or cement-based material (also pozzolans) that have adhesive properties.

Binder course (see also base course)

A regulating layer placed between sub-base and asphalt surface course, which is currently designed to be impermeable.

Bitumen

Viscous liquid or solid consisting essentially of hydrocarbons and their derivatives, which is soluble in trichloroethylene and is substantially non-volatile and softens gradually when heated. It is black or brown and possesses waterproofing and adhesive properties. It is obtained by refinery processes from petroleum and is also found as a natural deposit or a component of naturally occurring asphalt in which it is associated with mineral matter.

Bitumen emulsion

Dispersion of bitumen in water with an emulsifying agent.

Bleeding

Exudation of bituminous binder to form an exposed film on the wearing surface.

Bond (bonding)

The action of sticking separate layers together to make sure they act compositely.

Bond coat

A thin layer bitumen emulsion which may be (is generally) polymer modified used between adjacent layers in pavement to assist the action of bonding.

Bond pattern

A pattern in which block pavers are laid to form the surface course. Different patterns have varying capabilities of resisting forces transmitted to the pavement by the braking and turning action of vehicles.

Bump integrator

A machine which measures the surface roughness of a pavement by counting the amplitude of movement of a single wheel mounted in a standard suspension system.

California bearing ratio (CBR)

A measure of the bearing capacity of a material. The CBR test is a simple empirical penetration test; it is a measure of the shear strength, or stability, of a soil or granular road building material. Expressed as a percentage of the strength of a standard crushed rock material and measured by a constant rate of strain penetration machine in a laboratory. In the field there is a range of simple penetration tests which, with the help of the appropriate literature, can be correlated to the standard laboratory test.

Capping layer

A locally available low-cost material laid over soils with CBRs less than 5% to provide a stable working platform. A subgrade improvement layer, protecting the subgrade from damage.

Cationic bitumen emulsion

Bitumen emulsion in which the emulsifying agent coats the droplets of bitumen with a positively charged organic ion.

Carriageway

The part of the highway laid out for motor vehicles.

Chainage

Distance along a section from a reference point.

Channelisation

The narrowing of the normal lateral spread of traffic, which would be expected on a standard traffic lane of 3.65 m width.

Chart

A standardised system of visual inspection developed and used by UK DfT and others, it was developed principally for use on non-urban roads.

Close textured (granular)

A condition achieved in the uppermost surface of the sub-base, which may be assisted by the use of a geotextile layer during construction when the bedding course is prevented from migrating into the open void spaces of the underlying layer if the surface of the sub-base is naturally not close textured. The process is carried out by blinding with fine granular material.

Coated materials (macadam) (see also asphalt concrete)

Graded aggregate that has been coated with bitumen and/or tar (or other binder) in which the major part of the strength is derived from interlocking of the aggregates. In the UK BS 594987 governs its constituents.

Compaction

The process of expelling the air from a bituminous mix or granular layer to make the layer more dense. Carried out using a heavy weight, typically a roller that may or may not use vibration.

Continuously reinforced pavement

Rigid pavement or rigid composite pavement in which the high strength concrete slab is reinforced and has no construction or expansion joints. The principal reinforcing steel is longitudinal to limit crack width.

Core

A vertical section of pavement removed by rotary drilling, using either water or air flush to determine the thickness of the various layers of construction.

Crack and seat

Process whereby a failed concrete pavement is broken into relatively small slabs and compacted prior to overlaying to rehabilitate a pavement.

Creep

An irrecoverable movement caused in the wearing course of a pavement by a continuous long-term loading.

Cross-fall

The transverse slope across a carriageway (pavement), to facilitate drainage.

Curling

Twisting of a concrete slab due to the influence of thermal and/or traffic stresses.

Curviameter

A machine for collecting pavement deflection data, effectively a combination of a deflectograph and an FWD. Data measuring conceptually similar the traffic speed deflectograph.

Cut-back bitumen

A bitumen with the addition of a volatile flux oil. Used for low-grade mixes which may be stored without setting. Easier to lay than 'straight run' mixes. Use is not recommended due to problems of controlling the setting time.

Data capture device

A hand-held computer notebook for recording and managing defects.

Deflection

A recoverable movement of the surface of a pavement under transient load.

Deformation

The irreversible movement/compression of pavement layers, leading to rutting and settlement.

Deflectograph

A machine which is effectively a mechanised Benkelman beam and which measures deflection in both wheel paths automatically generated by a standard configuration truck.

Delamination

Separation of structural layers. This is also commonly associated with thin slurry surfacing where a thin layer peels off due to a lack of adhesion.

Design period

The number of years for which a pavement is designed. Usually 20 to 40 years. This presupposes consistency of traffic; it is not a preferred term and should be used with care.

Design traffic (load)

The predicted traffic occurring over the design period: usually expressed in terms of million standard axles (msa).

Design-mix asphalt

Wearing course of asphalt in which the proportions of bituminous binder is determined by specified mechanical tests.

Dynaflect

A small machine that generates a vibrating force which when transmitted to the pavement causes a deflection, the bowl shape of which is measured by geophones.

Elastic modulus (*E*)

A measure of material stiffness properties. In a bituminous layer it allows judgement on condition, it is not a measure of strength.

Edge restraint

A means of preventing the lateral spread of a pavement, especially block pavers in the surface course and preventing the loss of bedding course sand. Should be sufficiently robust to withstand overrun by any traffic, which will use the surface. Conceptually similar to edge beam stiffening of a bridge deck.

Elastic design

The process where a pavement is considered a structure and calculations are made of the stresses and strains in the various layers. These are then related to permissible limits in the same way as other engineering structures.

Elsym5

A public domain computer program developed by University of California (Berkeley) used for estimating the stresses and strains in a pavement.

Equivalent standard axles

The damaging effect of the many vehicle axles passing over a pavement during its design life. In the UK this is related to an 8 tonne axle, in the USA to a 18 kip (18 000 lbs) axle. The concept was developed in the Aasho road tests in the late 1950s in the US.

Falling weight deflectometer (FWD)

Machine for applying an impulse load to a carriageway and measuring the shape of deflection bowl caused. The load pulse approximates to that caused by a passing HGV.

Fatigue

The formation of cracks in pavement materials under repeated loading.

Fatting up

Exudation of bituminous binder to form an exposed film on the wearing surface.

FHWA

Federal Highway Administration (USA). Responsible for major federal interstate highways in the USA.

Filler

Fine non-plastic mineral matter used to stiffen bituminous binders and bituminous mixtures and to assist in filling voids in the mixtures.

Flexible composite pavement

Pavement containing a cement-bound roadbase and bituminous surfacing.

Flexible pavement

Pavement where all the bound layers are bound with a bituminous binder.

Formation

The surface of the subgrade in its final shape after completion of the earthworks.

Foundation

All materials on top of the sub-base. Needs to be sufficiently robust to permit compaction of the several layers of the pavement placed above it.

Fretting

An asphalt surface defect caused by ageing of the binder with consequent lack of adhesion and loss of aggregate, on newly laid surfaces. Also occurs at poorly formed joints due to insufficient compaction.

Geotextile

A polymer fabric material that permits the free passage of ground water but resists the movement of clay particles. Also used to prevent migration of sand fines in the bedding course to the sub-base in elemental construction. Can also be used as a reinforcement between layers in as asphalt pavement.

Geophone

A device which measures the velocity of response of the pavement surface resulting from an applied force. Deflection may be calculated by integrating the velocity signal once with time.

GPS

Global positioning by satellite. The ultimate locational referencing.

Griptester

Small machine for measuring skid resistance of pavements/surfaces.

Ground radar

Electronic process for determining construction layers in a pavement.

Growth factor

The proportional increase/decrease between the average 'whole life' traffic flow on a road and the flow at opening (or present flow).

Growth rate

The annual percentage increase in vehicle flow.

Heavy vehicle simulator

Machine which generates accelerated loading of a pavement. Can be static (fixed) or mobile and can be taken to site to load a pavement to destruction in a relatively short period.

High-speed road monitor (HRM)

Machine for measuring the roughness and other surface properties at normal road speed.

Inlay

The replacements of some of the layers of an existing pavement with new material where surface levels are the same after as they were before.

International Roughness Index (IRI)

Standard system of expressing the longitudinal roughness of a pavement. Developed by the World Bank in the 1970s and used extensively worldwide.

Interlock

The effect of frictional forces in the jointing sand between adjacent block pavers which inhibits an individual unit movement relative to its immediate neighbour.

Intervention level

The level of deterioration where serviceability becomes unacceptable and remedial work is required.

Investigatory level

The standard of the asset condition below which the need for treatment should be considered. This is sub-divided into safety, maintenance and serviceability.

Integral spacer nib

A small projection built into the clay or concrete block paver to ensure that blocks are laid a minimum distance apart.

Jointing sand

A fine dry sharp sand which when brushed between block pavers allows the development of interlock between adjacent units.

Kerb

The term used for an edge restraint; in the case of a pavement this is usually formed from concrete or stone and acts as a face to guide surface water to drains. It also inhibits vehicles mounting an adjacent footway.

Kerb race

The foundation to a kerb, usually in concrete and can either be formed from either wet or semi-dry concrete.

Lightly trafficked pavement

Usually considered to be a pavement carrying a design load less than 1.5 msa in the design period.

Lime stabilisation

The technique of improving the strength of clay soils (subgrades) by the incorporation of lime. This provides an improved working platform and allows a reduction in the overall pavement thickness.

Macro texture

The visible roughness of a surfacing material, enabling drainage of water, etc.

Micro-texture

The microscopic properties of the surface which enable it to develop friction and thus to provide skidding resistance.

Maintenance investigatory level

Indicates the stage where consideration must be given to some form of maintenance in a future programme, which could be several years away.

Maintenance treatment level

The optimum level of deterioration at which to carry out remedial works. Prevention of further deterioration becomes more cost effective than allowing continuing deterioration to occur hence incurring greater maintenance costs.

March

A standardised system of visual survey, developed for use in urban areas, which is used extensively in the UK.

Mastic asphalt

A dense asphalt mixture of aggregates and filler in which the binder content is optimised to fill all air voids in the aggregate. It is solid at normal temperature but pourable upon heating. It can be applied by hand or using special equipment to provide an impermeable surface layer.

Modified binder

A bituminous binder, the properties of which have been modified by the incorporation of an additive, usually a polymer or rubber blend.

Modulus (E)

The ratio, stress/strain generally referred to in strength of materials texts as 'Young's modulus'.

Modulus

Computer program for elastic design/back calculation of pavements. Developed by Texas A&M University, public domain; used by FHWA as a standard evaluation program.

msa

Million standard axles.

Overlay

To strengthen of a pavement by placing bituminous or concrete material on top of the existing pavement.

Partial reconstruction

Replacement of some of the construction layers in a pavement as a means of strengthening.

Pavement

All layers above the natural soil formation.

Pandef

Computer program used by UK DfT for processing deflectograph measurements; supersedes Deflec.

Paver

A purpose-made product intended to be laid in an interlocking bond pattern to form the surface course of a pavement. Can be made either from clay, concrete or natural stone – typically granite or sandstone. Typical size is 200 × 100 × 65, rectangular in plan if clay or concrete. Can be thicker and also differently shaped.

PAVER

Computerised system of pavement management developed by US Army Corps of Engineers.

Pavior

Artisan who lays pavements.

Pavscan

Dedicated processor developed by WDM (UK) for processing Deflectograph measurements.

PCI

Pavement condition index (USA) based on new pavement having 'score' of 100; defects are calculated as 'deduct' values.

Pervious macadam

Open-textured bituminous macadam which allows for water to

drain through it. Used to minimise water spray when wet.

PFI

Private finance initiative where a company (usually a consortium) design and construct an infrastructure asset (not necessarily a pavement) and maintain it for a period (usually 40 years).

Profile

The variation of the longitudinal or transverse level along the length or width of a pavement .

Poisson's ratio

The ratio between the vertical and horizontal stresses. It is material-dependent and in a pavement is usually in the range 0.35 to 0.45.

Reconstruction

The replacement of all layers of an existing pavement with new or recycled materials.

Regulating course

Layer of variable thickness used to adjust levels in preparation for an overlaying course of regular thickness. Part of the construction process rather than contributing to the strength of a pavement.

Reinforcement

Process of making stronger.
Steel mesh used to increase the tensile strength of concrete.

Rigid composite pavement

Pavement in which the main structural element is a high-strength concrete slab over which a bituminous surface is placed.

Rigid pavement

Concrete roadbase and surfacing.

Road formation

Level on which the pavement is constructed, usually the top of the subgrade (natural soil).

Roadbase

Main structural layer of the pavement, generally bound material – either bituminous or cement; placed above the sub-base.

Rolled asphalt

Mixture of aggregates and bituminous binder used as a dense wearing course or basecourse. Very impermeable; strength gained from stiffness of the bituminous mortar rather than aggregate interlock. Controlled in UK by BS 594.

Rut

Groove or depression formed in the surface of a pavement by the action of traffic. May be confined to the surface (wearing) course or may be structural if it affects lowers layers in the pavement.

Screeding

In elemental construction, the process of laying the bedding course sand to the correct line and levels.

Sett

A natural stone, typically granite or sandstone – cubic in shape, used in the construction of pavements from about 1650 onwards. Timber setts have been found in some urban areas.

Scrim

Sideways force coefficient routine investigation machine. A standard machine for assessing the skidding resistance of a pavement surface.

Skidding resistance

The resistance to skidding in wet conditions measured by a standard test. Close approximation of coefficient of friction.

Slurry seal

Mixture of binder, fine aggregate and mineral filler with water added to produce a material of slurry consistency.

Standard axle

An axle with an 80 kN total force.

Stiffness modulus (E)

The equivalent of elastic modulus but for materials whose stiffness varies (e.g. with temperature, stress state, etc.).

Strategic Highway Research Program (SHRP)

Major research programme undertaken primarily in the USA by FHWA. Very far-reaching, and ongoing. Developed new materials and has long-term performance monitoring on a large number of pavements.

Stripping

Displacement of bituminous binder from the surface of aggregate, usually by the action of water.

Sub-base

A platform layer upon which the main structure of the pavement may be laid.

Sub-formation

Top of subgrade level if a capping layer is used.

Subgrade

The naturally occurring material upon which all subsequent layers of construction are placed and which supports the loadings transmitted by them.

Surface dressing (chip seal)

A single, double or triple layer of stones attached to the pavement surface by a layer of bituminous binder.

Surfacing (surface course)

Upper layers above roadbase designed to carry traffic directly.

Tack coat (bond coat)

Layer of bituminous emulsion used to improve adhesion between layers in a pavement.

UK DfT

Ministerial department, which oversees all transport issues (road, rail, air, shipping).

UK HA

Executive agency responsible to UK DfT for the procurement and operation of the UK motorway and trunk road network.

UKPMS (HAPMS)

United Kingdom Pavement Management System, used by all highway authorities in the UK, except the Highways Agency – Highways Agency PMS is conceptually similar but confined to the national road network.

Vehicle category

Description of vehicle by general weight/damaging power, for example 'Other goods vehicle category 2 (OGV)'.

Vehicle class

Description of vehicle by type and number of axles, for example '3-axle articulated or buses and coaches'.

Warping

Deformation of a concrete slab due to differential stresses caused by thermal and/or traffic loading.

Water table

The natural level of ground water in the subgrade. This level varies depending on the time of year, weather conditions, etc. and can significantly affect the strength or performance of the sub-grade and consequently the pavement.

Wearing course (surface course)

The uppermost layer of a pavement, which is in contact with the traffic, part of the surfacing.

see also:

BSI (1985) BS 6100: *Glossary of highway engineering terms.* BSI, London.

Deterioration and Maintenance of Pavements
ISBN: 978-0-7277-4114-1

ICE Publishing. All rights reserved
http://dx.doi.org/10.1680/dmp.41141.279

Index